Charity's
The Tway It Was

Lois Carter Kelly

To Diana ♥ From Lois Carter Kelly Jubilate Dio

Wolf Creek Press

Requests for such permission should be addressed to:
    Wolf Creek Press
    P. O. Box 423
    Avondale Estates, GA, 30002

Kelly, Lois Carter
    Charity's Children: The Tway it Was

Cover Design: Manjari Graphics
Layout: J. L. Saloff
Fonts used: Goudy, Brush Script

10-Digit ISBN: 0-9777478-0-8
13-Digit ISBN: 978-0-9777478-0-1

Library of Congress Control Number: 2006901237
Copyright information available upon request.

First Edition

Printed on acid free paper in The United States of America

This book is lovingly dedicated to Charlie Kelly,
a patient listener who for fifty-five years has kept me in line,
and to our sons and daughters-in-love,
Tad and Jenny Kelly and Alex and Shane Kelly and grandson Burke

Acknowledgments

There would not be a book had it not been for the literary and typing skills of my dear friend Bettie LaDuke. She typed, laughed, cried, and changed the manuscript in ways that only someone of her caliber could do. Thank you, Bettie. Special thanks to Ann Hoeke and Glenda Willis who were able to read my cursive writing—somewhat. Jamie Saloff and Manjari Henderson turned the typewritten manuscript into a book. Their knowledge was invaluable. When I was struggling with the title, Joy Durham who was visiting looked at me and blurted out the title. And thanks to all those patient souls who listened to chapters being read aloud, including former teachers, coaches, and a principal. Others from whom I have received encouragement include my local banker, the copy machine operators at my local office supply store, and the checkout people who always asked, "When will your book be ready?" They have kept me going.

Foreword

The first nine years of my life were set in Harlan County, Kentucky, in the coal mining camp of R. C. Tway. The city of Harlan was widely known, infamous, rich with "black diamonds," the finest bituminous coal in the world, and centered by its historic and tumultuous courthouse. It is also known as Bloody Harlan.

I grew up in R. C. Tway Coal Mining Camp, a tight community of blacks in upper camp and whites in lower camp. In my book I describe the rituals, the food, the education, finances, love and death, the swing of the pendulum from exotic energy to economic hardship.

As a young child, I was uniquely exposed to the wonders of a significant time when new forces were confronting the country. The Great Depression, political concerns—the Communist Party, education, communications, racial differences—were all occurring simultaneously. It was my fortune to experience the effects of these movements and events at the most formative time of my life.

Theodore Dreiser visited Harlan. The famous reporter, Lowell Thomas, broadcast from Harlan on the CBS network. John L. Lewis struggled to organize the miners into the United Mine Workers.

This is not a book of fiction. It is autobiographical. It did happen. Furthermore, as Maya Angelou has noted, we all do have the same life.

Harlan, Kentucky

Harlan County lay in the southeastern range of the great wild Appalachian Mountains. It had no name when Daniel Boone explored the dark and bloody hunting ground. And certainly he was unaware of the black diamonds that lay in rich seams in that part of the range known as The Cumberland Mountains. The mountains were created before time began when they heaved out of oceans teeming with fish. Fish, pressed between layers of slate, were preserved in perfect detail. And coal was layered in rich, abundant seams reputed to be the finest and best burning coal ever produced.

Someone discovered coal in Harlan County sometime around the turn of the century. And that place became a town of legendary fame. Harlan lay in a wide valley in Harlan County that butted up to Ivy Hill. Harlan had paved streets and new brick buildings. One end of Main Street began with the great Atlantic and Pacific Grocery Store abbreviated to the A&P. Up a way was J.J. Newberry Five and Dime; across the street was Dr. Tye's Drug Store, a classic drug store with a marble soda fountain and round marble tables with wireback chairs for customers who wanted to sit and enjoy some refreshment. The genteel and well-educated Dr. Tye oversaw it all. The Quality Shop, Bowers Department Store, Powers and Hortons kept a Harlan clientele well dressed. Doctors and lawyers were on the second floor of these fine brick buildings.

At the end of Main Street rose the imposing First Baptist Church, brick, two story, with yellow marble dome-like windows. The church had a telephone and downstairs were two restrooms with commodes. From anywhere within the city limits the cross-topped bell tower proclaimed deliverance and salvation. Dr. W. J. Bolt pastored the congregation from the cradle to the grave.

Restaurants touting mixtures of ethnic food blended with what was available in Harlan to create Hungarian, Italian, French, English, Irish, and pure mountain food cooked by first generation cooks, who had originally come to work the mines but had stayed to cook for the miners.

Harlan County thrived on lumber and coal, and the city of Harlan was the center of command. On Saturday folks dressed up arrived early and stayed late. They came from the coal mining camps to eat, get haircuts, groceries, gold fish, hairpins, pink panties, Tangee lipstick, medicine and bet on the horses.

The A&P was a major stop. The store was an unheard of self-serve. Unlike the commissaries, customers were free to walk anywhere and pick up what they wanted. Open barrels of pinto beans with a scoop and brown paper bags set in the aisles. Slabs of streak of lean and thick-sliced bacon, Eight-O-Clock coffee in red packages with a package of Eight-O-Clock flower seeds attached to the side, macaroni, spaghetti, Irish potatoes, fresh heads of cabbages, red beets, white and yellow onions, lard, salt, apples, grapes, cantaloupe, loaves of light bread for sandwiches, peanut butter, jelly, Karo syrup, matches, waxed paper were all items that were bought every Saturday night. It was all cheaper than at the commissaries, and it was all paid for in genuine U.S. currency—not company money called scrip.

It was to this thriving town that Ida Cox Moses came with her brood. She chose Elcome, a small mining camp on the outskirts of Harlan. She cooked and prepared buckets for the miners who roomed at the boarding house.

Wherein Ida Makes Her Way to Harlan

Charity Angeline Moses was born December 29, 1907, to William I. Moses and Ida Dyalthia Cox Moses in Procter, Tennessee. Her grandparents on both sides owned large farms; their relatives owned large farms. The farms on the Moses side were all traced to Joshua Moses Sr., who was born in 1748, fought in the Revolutionary War, was wounded, captured at the battle of Eutah Springs, S.C., and then taken to James Island where after nine months he escaped and returned home to North Carolina. Sometime later he journeyed to Pleasant View, Kentucky. He claimed land and had a family. Charity is the seventh generation of Joshua Moses progeny and she had ten brothers and sisters. They were: Chester; Girtrude, 1894; Millard, 1896; Pearlie May, 1898; Emma, 1900; Mary, 1903; Otis, 1905; Charity, 1907; Nannie, 1909; Van, 1911; and Willie, 1914.

Charity's father, for some unknown reason, left the land and farming for a job in the Procter coal mines. This family, like all others, lived simple lives with simple pleasures. William belonged to the "The Mechanics" organization and worked on machinery near the driftmouth of Procter mines. In spare time the family gathered around the pump organ and sang hymns, told stories, and read the Bible. About every two years, Ida wrote a new name in the Bible.

Ida was an outstanding cook and a superb seamstress. She taught each girl how to knit, embroidery, and quilt. She taught them how to cook. Each girl learned to cook meat and vegetables and to make a pie and the famous apple stack cake. Boys could work the garden, hunt squirrels and rabbits, fish, and carry coal. Finally, she taught them that "cleanliness is next to godliness."

The boys slept in the loft on corn-shuck mattresses. The girls slept in a room of their own. Each older girl took a younger one as soon as the baby left the nursing mother. And so it was that Pearlie May chose Charity Angeline when she was born. Charity was a beautiful baby with blue eyes and soft downy fuzz on her head that reminded the doctor of a baby gosling. The doctor offered to take the baby. His wife had no children. Ida thanked him kindly but kept the baby. And so it was that the family "grew in wisdom and stature and in favor with God and man."

Then great tragedy struck. Pearlie, who was now thirteen, and Emma went out into the mountains to pick a bouquet of flowers and to meet the Green boy from the next farm. He was carrying a shotgun. He came to the bobbed-wired fence and leaned over to pull the two strands apart and climb through as he had done on numerous occasions. The gun came across his shoulder and someway caught in his overalls strap, fired and blew Pearlie May's head away, exploding, against a cobalt sky. Ida heard the noise and some minutes later she heard Emma screaming. She ran out the door with Charity and Nannie behind her. She could not understand Emma. Emma turned and ran. Ida and the girls followed. Everything was in slow motion. Emma disappeared down the steep side of the mountain. Finally Ida got there and looked down. Pearlie's headless body had rolled down the hill, blood soaking her clothes her arms; she lay in a bloody heap, her hand clutching a bouquet of daisies and bluettes.

Pearlie slept with Charity, the two sharing a bed. Pearlie dressed Charity, helped her at the table, bathed her, loved her. On a cold winter's night she would draw Charity into the curve of her body to keep her warm. Charity was closer to Pearlie than she was to her own mother. That night, when it came bedtime, Charity walked up to the bed, stopped, then laid her hand on Pearlie's pillow with its bright-embroidered birds and began walking down the side of the bed. "Where's Pearlie? Where's Pearlie?"

Sometime between 1912 and 1913 William came home from the mines sick. The doctor could not diagnose the illness. He was hot; he sweated; he lost weight; he had no energy. Ida was pregnant with Willie. One morning William died with typhoid fever caught from a contaminated spring near the mines. In 1917 Otis died from influenza. Girtrude had married Andrew Dopel and Emma had married Lonzo Shown. Ida, after much reading of the Bible and much prayer, packed up her family and moved to the Promised Land—Harlan Kentucky.

Wherein Lois Jean Is Born

Charity and Nannie helped Ida as much as they could, which was not much. They could help clean the tables at the boarding house in Elcombe where Ida ran the kitchen and packed lunch buckets for the miners. Charity and Nannie attended school in Harlan; however, they did not feel accepted. Someone in Harlan told Ida about Pine Mountain Settlement School across Pine Mountain that was operated by Miss Petit and Miz Aundi. Ida sent Charity and Nannie. The girls learned to garden, raising and preparing vegetables that they had never heard of, Swiss chard, asparagus, and hominy, dried corn kernels cooked in lye water. They learned to keep their bodies clean and their hearts and minds pure. "Cleanliness is next to godliness." They slept on a screened-in porch from May to September. They sat up straight at the table, the span of one's hand from navel to table and from back to chair. And before every meal they prayed:

> "Be our good Shepherd, O Lord, we entreat Thee,
> And may we receive all good things from thy
> sweetness. Amen."

Although the girls could have gone on to Berea College, Charity and Nannie stayed only a few months at Pine Mountain Settlement School and returned to Harlan. Charity would say that she didn't have shoes. She worked at the Eagle Laundry. Then she worked cleaning houses for the "rich people" in Harlan. Finally, she worked in the stockroom at J.J. Newberry's Five and Dime store. One night her appendix ruptured and she was taken to the Harlan Hospital. There she met James L. Carter. James, handsome, eyes outlined in fine coal dust, black hair, white linen suit, hands coarse from the mines, a fine figure of a man. Furthermore, he was respected as a coal miner.

James L. Carter's lineage was as long as Charity's. His family, however, had kept their farm in Whitely County, and his parents, Madison and Nannie, planned to return when the mines worked out.

Charity Angeline Moses slipped off and married James L. Carter after her appendix operation healed. They were "united in holy matrimony on the 26th day of May in the year of our Lord 1930 at Middlesboro, Kentucky, by Reverand A. B. Reeves. Witnesses, Elois Reeves and Miz. Reeves."

Charity stood in the sunshine reading the certificate. She was beautiful in her sheer organza dress, embroidered with tiny blue flowers that matched the color of her eyes. The dress was belted around her petite waist. She had on white suede slippers that matched her pocketbook and carried matching gloves. Sliding the wedding certificate into the suede pocketbook, she looked sweetly at the three and said, "I am a virgin. I can truthfully say, I am a virgin."

James drove back to Harlan. Charity changed clothes in the stockroom at J. J. Newberry's, put the wedding outfit in a box. James dropped her off at her sister Mary's house. Mary had married Murphy Tweed. Murphy had built a grocery store and they had lost their first baby. For some reason, James and Charity had decided to keep their marriage a secret. James drove to R.C. Tway Mining Camp, changed out of his dress clothes, picked up his bucket from the boarding house and went to the mines.

Ten months later on March 10, 1931, Lois Jean was born in the Harlan Hospital. The story is that Captain T. M. Gibson, who was living in a brick house with running water and indoor toilet and who was in charge of the mining operation in Tway Mining Camp, was visiting the hospital when Lois was born. The beautiful, red haired nurse, Carrie Forsyth had just washed the baby, put on baby powder, new swaddling clothes and laid her in a baby bed. Captain Gibson took out his fountain pen, leaned over the bed, opened up the tiny little hand and gently lay the pen in her hand and held it, saying, "the first thing that a baby touches is what she will do the rest of her life."

After ten days, James took Charity and the baby home to R.C. Tway Mining Camp to the shotgun house between the lower white camp and upper colored camp. The house had weathered to a natural gray color with a silver tin roof. Ten wooden steps led up to a long front porch, and the front door led into the front room. To the left was the bedroom and to the right the kitchen. Out the kitchen door was the back porch. Under the front porch was a space tall enough for a cow to be kept. Canned jars of food could be stored near the chimney and kindling was kept dry to start the fire in the cook stove. On the bedroom side and about twenty-five feet away from the house was a two-hole toilet that was shared with the Smiths. On the kitchen side of the house the mountain sloped into a lower spread and the third shotgun house stood there. These three shotgun houses were the only ones in Tway Coal Company. Charity and James had already applied for the first four-room house to become available in lower white camp.

There was traffic day and night on the one-lane dirt road used by both foot traffic and an occasional car; the road forked here. Left side led to upper colored camp, and the right side went to upper white camp. This mining camp was small, well organized, a fine brick commissary with a coffered ceiling and ceiling fans. The office was located behind a window on the wide concrete porch issuing the mine's own currency, scrip, which could be used only for Tway Coal Company.

Wherein Death Comes for the Fish

James was now thirty-one and the best dynamiter in Tways. Charity was twenty-six and Lois Jean was going on four.

Their lives were wound tightly into routine, the circumference of which included a trip every Saturday night to buy as much as they could at the A&P (with real money, not scrip), take a trip to J. J. Newberry Five and Dime and maybe a show at the Margie Grand Theater. This trip in the spring of 1934 was like so many others except. . . except for the goldfish. Charity saw the fish before Lois Jean did. "Emily, do you think she could enjoy gold fish?"

"Honey, she might not, but you sure could. They are so easy. All you need to do is give them a pinch of food—just a pinch and clean the bowl about once a week."

Emily Dickenson Jones (her mother named her after a poet) was well educated. But she had had a nervous breakdown and had to come home her senior year from Center College. Everybody knew that Emily was nervous. She was taking time to recover.

"Honey," her voice soft and soothing, "don't overfeed them. They don't know when to stop eating. They will eat and eat. They have no self-control." She looked off into her world and sighed. "Change the water and don't tap on the bowl. It will frighten Harriet Beecher Stowe and Herman Melvin."

"I'll take them. Wait! How much are two?"

"Why, ten cents for the fish, fifteen for the bowl, and I will give you some food. A box was opened for these in the store and you can have the rest."

"Thank you, Emily. When will you be going back to school?"

"I'm not sure that I will ever go back. I rather like being in charge of fish. Now, take care of Herman and Harriet."

She handed Lois Jean the little box of fish. The box had water in it so the fish could swim all the way home.

"Here, I'll carry it," and Charity took the box by the wire handle, put the food in the bowl, and out the door they swooped.

The next morning Lois Jean was up earlier than Charity or James. She went into the front room and looked up through the fish bowl that was on top of the radio that set catty-cornered in the front room. The two "golden fishes" were not moving. They were asleep. She called softly, "Fishes." The little fish were floating on top of the water. "Little fishes." Nothing. No darting in fearful ecstasy. Just floating on the top. They lay on their sides peacefully asleep. She took her finger, stood on tiptoe, but could not reach inside the bowl.

"Oh, sheee, he's done it again! Move, Lois Jean. James has killed the fish. He's given them a whole sheet of food and the fish are dead."

Lois stood there.

"Yes, they are dead."

"Wake 'em up, wake 'em up!" Lois was scared.

Hadn't Emily said "only a pinch—only a pinch. Fish don't know when to stop eating. Fish need a little pinch."

James had come in from night shift at the mines. Checked on the two girls, fixed himself a bite and then noticed the fish bowl on top of the radio that set across the corner of the front room. James enjoyed the fish. He knew that Charity was starving them, and he had laid a whole silvery sheet of the food on top of the water. The fish darted and darted, darted and dived, swam back to the top again and again. James left them in the frenzy of a joyous death.

Charity took her finger and touched the floating fish. No movement. She smiled sweetly and said, "They are dead. Dead. The fish are dead, Lois Jean; they will never move. That's the way it is when you die. You don't move. You don't talk. You don't sing. You don't dance. You don't. . . ," her voice trailed off into a wail.

She stopped as suddenly as she had begun. She scooped up the two fish, held out her hand.

"Here, go throw these away. Put them in the pee bucket. Throw them down the toilet. Do it!" She screamed. "Do it now!"

Lois danced in fear.

"Dead, dead, Charity."

"Don't call me Charity." She screamed. "You call me Mother—you call me Mother." She dropped the two fish, reached for Lois Jean and began shaking her.

"Honey, don't cry." It was James. Just his pants on, and coal dust around his eyes. He swooped Lois up with the big, toughened hands callused with fifteen years of coal mining. Comforting hands.

"Honey, we gonna bury the fish." He carried her to the kitchen, set her in her chair at the table, picked up the big box of kitchen matches, poured them out on the oil-clothed table. He went to the bedroom, came back with a clean, white, ironed and folded handkerchief, laid it out, took his big dirty looking hand, the hand on which years of mining had left its mark, and gently pulled the handkerchief into the corners of the box, letting one side hang out of the box.

"Let's put the fish side by side here in this little casket."

Without hesitation she walked into the front room, picked up the two cold, slimy fish and came back.

"I gonna cry."

"No. You gonna bury the little fishes. They need you. They really need you."

Charity was outside this dance, and she liked being away from it. Charity was frying pork chops and eggs; she had rolled out biscuits. Blackberry jelly was on the table. She was involved in her own dance.

James pulled the handkerchief down, tucking in the sides until there was not a wrinkle anywhere, slid the box into its open-ended part and breathed deeply.

"OK, pick them up, honey, and let's go bury them"

Just as she reached out, Charity hit the iron skillet with the egg turner and Lois dropped the box.

"That's enough, Charity."

They went outside, just the two.

They went outside to the dew-pearled hillside, dug a little hole, and buried Herman and Harriet.

"Now you pick them violets over yonder; put 'em on the top. And we'll sing."

"James, breakfast is ready." He ignored her. Lois Jean picked three violets and lay them on the little mound of dirt. "We'll sing. No, you sing and say your prayer. She sang "Jesus loves me this I know;" and prayed,

"Now I lay me down to sleep.

I pray, Thee Lord, my soul to keep.

Fi-shou-di before I wake,

I pray the Lord my soul to take. Amen."

She got up, put out her hand. He took it and led her to the table.

James ate three pork chops, four eggs, biscuits—hot biscuits with gravy and blackberry jelly—and drank three cups of hot Eight o'clock coffee and smoked a Duke's Mixture roll-your-own cigarette.

Later that day Lois and Charity went out and looked at the grave; the violets were wilted. That day Lois Jean learned three words: dead, casket, and grave.

The next morning she went into the kitchen. Charity was holding the match box filled with matches. A clean freshly ironed handkerchief lay on the table.

Wherein the Rule Is Broken

There was a rule: don't get on the bed. Every morning Charity took everything off the bed and then put it all back. First the sheet, then the log-cabin quilt, then the bright pink silk bedspread and the two silk shams. The only time that the bed was sat on or slept in during the day was illness—or if a new baby were to come. Then a woman lay in bed for ten days.

Lois Jean, being moved by her spirit—but not knowing which one, since she had not reached the age of accountability—climbed upon the bed. She had on brown lace-up shoes. She put one foot on one pink satin pillow sham and the other foot on the other one. The headboard was ornate, decorated with wooden inlays working like a delicate vine along the edges to meet on either side of an oval inlay in the center of the headboard.

Lois Jean looked at the oval inlay. Suddenly, there stood an ugly little man with a skull for a head and thin legs and a walking stick. One leg raised in a dance.

It was the Devil. "Omity," she moaned. "It's the Boogie man." He was looking directly at her. Suddenly emboldened, she commenced jumping up and down on the pink satin shams, singing:

> *"You—can't—get—me*
> *You—can't—get me*
> *Ha! Ha! Ha! You can't get me."*

Holding on tight, one hand on either side of the inlay and jumping high on the bed, she sang, "You can't get me. . ." Suddenly she was being lifted off the bed, moving through the air.

"You can't get on the bed. You can't get on the bed." Charity jerked her by the arm and dragged her into the kitchen, opened the cabinet drawer, took out the egg turner, began hitting her legs again, again, and again. Lois had never felt such hot, stinging pain. Charity hit and hit and hit and hit. Lois screamed and screamed. Finally, the blows stopped and she lay snubbing and exhausted on the kitchen floor. Charity looked at her legs, went to a drawer, got Lois' pajamas and put them on her. She put the egg turner back in the drawer. Lois was lying on the kitchen floor. When she woke up, she went looking for Charity, who was in the bedroom. Charity was walking down the side of the bed, her hand moving slowly along the pink silk spread down one side, across the foot and up the other side then back down—all the while whispering, "Pearlie, Pearlie, oh, Pearlie." She was in her own world. Suddenly she saw Lois and went toward her. Lois Jean sat down, drew her knees up under her chin, closed her eyes tightly, and waited for the blow. Charity stood looking. She sat down in the floor, reached for her little girl. They both cried.

Wherein There Is a Detour
to The Garden of Eden

James was at the mines and would not be home until midnight.

"Come on, let's go see Miz Brannon." That meant lower camp. Charity put the thumb lock on the back door and locked the front door with a key. In lower camp, the houses were bigger, yards cut, and fruit trees and flowers growing profusely. Lower camp was a different place. Folks in lower camp had been there for years. They had families with children in the two-room school up the mountain, and others at Hall High School. Frankie Brannon was in the first year of high school. Charity and James hoped one day to find a house in lower camp. That was wishful thinking. Families had left large farms to come when mining first opened in Harlan and they stayed.

"Come on, and let's go see Miz Brannon." Charity called people by their last name. Miz McCurg, Miz Gibson, Miz Miller. If people were her age and danced, played cards or went to a roadhouse—even if one was her own sister, she called them Nell, Nannie, or Flossie. If they had been caught sinning, then "that" plus "ol'" was added, as in "that ol' Polly", "that ol' Lurie."

Miz Brannon was Miz Brannon; much respected. She was married to Jim Brannon; they had Frankie, Jewel, and Virginia. Beautiful girls. Lois Jean loved to go to Miz Brannon's. The girls, especially Jenny, made over her. That's where Charity went to visit and learn new ways of doing things.

At Miz Brannon's someone was always churning milk, making butter, cleaning chickens. Miz Brannon molded the butter for neighbors in lower camp. Her house was clean; her apron was clean; her hands were clean.

Charity and Lois Jean left the house, went down the front porch steps, down a little path onto the dirt road, down the dirt road, steep mountain on one side and an embankment on the other side that swept down to the branch. Across the branch was the Garden of Eden. Chickens nested there, laid eggs, hatched diddles; rabbits, possums ambled in; frogs, cardinals, hawks, black birds, blue jays made it their home. On hot summer days butterflies and June bugs abounded, and on cool summer nights lunar moths floated in at night, seeking light and often mounting the screen doors and windows.

There were chickapin trees bearing delicious three-cornered nuts, polk salad, apple trees, paw-paw bushes, and cool green moss, and for pure beauty, dandelions, violets, jack-in-the-pulpits, rhododendron, and mountain laurel.

Beneath it all was rich loam deposited for generations that grew anything except weeds. For this generation of the Great Depression, it grew half runner white beans, tomatoes, peppers, cabbage, and onions.

The Garden of Eden was an ideal place to play Adam and Eve. Nothing was better than to slip off, go down the steep front porch steps, down the bank, across the dirt road, down another steep bank, across the branch into the Garden of Eden. Crossing the rocks and stooping to look at the fish dart in the freedom of their watery world.

It was the Garden of Eden because Charity had told her about Adam and Eve and how they were so poor that they did not have any clothes except some made out of leaves, and they ate apples. Lois remembered this story to the extent of recreating it. She would never forget how it happened. One day she had slipped off to the Garden of Eden. She sat down on a rock, looked around, and then there came a delicious thought. There stood a paw-paw bush. Paw-paws, green and looking like short bananas. She pulled one. It was bitter to the taste. She spit it out, threw it as far as she could. Nothing came to her. What could she do? Then came the picture. Be Adam and Eve.

She picked some of the leaves from the bush, stuck them on her dress; they wouldn't stay. She took off her dress, stuck one on her belly; it stayed just a little while, then off it fell. Then another picture came. Wet it in the branch and stick it on. That she did. On her belly, her arms, and then she took off her panties and stuck the wet leaves on her tail and legs. That was when she heard Charity call her. Charity was hurrying and calling. It was not a good call; it was a spanking call. She was coming closer and closer. There was no hiding place. There she stood.

At first Charity could not take it all in; she started toward her, stopped. Then she began laughing. She laughed until tears ran down her face. "That head of yours is filled with sense." She knelt down and hugged her, pulled off the leaves, put her clothes on. "God's in His Heaven. All's right with the world." Lois Jean loved this happy time.

Wherein Miz Brannon Offers a Way Up

Miz Brannon was clean as a pin. She lived in the first house on the left, across from the pump. Charity and Lois passed the Mitchell house, turned into lower camp, rounded the curve; there was Miz Brannon's. Fenced yard—fenced with hog-pen wire. A maple tree shaded the front porch. Over in the corner of the front yard was an apple tree, and by the side of it grew "Eight-O-Clocks." She got the seeds out of the Eight-O-Clock package on the side of Eight-O-Clock Coffee. She also had dahlias and hollyhocks.

Inside the house, she had linoleum floors, lace curtains, painted walls, nice bedroom sets. She was clean as a pin. She kept chickens and a milk cow and sold milk, butter, eggs and cleaned fryers ready to cook. She had three fine girls, and Jim Brannon owned a Ford. Miz Brannon was well-to-do.

Charity glanced at the pump. Nell Farmer was in earnest talk with some woman new to the camp. There were four pumps in R.C. Tway Mining Camp; one in the upper colored camp, one near the boarding house, the one across from Miz Brannon, and the one below the Miller's house. Some three or four houses near the commissary had indoor plumbing. The Owen's house, the Miller's house did. On a warm day someone in a good mood would say, "Hold out your foot," and would pump glorious, cold mountain water and pat you on the head.

Charity and Lois Jean went to the back door and Miz Brannon called, "Come in, Charity, come in honey—how are you?"

"I'm fine."

Virginia ran in, grabbed Lois. She hugged her.

"Let's go play."

"Virginia, you can't play."

"Mommie," Ginny whined.

"Churn, Virginia. You've got to take the Miller's milk and butter in time for supper. Charity, when are you due?"

"Sometime in May."

"Are you going to Harlan Hospital."

"No, with this one I am going to stay home."

"Why, Charity, you could go to the hospital for $20.00 and it could be cut from his pay."

"Things are. . . ," and she trailed off. Ted, James' younger brother, had taken the scrip card and checked out money to go on the train to Berea College. James told Ted that it was all right with him.

"I'm going to let Lois Jean stay with Mr. and Miz Carter."

"Oh, Charity."

"It'll be no more than two nights at the most."

"Oh, well. I know how you feel."

Virginia said, "Lois, would you like to churn some?"

"Could I? Mother, could I?"

"Please, Miz Carter, could she?"

"Well." "Well" actually meant yes, she could. Lois stepped up to the churn and took hold of the paddle handle with both hands and began to push the wooden paddle down with all her might. But try as she might, the paddle wouldn't go all the way to the bottom. She was too short; Ginny took the handle and put her hands over Lois'; down they went. Down they went— again and again, together. Churning, churning. In the sunny kitchen, clean curtains blowing in the breeze. Everything working as it should.

Lois got tired, but Ginny said that the butter was coming. It was almost ready. She stopped churning. Lois opened up her hands and there were little blisters, but she didn't care. Ginny stopped, eased the paddle to the top of the churn.

"Charity, hand me that bowl. Ginny, hold up the paddle. Lois sit here." There was butter all on the top of the milk.

"Stand back. You don't want yer hair to fall in. . ." Out came a wooden spoon and the butter was scooped up into the bowl. It was white butter. She put it in a yellow bowl with a blue band at the top, a big bowl, and commenced to mash and mash and mold the butter around in the bowl.

White milk came out and she continued to squeeze that butter. And, lo and behold, it began to turn yellow. How nice. How golden. How satisfying. She poured the milk back into the churn. Took the mold and packed the golden butter in the cool mold, pushed down on the handle, and out came a perfect pound of butter with a four-leaf clover engraved on the top. All butter. She made two molds of butter.

Then she began to pour the buttermilk into the clean dishpan, and, using a tin cup with markings on the side, she filled the quart jars and pressed a small, round cardboard lid onto each quart glass bottle.

Charity watched.

"How much is your butter?"

"It's 15 cents to you, Charity."

"And milk?"

"10 cents to you."

"Now, I don't want a handout."

"I know, but Lois helped make it." She smiled at Lois.

Charity reached down inside her dress and pulled out a handkerchief, untied the knot, and found two dimes and a nickel. "Here, thank you, Miz Brannon."

"Charity, why don't you buy some little chickens and raise them?"

"Miz Brannon, I have fresh eggs everyday. Wild chickens are in Lois' Garden of Eden. I go over there every morning and find at least six eggs fresh waiting from them wild chickens."

"I know, Charity, but let me show you something." She unbuttoned that top button on the dress made out of mingley goods. She reached down the opening on the left side and pulled out a Duke's Mixture bag. She pulled the little yellow strings apart and, lo and behold, out came nothing. Then she stuck two fingers in and pulled out bills. Said in a low voice, "Count." Charity counted three tens, two fives, and three ones.

"Theylaume! Theylaumee! Miz Brannon, theylaume. How'd you do that? How did you do that?"

"Chickens and cows, Charity. Chickens and cows. Now, the milk business is so demanding and I'm not goin' to do chickens after this year. I'm a gitten me another cow. Why don't you order you some diddles?"

"How?"

"You can order them from the catalog, or you can get them from McComb's Supply in Harlan. Charity, get them at Easter for the children. Give them diddles."

"Easter has passed. Do I wait till next year?"

"Lau, no. Go Saturday and get the ones that are left over. Charity, here, take this dollar. I know that you are having to help Ted in Berea. You can pay me back with a fine dressed chicken or two."

Charity just sat there. She felt a little like crying. But, she never cried.

Nobody in her family had ever seen her cry. Not since Pearlie died when she was a little girl. The tears were gone, all gone, except when she laughed with Ida Brannon.

She took the dollar, rolled it up and put it on the right side of her bosom, and it stayed there. "Thank you, Miz Brannon. I won't forget this. I'll never, never forget this. Theylaume, it's dark. Come on Lois, let's go home."

Wherein Jess and Joe Celebrate the Coming of Age

It was way past sundown and the moon had not come across the mountain, the rough, unpaved road was hard to follow in the dark. Lois begged to be carried. "Hoshee baby, Charity. Hoshee, baby."

"No, I'm not going to carry you. You are too big. You walk. I won't be a carrying you. You can walk." But she held her hand and lifted her high over the rocks. Suddenly the full moon came across the mountain; the whole side of the mountain was alive with sights and sound. Frogs were jumping around going down to the branch. An ol' hoot owl had commenced. And then a strange thing happened. A rooster crowed. "That's bad luck," she muttered to herself. "A rooster crowed when Peter denied our Lord. It crowed three times when Peter denied our Lord. That's bad luck. One of these days I'm a going have a flashlight so as we can see."

"Charity, we are a making shadows."

Then they went round the curve and it got darker. The tall hemlocks, the walnut trees, the magnolia trees hung over the road like lacy curtains keeping out the moonlight. It was cool. Lois stumbled. Charity didn't let her fall. They began to walk a little faster.

"I can't, Charity. I can't."

"Yes, you can. Come on. I don't like that rooster a crowing one little bit." They went on, and everything was quiet. Just then they got to the bank, climbed the bank, went up on the front porch. She opened the door and stepped into the pitch-black front room. She went over to the middle of the room and reached up to push the little button on the single light bulb that dangled down from the beaded ceiling. She couldn't find it. Lois held onto Charity's dress tail. Lois could feel the dress tail lifted as Charity swung and swung. No light. She ran to the kitchen and swung and swung. No light.

"I'm going crazy. I can't find the light."

Lois, catching her mother's fear, began to cry.

"Shut up." Charity pulled free, leaving her standing in the dark.

She ran to the bedroom, stumbling once, swinging her arms frantically. No light.

"I'm having an attack. There's no light. I can't find the damned light. The damned light. I can't find it." And she was crying. She fell on her knees.

"Sweet Jesus, don't let me lose the baby. Don't let me lose James. Don't let me lose my mind. Sweet Jesus, help me find the damned light bulbs and. . ."

Suddenly she knew that there were no lights in the house—none! She left Lois in the bedroom and ran back through the house, waving and waving in the dark, screaming in happy relief.

"There are no lights—no lights. Somebody has taken all the lights in this house. Oh, God. They're gone! Lois Jean the lights are gone!"

She was happy—real happy.

"Now you stay here and I'm going across the branch to the boarding house and tell Mr. Moore that the lights are gone. She left her in the bedroom and ran out into the dark.

Lois sat there in the dark, then crawled over to where her bed was, reached through the wooden bars and pulled out the naked, rubber doll, ol' Bettalu. She loved Bettalu. She pulled her blanket through the bars, crawled under the bed and went to sleep.

Charity and C.C. Moore, who kept law and order during the day in both upper and lower camps, stepped into the kitchen. "Lois," she called. "Oh, Lois, come here." No answer. "She's gone. She's gone. Oh, God, she's gone."

"Charity, slow down, hold on, or you're goin' to have that baby here and now. She is somewhere in this house."

"Lois Jean, answer me!"

C.C. Moore shined his flashlight around the front room, walked over to the baby bed, and slipped Lois Jean and Bettalu out from under the bed. Charity grabbed her, squeezed her tightly. C.C. continued to shine the light around the front room, then into the bedroom and back through the front room and in the kitchen. "I told Russ to call the tipple and get James down here. He will arrive shortly. Yes, somebody has pulled all the electricity out of the house."

"James will be a needing some water to bathe in when he comes. I'll put the tea kettle on."

"Charity, they's no time for bathing."

She pulled in the number two galvanized tin tub and set it next to the kitchen stove.

"Shine yer light here, Mr. Moore. He'll be hungry, too."

"Charity, he has his lunch bucket filled with them fine samaches that you make for him."

He stepped out on the back porch and looked up at the mountain. He could see a light moving down the mountain. Russ had called the driftmouth and Jim was coming down the mountain, from the right side of Tways. Nice laid out mine. The houses arrayed up the main road. Split at the boarding house, "colored camp" on the left side. "Upper white" on the right side. All cozy. Everybody asleep. C.C. liked it like that. He rubbed his perfectly bald head except for the dark fringe all around his head. He let one side of the fringe grow long and combed it across his bald head. All at once, he had the urge to measure his hair. He, on the dark porch, reached across his head and pulled that long piece of hair across his head. It came down to his shoulder. Quickly he rearranged it and came into the kitchen. Charity was working in the dark. She knew where everything was. She would fix James a molasses biscuit, and he could eat it while he got the clothes covered with coal dust off and, behind the cook stove, took a bath.

Jim was a dresser. White suit and straw hat in the summer and pin-stripped suit with the felt hat in the winter. Before he married Charity, he had his white shirts "laundered." That's how she had first heard of Jim Carter—dresser. He brought his shirts to the Eagle Laundry. Charity had left Pine Mountain Settlement School to get a job and buy some shoes. She was in the eighth grade when she left. She left everybody, including Jean Richie and her dulcimer. One day, Charity and Nannie just left the Pine Mountain Settlement School, never to return. Charity had worked in the homes of Harlan's well-to-do mine owners and personnel. She moved up to the Eagle Laundry and finally to J.J. Newberry's Five and Dime store. She was in the eighth grade when she began her life of independence. It was hard to believe that she was now twenty-six years old and waiting for her second child to be born.

Suddenly, Jim was at the door.

"Charity, is Lois. . .where is Lois?"

"She's asleep in her bed. Here, take a bath."

"Jim, no time for that. The boys are coming on horses and we goin' find out who did this thing—who came in and violated your living quarters."

Jim had his clothes off in the dark room and had commenced with the cake of P&G soap, the only soap strong enough to get to the coal dust.

"Horses ain't going to help."

"James," Charity interrupted, "remember: say 'ain't', you'll fall into a can of paint."

That is what she had learned at Pine Mountain Settlement School. Charity never said "ain't".

"What did you say, Charity?"

"Awe, just ignore her, C.C. She ain't"—and he said it a second time—ain't gonna change me."

"Well, I just hope not. Ain't seen you at the boarding house for a while. You settling down?"

James didn't answer. How could he answer a question like that? He did not have time to consider it. That was like asking that question about being "saved". Had he given up drinking? Had he given up playing banjo and piano? Did he have the time to entertain himself by reading the book of Revelation or learning the fine art of making moonshine or making love to some fine women? What does a man give up?

"Charity, get me some drawers and a clean pair of pants. Hurry. They here yet, C.C.?"

"Naw."

"You want a molasses biscuit, Mr. Moore?"

"Don't mind if I do, Charity. I will need the energy before the night wanes."

She began putting the molasses on the breakfast biscuits. They were flaky, at the same time holding together, not crumbling apart. Nanny Carter had the reputation of making the best. Hers were "choked out". Charity's were "rolled out". She would pull the cabinet table top out, sift down some flour in her hand, flour the cabinet top, and roll the biscuits out with the rolling pin.

Jim picked up the tub, went out the back door, and threw the water off the end of the porch, where the tomato plants were. Here it was May and they were in bloom. Thanks to Mom. As he drew his head back after pitching the water, he was aware that he was aware of something. He froze. Not moving any part of his body, holding the tin tub at arms length. What was it? His gun was in the bedroom and the rifle behind the kitchen door. Both ready. What was it?

All at once, he looked up. It was the Aurora Borealis. The sky was lit up over schoolhouse hill. The whole sky was lit up. Not a quarter a mile up the side of the mountain. Up on schoolhouse hill. All lit up.

"C.C., come here."

C.C. had been commenting on the flaky quality of the biscuit and black-berry jelly. He didn't care for molasses. Too much like tar. He laughed. The flashlight lay on the table. He had asked for a little buttermilk, "if it's no bother."

"Lau no, it's no bother."

C.C. leisurely rose and strolled across the floor, leather boots and his fine jodhpurs brushing against the screen door.

"Look up there."

C.C. stood, not moving. "Joe and Jess Young."

Suddenly, they both turned and C.C. pulled his gun. They had heard something moving in the lower backyard.

"Who's there? Speak up."

" It is I, Chief Miller, night watchman for R.C. Tway Coal Company, lending service." He was laughing, remembering what a coward C.C was without his gun.

"Chief, do you have your pistol?"

"Of course, I was at the shack when the message arrived that perhaps my help may be needed."

Chief always spoke in complete sentences and could correctly spell any word in the dictionary and define it. Chief was old, maybe in his fifties, and married to Miz Miller. Miz Miller never ever went out of the yard, as far as the yard, no farther. She stayed inside all the time, most of the time with the shades pulled. No child had ever delivered milk, or eggs, or anything to their kitchen table and gone home to report what the inside of the house was like. Chief Miller and Miz Miller carried a painful secret.

"Do all of you have yer pant legs down in yer shoes? Rattlers don't sleep at night, ye know." James had stooped over and was putting the tops of his pants inside his mining shoes.

Then quiet. The three men began the climb up schoolhouse hill. This was the same climb that the children from upper white camp made every day for school. The moon lay a faint, lacy pattern through the trees. The only sound was the sound of their breathing.

"I smell cooking. Do you smell cooking?" It was James. Then they heard the radio. Bluegrass music played on the radio. All three stopped.

There was Joe Young out under the basketball hoop, dancing around with the only basketball within three miles. The school's only basketball. He was dancing around, tossing that ball into the basket, not missing a single shot. He was good.

"He is extremely talented. Superb coordination. My practiced eye has never seen such agility. It is a tragedy that such hubris and error of judgment overtakes his better instincts." Chief, C.C, and Jim just stood, trying to take in the scene. The radio was a playing.

> *"Down to the barnyard he stumbled*
> *fell down by the door.*
> *The very next words that he uttered,*
> *'I'll never get drunk no more.'"*

Then real high,

> *"Beautiful, beautiful blue eyes*
> *Beautiful, beautiful blue eyes*
> *Beautiful, beautiful blue eyes,*
> *I'll never get drunk no more."*

Then rifting into blue grass that would cause a grown man to chill all over.

"Joe, this is ready." Jess Young called to his big brother

Jess was frail and not interested in much. He knew how to cook. And he loved music.

Joe was moving and scoring! He was at the University of Kentucky with a million people, all a shouting his name because UK was beating the hell out of Tennessee! He was better than the best. He twirled, ducked, bounced up to the goal, swung his hips to outplay the guards. The score was 13 to 0 in the first three minutes of play.

"Joe, this chicken won't be fit to eat and the taders 'ul get cold. Come on."

Joe stuck the ball under his arm, wiped the sweat off his forehead, and loped over to the fire.

"Byronesque," whispered Chief. "The boy is Byronesque."

Joe sat on his heels, reached over to the fire and lifted gingerly the stick holding the hen, pulled the roasted hen apart. Clear juices oozed. The potatoes sizzled, the skins all puffed out and crisp. The coal was hot when Jess dipped them in cold spring water, shook them, and laid them in the hot ashes.

"God, wish I had me some salt," said Joe.

"Oh poot, I forgot the salt." Jess rummaged in his pocket and brought out salt in a little Duke's Mixture bag.

"Never be without salt, I say."

He sprinkled the salt over the chicken and the potatoes.

"Wher'd you get them taters?"

"Ma's, nunder the floor."

"Nunder the floor?"

"Yeah, wintered over good, didn't they?"

The music played on. The night was cool, the fire warm.

"Halt, in the name of the law!" It was C.C. He had his gun aimed at them.

"You boys are arrested by the authority vested in me by the Tway Coal Company and the Commonwealth of the State of Kentucky."

Suddenly, Jess began to cough and bend over. When he looked up, blood was a running out of his nose and mouth.

"Gotamitee! Anyone got anything to wipe his mouth?" James realized Jess was a sick boy who needed more than any of them could give him.

Chief reached into his pocket and brought up a white, folded handkerhief and handed it to Jess.

Covering his mouth, Jess wailed, "Hit's the TB."

C.C. started toward him with the cuffs.

"Don't do that, C.C. The boy needs access to his mouth." Chief Miller was remembering something so painful that it could never be put into words.

C.C. felt nothing. "He needs handcuffs. He has broke the law of the Commonwealth of the State of Kentucky. And Joe. . ." Joe was gone. They looked around. He was gone. The basketball was rolling down the sandy court.

"Now, boys Joe's gone. I went in the mines at four o'clock, and I left my bucket at the mines. I'm hungry. Let's eat. Jess, sit down. Maybe that'll help yer cough." He reached for the hen. "This would be good if we had some salt."

Jess, covering his mouth with the one hand where the blood oozed through the folded handkerchief, reached in his pocket and handed Jim the Duke's Mixture bag.

"Much obliged, Jess."

They tuned down the music coming from a large radio. They broke off sticks, stuck them in the potatoes, and ran them around in the chicken juice.

"Mitey fine—mitey fine, boys. Jess, you've done mitey fine." James complimented him. Jess wiped the blood and ate the chicken.

They did need something to drink. Over by the schoolhouse porch was the galvanized water bucket for the school. Usually Gerald Carter, Aunt Ella and Uncle Tom's boy, went after the water at the spring. Every child could make a cup out of a piece of Blue Horse notebook paper that had a pointy bottom; the "cup" looked like a little pointy hat, with flaps. No one was supposed to drink out of the dipper. One person would pour into the cups.

Jim went after the bucket. Returned. "Jess, go get some water."

"James, the perpetrator could escape, couldn't he?" offered Chief.

"Is there any residue in the bucket?"

"I reckon that if yer talking about water in the bottom, there is."

"I suggest that we pour the residue into this bottle and that we pass the bottle." Whereupon he pulled out an Early Times bottle with about four fingers left in the bottom. By the light of the fire, Jim poured while Chief held the bottle. He made the bucket pour the tiniest stream. Then he began to raise the bucket higher and higher. The stream never missed the center of the bottle.

Chief looked up. There stood Jess with that black, curly hair, handsome features.

"What a loss."

"What'd you say?"

"I just made a significant observation, James L."

"Jess, go home," said C.C., chewing on the last of his chicken. "I'll pick you up tomorrow for jail, ifn't you are not too bad."

"Hell far, boys, I'm not going home without my juice. I need juice."

No one wanted to drink after Jess. What could they do?

"Don't worry, I know you'ens don't want to drink after me. I carry this." He reached into his pocket and handed Chief a little tin collapsible cup. Chief poured Jess' first and the other three sat in the spring night and had their own communion and thanked God that they were all well. Some time passed listening to the night sounds and away from all care. The fire died to a few embers. Jess never coughed. James broke the silence.

"Now, let's take down this electrical wire so I can put it back in the house."

"Jim, just how you going to handle that electricity?" C.C. said, running his greasy hand across his head, pasting down the fringe hair.

"Easy. Joe Young's not the only one who knows about juice." He walked toward the schoolhouse. The box holding the fuses was just inside the door. He went inside.

Suddenly, he stopped. What a smell! A warm, cozy, childhood smell. Chalk. And childhood sweat, play sweat. Happy time! He had never gone to school here. He went into the mines for pay when he was sixteen. He had tried Berea College. It wasn't for him.

He opened the fuse box, struck a match, saw what had to be detached, called out to C.C. for the flashlight and began with his pocket knife, careful not to touch the second wire.

"CC, it's gonna be dark for a minute or two. Shine the light here. He forgot for one second and "here" was punctuated with 110 volts going through his body. It held him. He jerked and by some miracle the juice let go. He stood there. Feeling good. Feeling fine! The significant thing is fear factor. Don't let fear take hold. He quickly rewired the wires, took his wire and was out the door, rolling it around his arm as he walked to the radio. It was a large radio, just out of the box.

"How'd you do that, Jess?"

"See," seys Jess. "We got it last time and hid it nunder the floor. We sold our cow and Ma never went down nunder the floor. So we set it back nunder the back. See, hit's my birthday and this is my party. So me and Joe carried it up here and got this ol' chicken on her nest and decided to take your lights out of yer house. See, and we come up here for my pardy."

"How old are you?"

"I'm thirteen."

"Age of accountability." Chief observed.

"Here boy, take a swig of this. It will give you something to celebrate," This from C.C., who had planned the last sip for himself.

Jess took the bottle and drank a little, than a little more. Emptied the bottle.

"Jess, boys, let's go home."

Wherein Mickey is Born

Very early in the next morning Charity got up to start the fire in the cook stove and to fix breakfast. James had gone back to the mines, leaving the wire rolled on the back porch. With the baby coming, they needed every penny that he could make.

She put on her clothes. Tied her apron. Went out the back door, across the back porch and down the steep yard and under the porch to get dry kindling for the stove.

"I'll make biscuits, fry eggs, fry some of the last of the bacon and have blackberry jam, milk, coffee and make a showing of the fresh butter." By now she was completely under the floor. She moved her hand out for a last piece of kindling. That's when she saw the two shoes with two feet in them. Gently, gently, she laid down the kindling and got down on her knees, and backed out from under the floor. She pulled her dress above her knees and ran down the steep embankment across the dirt road across the branch, through the yard and up the front porch of Miz Amics' boarding house. She ran up the steps and down the hall to the kitchen.

"Help, help. Somebody help. Miz Amics, help!" Out came Miz Amics, wiping her hands on her apron.

"Charity, what's wrong?"

"They's a man up under the floor. He could be dead," her voice rising in total fear as she began to take in what had happened. "Oh God, Oh God. Lois Jean is there. Help me. Help me."

Miz Amics went to the bottom of the stairs.

"Mr. Moore." Her voice climbed sweetly up a whole octave as she called out to him.

"Come, Mr. Moore." It sang.

Then she began the refrain again.

C.C. appeared at the top of the steps, hastily putting on his gun. His hair hanging down to his shoulder on one side.

"They's a man at Charity's under the floor, Mr. Moore. I'll keep your breakfast in the warmer 'til you return, Mr. Moore."

"Alright, Miz. Amics."

"Charity, it's Joe Young." He looked at her. With awareness this time. Even pregnant, she was beautiful. Blond, dishwater blond, beautiful face with blue eyes, full lips—full lips. And something else. What was it? Something else.

"Lois Jean is there. Hurry, Mr. Moore, hurry," she said, running out the door. "Oh God, oh God, oh God," she said with every step. "Lois Jean, oh God."

"Hush, Charity, or you'll wake up Joe and he might have a gun." On they went, he behind her. They crossed the branch, went up the hill, and under the porch.

He got down on his knees, crawling his way closer and closer to the two feet. The soles of the shoes just inches past the chimney. He clamped his hands around the ankles.

"Joe, in the name of the law in the Commonwealth of Kentucky, come out."

Joe raised up.

C.C. heard his head hit a 2x4. He moaned and slid forward on his back.

"Let go my legs; I can't move."

"Tough titty, my boy. Move."

Joe squirmed out.

C.C. let go, pulled his gun. "You know, I could shoot the hell outta you now and nobody would care. Nobody save Jesse would care. This time yer going to jail in Harlan."

Joe came out, blinking in the bright sun. James had come upon the scene.

Joe looked silently at James and Charity. C.C. shoved him and Joe fell and slid forward on his face.

Jim and Charity started up the backyard to the back door. Suddenly she stopped and drew in her breath sharply. He stopped.

"Charity, you all right."

"James, the baby's coming."

He swooped her up as light as a feather. She looked up at him.

"I do love you," he said.

She lay in his big arms, hands folded. "Charity, put your arms around my neck. That'll help."

She lay still. He carried her up the steps, into the kitchen.

"Lois, honey, what you doing out of the bed?"

"I climbed out, Daddy. You know I can climb out." She went over to the cabinet that was catty-cornered where Charity kept the apples in a basket. She turned around, stuck out one hip, and began to hit the cabinet door with her behind.

"Appa, appa, appa."

They laughed—sun up, birds singing.

He set Charity down and went back for the kindling. Charity always built the fire. Why would that dumb ass Joe come back and crawl under the porch? Why in hell? Because that would be the last place anybody would look. He picked up the kindling and built the fire. The secret to a good fire, he thought, was fine, dry kindling.

Charity was sifting down the flour for biscuits. She had just turned to get the buttermilk when a pain shot round her waist. She stood frozen, eyes wide. It stopped. She went about her business. Frying bacon crisp, draining it in a bag, the precious brown paper bags that she folded carefully and slid behind the leg of the icebox and the wall. Then came the eggs, while the biscuits were baking.

"James, put something sweet on the table, not molasses, apple butter."

"How 'bout some Karo. You got a bucket of that."

"Okay. Nothing can beat syrup'n'biscuits."

"Yeah, especially if you lay a slab of butter on that biscuit first."

In the little cozy kitchen with the oil cloth on the table, four chairs, stove, icebox, and the cabinet was a white-enameled table with the galvanized water bucket and dipper. They all drank out of the dipper. The jelly jars were in the cabinet and they had a set of four plates, a platter and bowl that Mr. and Miz Carter had given them when they got married. Different ones had given them an egg turner, some called it a spatula, an ice pick, a can opener, a rolling pin with instructions to use it on Jim, if necessary.

He sat down in his place. She reached for the biscuits. The pain again. This time she dropped the pan. The whole pan.

"Oh, God! Oh, God! James help me, help me, James."

"I'll go for the doctor, Charity. I'll get Miz Amics. Lay down. Lay down on the floor."

The pain had subsided.

"No, I've got to bathe and change clothes!"

"Charity, get in the bed or you'll drop that baby on its head."

He swooped up this tiny, blue-eyed, unpredictable woman and bolted through the front room into the bedroom and laid her gently on the pink bedspread. "I'm goin' to Miz Amics and call for the doctor."

As soon as the door closed, up she got, opened the chifforobe, pulled out the drawer, and put on the pink silk gown that she had secretly stored there. She reached under the bed, pulled out the precious horde of newspapers. Spread out the sheets of the Harlan Daily Enterprise, layer after layer. Got the clean, soft feed sacks that she got from Miz Brannon, put two that she had cut down the side seam and across the bottom onto the mattress. She had put them through lye water and they were soft. She pulled the shades down and turned on the floor lamp.

Ted had made the floor lamp in a class at Berea College. Only Ted would make a floor lamp light like this. He called it "the natural wicker look." Frank Lloyd Wright had talked about the "prairie look". He had begun at the platform on the bottom and wound natural wicker around the base, up the stand that was a pole as big around as a baseball bat. It had two lights. The shade was as wide as her arm was long. It was a wicker shade, lined in pink silk. The lamp was a wedding present, a gift of gratitude to Jim and Charity for financial help to Berea College. Charity hated the lamp because Ted had made it. Theodore F. Carter took money from James to go to Berea College and to Charity, that was unfair.

Another pain shot through her body. She screamed. Lois Jean came in.

"Climb in yer bed, Lois Jean. Climb in yer bed."

Lois went over in the corner and climbed into the bed, just as Miz Amics came into the room.

"Oh, Charity, honey. Has yer water broke?"

"No, not yet."

"Honey, it's gonna mess up that gorgeous gown. Don't you want yer slip?"

A slip was made out of a cow feed bag or a chicken feed bag. The feed came in nice sacks, sometimes with flowers printed on it. Everybody who had a cow and a little girl made that little girl a pinafore for school out of feed sacks when it got warm weather. Sometimes, somebody would say, "Yer wearing a cow-feed dress." They were more complimentary if it had rick-rack trimming it.

"No, Miz Amics," she said condescendingly. "I want this pink satin gown."

"Here, James, let me take Lois. Don't worry. Me 'n Helen will keep her. And if need be, she can spend the night."

"Ma will come get her if need be."

"Charity, honey, ye'll be all right when the doctor gets here. Say bye-bye, honey. Say bye-bye. Wave bye-bye."

Charity closed her eyes, folded her hands across her stomach. She said nothing.

When Miz Amics started down the hill to the dirt road, she ran into the company doctor. Fortunately, he had been at the boarding house. Unfortunately, he had laid out all night long, coming in at about three or four o'clock.

Nobody knew much about this little thin man with the white hands and manicured nails. You could tell that he took great pride in his delicate white hands. He wore a watch and somebody said something about his being from West Point. Was that place in Kentucky? Anyway. he stayed in Harlan a lot. Every miner in Tways, black and white, was cut two dollars a month for the company doctor. And, furthermore, he didn't do all that much. He delivered babies, of course, and helped with the miners when they "got mashed" in the mines. But it made one wonder.

There he was in the room.

Her water broke. She began to scream.

He bent down, lower.

"Lady, what is your name?"

James was in the kitchen making sure there was plenty of hot water.

"Charity, Charity Angeline Moses Carter."

He bent closer.

She smelled the whiskey. "You've been drinking."

"Charity Angeline Moses Carter, we are going to get this baby here in fine shape. You are with one of the finest surgeons in the whole world. I could cut you open and take that baby, sew you back up and you could dance in Harlan ten days from now."

"You've been drinking."

"No, sweet Charity, that was last night. This is today. Let's see. May. . . May 14, 1934, sweet Charity."

Just then James stepped into the bedroom carrying a pan of water. He set it down on the art deco dresser. It was hot water, and it would leave the faintest white ring forever on the dresser. He reached into the drawer and pulled out the pistol.

"Doc, do you need something?"

The doctor looked up. He saw James' front and back (reflected in the mirror) at the same time. He saw the pan of water and the gun.

Doc jumped back, hitting the floor lamp. He jerked forward; the wicker shade with pink lights slid gently, covering him completely. He staggered, pushing the shade back.

Charity screamed.

"Push down, Mrs. Carter." James shoved the doctor out of the way and grabbed Charity's hands. "Push, Charity, with all your might."

"It's coming; it's coming. Oh, God, this baby's coming." She drew back, drew all the muscles in her body tight. Nothing happened.

"Relax, Charity, relax!"

"Look at me, look at me, relax—let go—let go like you did when we started this baby. Turn everything loose."

Doc stood back. Adjusting the lamp shade, screwing it around until he found the top of the harp and felt it slide into the anchor.

"Charity, look me in the eyes and let go; let go; let go." Out slid the little baby.

"Here, sir, I'll take it from there, if you don't mind, sir."

"Much obliged, Doc."

The lamp was shoved into the corner.

"Hell fire, I've left the kettle on. It's probably burned through." Out he went.

"Mrs. Carter, we will clean up." He cut the umbilical cord, took the little baby over to the dresser and bathed her gently, gently.

"Where's her some clothes?"

"In the left-hand dresser drawer."

He took out a little shirt—a little knit undershirt. Put on a square Birdseye soft diaper. Looked at her little pink mouth yelling her head off and carried her over to her mother.

Charity was struggling to get up.

"I'm in a mess. I've got to get up and wash."

"No, I'm going to do that. I will disassemble the birth bed. Perhaps you have some store bags."

"Yes, behind the icebox in the kitchen."

He went in the kitchen. Jim Carter was stirring red-eye gravy for the biscuits.

"Doc, we'll eat directly."

Doc bent over and felt his gorge rise. He grabbed the bags and went back to the bedroom.

He rolled Charity over and removed the bed mess.

"Now, separate them feed sacks from them newspapers." She was propped up with her head on her elbow and was directing the doctor.

He pulled out the papers, pulled off the two feed sacks.

"They's a clean sheet in the chifforobe. Get it and the matching pillow-cases."

"Charity, Mrs. Carter, there is nothing on the pillowcases."

"I don't care. They don't match. Get the set, doctor. Get the set. I was a virgin when I married James."

He opened the drawer. There was a set. He came back to the bed.

She rolled over.

"Oh, Ch—Mrs. Carter, don't you want to hold your newborn infant?"

"Well, I guess."

He took the tiny bundle out of Lois Jean's bed. Here. The little thing was crying.

"Has your milk come down?"

He was pulling at the pink satin gown. "It's got to come off." He went to the drawer, opened it. Sure enough there was a straight slip. Soft.

"Take this bloody thing off, and put on this."

"Turn your head." The baby lay beside her; off came the gown. On went the clean slip.

"Charity, what we going to name this baby?"

"I don't know. Her head is bony. The bones stick up on both sides and she doesn't have hair. She looks like a mouse."

"Like Mickey Mouse," gorge rising as he worked with squeezing the mess into bags.

"Like a little mouse!"

"Like Mickey Mouse. How about Mickey Mouse?"

"I like Mickey."

Suddenly she said, "What's your name, doctor?"

He paused. "My name, he mused. I lost my good name."

What a strange thing to say. "I lost my good name."

"My name is Jonathan Fowe Anderson. My middle name is Fowe.

Charity said, "She is Mickey Fowe." And she was.

The doctor hurried out of the room.

Charity lay back, closing her eyes, and Mickey Fowe lay curled beside her asleep. Jim, standing in the kitchen stirring the gravy, heard Buchell Creech in his ice wagon coming to deliver the ice. Jim heard a knock at the door. There stood Uncle Tom Becker.

"Jim."

"Tom."

The men shook hands and Tom laid his hand on the clasp.

"Come in, come in." Buchel Creech was behind Tom. He was carrying a twenty-five pound block of ice.

"Jim, I just heard from Doc that you are now living with three women."

"Come here and look, Tom. Let me show you a sight for sore eyes." Uncle Tom, Buchel, and James peeped into the bedroom. Charity was asleep. Mickey Fowe lay beside her.

"That's a fine scene," Uncle Tom nodded. The three went back to the kitchen and sat down at the table. Never mind that Uncle Tom was from colored camp. There the three sat at the table at Charity's house eating cut-out biscuits.

Sun came in through the screen door. Jim poured the coffee and sat down. Uncle Tom ran his hand across the cool oil-cloth table and leaned back.

"Mighty fine, Jim, mighty fine." Suddenly Buchel destroyed the moment.

"Jim, you still doing business?" Uncle Tom cleared his throat, and Jim got the signal.

"No, married life sets a man straight. A man can't make moonshine with a wife and two little girls.

"I'z just asking. Butchell stuck his finger in his ear and turned it, examined it and wiped it across his pant leg. "I'z just asking."

"I know. I know."

"Tom, how's Miz Becker?"

Miz Becker—no Negroes were called Miz, Mr., or by their first names, or Nigger. But R.C. Tway was different. Matt Carter had told James that in the sight of God all were created equal. Furthermore, there soon would be more colored men working R.C. Tways than there would be whites, especially if anybody tried to unionize Tways.

T.M. Gibson was going to have more jobs for colored men than for white men. Colored men could not join the union. They knew their place and they would be forced to keep it. Strange thing. When miners were deep in the mines, nobody cared what color anybody was. Near the end of a shift they often passed the bottle around and everybody took a little swig of James' best.

"Well, got to be goin'. Come on, Uncle Tom," says Butchell. "Let's take them Niggers some ice."He loved saying it. It was a dare.

"Yes, young man, let's go. Thanks for the breakfast. See you tonight."

Jim cleaned up, put the clean dishes up in the cabinet. Charity had carried extra water. The house was quiet and sweet smelling.

He went up the steps of the boarding house, and there sat Lois Jean in the swing with Helen. Helen was beautiful, red hair, fair complexion, and a fine figure. She had on a satin kimono. "Helen, how are you?"

"I hear that you have a blond girl, Jim. Buchel told us."

"Yes, I have." How the hell could he explain that the woman, this unexplainable woman, had named his baby, his bony headed, bald girl, Mickey Fowe. "Oh, Gotamitee, Gotamitee, Gotamitee," he prayed.

"Gotamitee, Daddy, let's go."

"Don't say Gotamitee, Lois. Yer mother wouldn't like it. Let's go see Gramma." He went in and thanked Miz Amics.

They were passing Frank and Hanner Young's house, where Frank and Hanner, Jess, Joe, Frank, Jr. and Charles lived. They had just passed Lurie Cloud's and her man's house. Some even said that her man was an Indian, from up off Bird Eye Rock. They passed the McVey's, soon to be moving out into the holler near the garages. Then an empty where Uncle Tom and Miz. Becker had lived next to the Carters while they were waiting to get a house in colored camp.

They came to the Carter's house. Up the steep hill, up the steps onto the porch, and into the front room. Matt and Nannie had a four-room mining house. They had lived there since R.C. Tway opened. He reached over in the corner in the front room, grabbed the guitar, commenced to singing.

> "I've got me a mity sword.
> I've got me a mity sword.
> Ho dommie diddle dommie, diddle dommie do,
> I've got me a mity sword."

James had entered the mines when he was a boy. He was not afraid to crawl through the hole and back into the mines. When a miner went back a couple hundred feet, he could stand up. It was a room. A black room. Jim went in young and began to get paid when he was sixteen years old.

Matt Carter was welcomed at anybody's camp. He came with five boys, and the younger ones worked for almost free. Matthew Carter had closed up a huge farm in Whitley County, Kentucky, and come to Harlan, with his family.

"What the hell, Jim. You lost your mind?"

"Has Charity had the baby?"

"Yes, a little girl, Mickey Fowe." He told them about the delivery and about Tom and Buchel. At that minute he realized that Lois was not in the room. She had gone to the kitchen, taken the cornbread off the table, and was going toward the kitchen door, where at least five hungry dogs waited. They all ran. Nannie was there first and swooped her up, squeezed her tightly against her bosoms. They all knew that the first lesson is to learn to anticipate the evil deed. "Jim, go back and lay down."

"I've not slept."

"Go back and lay down," said Matt.

"I might just do that."

He was dog tired and would need to be up again ready for the night shift.

He was in his Dad's and Mom's bedroom. Surrounded by their familiar things, he took off his shoes and threw himself into the bed. The old Seth Thomas clock on the wall said 1:47. How good the feather bed felt. The feather pillows. The soft, soft quilts—one was the Star of Texas; the other he couldn't remember. The room was cool and dark and soft, and the branch below the hill was gurgling, splashing. He was alone and sleeping.

"Gramma, Gramma, show me, show me your prize."

"Matt, this is one smart child." She was holding Lois on her big, soft lap.

Let's see. Cora's two children, Alma and Junior. Bill's two girls, and now Lois Jean and Mickey Fowe. She was relieved it wasn't "Nannie"; she hated "Nannie". Nannie Caddell Carter was her name. A Caddell from up on Wolf Creek. Her brother Clyde read law.

Matthew Carter had brought wife and children from Buck Creek at Rockhold in Whitley County. His was one of the first families to settle in the new coal mines, R. C. Tway in Harlan County, Kentucky.

Tways was not a large camp like even Mary Helen, or the big ones on up the road, but it suited him fine. Leige, Bill, James, Arthur, and Ted. Not many miners had that many boys to follow in the mines. For that reason Matt was looked up to and he introduced each boy into the mines early on. They either did or they did not stay. Only Jim really took to it. The rest would manage to leave as soon as they could and get out. Ted went to Berea. He came in and used James' scrip card for funds. Berea was a college run by northerners and supported by rich northerners. Everyone worked. You worked your way through four years of superb education. Ted would be the first in the family to graduate and become a dentist. Matt and Nannie believed in letting children find what they wanted to do.

Jim was the best in the mining business. He was not afraid of the claustrophobic driftmouth that led to the seams of bituminous coal. He never carried one of the canary birds in. He could do any job assigned to him to mine coal. He could place timbers, cut coal, shovel coal and shoot dynamite. He was the one with the muscles and the brains and he was handsome. Furthermore, he was a coal miner's coal miner. He could do anything with electricity and fix any machine. He could fix cars. He could shoot a gun and fry an egg or dress a mine wound as well as anyone. He had completely shocked the family when he came in and told them that he had married Charity Angeline Moses. The Carters knew the family. Charity's mother, Ida Cox, was a fine, talented woman who had done nothing to deserve her fate.

The Moses' were a tribe. They owned farms and were enterprising. They traced their genealogy back to Joshua Moses, born in North Carolina in 1748; died in Whitley County, Kentucky. He fought in the Revolutionary War and had a pension of some $50 per annum until he died.

"Sit in this chair, honey, and you can hold it." Nannie came to the front room holding the largest, round ball of silver foil in Harlan County. She, with Matt's help, had saved foil from the Teaberry chewing gum wrappers and foil from black electrical tape for years. Others had saved silver foil, but nothing like this. It was as large as a small pumpkin! She used it to hold the door to the front porch open in summer time. People came from miles around to see this wonder.

Lois Jean sat and waited for the ball to be placed in her lap. Nannie placed it gently in her lap, and Lois put her hands on either side.

Nannie took those little hands; looked at them. Then suddenly she ran her finger across the top of the little ear. Her little left ear. There it was—the mark of the beast. She smiled; there it was. No bigger than the head of a straight pin and coming to a point. That tiny bit of cartilage was on both of Jim's ears. It was on Matt's ear.

But the deep secret was that Elizabeth Jane Caddell was a distant cousin to James L. Carter. Elizabeth Jane Caddell (4) b March 13, 1847, daughter of William and Louisa (Moses 3) Caddell, daughter of Joshua Moses 2, son of Joshua Moses 1, married James Moses 4, son of John Moses 3, son of Joshua Moses 2, son of Joshua Moses 1. James Moses was born Oct 30, 1848. Died March 31, 1931. Nannie Caddell was related to Charity Moses. Charity didn't know it and Nannie wouldn't tell her. They both had blue eyes.

The dishes were on the table and the dogs around the back door. Outside it was May. The morning glories were climbing over everything. They had climbed over three of the four posts on the back porch. The back porch was an important place.

So much depended on the #2 tub. A #2 lasted a long time. It was used for everything! Two were on Nannie's porch. Geraniums in the Karo syrup cans ringed the banisters. Nannie could grow geraniums year after year by just setting the cans, after blooming was gone, under the floor.

On the front porch were the chairs. The rocking chairs, the straight chairs. And again the red geraniums grew in the cans around the banister. There was a front porch swing. The girls, Ora, Ruth, and their niece Alma, sat on cool evenings swinging, pushing back with one foot and holding out the other leg. The lovely, shapely leg. The swing moved slowly from spring until the first frost.

It was May. The yard was burgeoning. Tomatoes were hanging green on the vines. The corn was up. Half-runner white beans and pole beans were set. Nannie Carter also had some fine pepper plants. She had nursed them from seeds that one of the women from across the branch had brought from Alabama. That same woman gave Miz Brannon a peach switch, which Miz Brannon planted. It grew, as Nannie described it, "profusely," giving off peaches the second spring. Nannie, on the way to the courthouse, picked up one of the peaches for the pit, brought it home, nurtured it with everything from warm water on. Put it in a syrup can (she saved everything, everything). The little thing began to bear green life. She nurtured it by letting it be in the kitchen window sill. When there was no danger of frost, she set it in a quiet corner of the upper backyard. And it increased. Before June, it had put out three delicate blossoms. She went to it everyday and talked to it. "Come on little tree, grow, make peaches, and I'll make us something good to drink!" There was nothing as delicious as peach brandy. And it was a wonderful experience every time you took a little sip.

The well-made spirits were made by women in the Caddell family. Most stopped when they were "saved". Either Nannie was "saved" and given permission by God to continue, or she was not "saved" yet. Eventually everybody was "saved". Unless they were caught dead! That happened often. However. . .

> "Between the stirrup and the ground
> Mercy sought and mercy found."

That made little sense to a lot of folks. However, they had not fallen from a horse as Nannie had. The thing to do was to enjoy life. Live each day. "The French have a word for that," says Ted. "Carpe Diem." She had him write that out, and she embroidered that on her pillowcases! A pair she kept in the trunk.

Wherein Princess Is Killed by a Panther

They had all settled down. Ruth, Alma, Ora, Junior, Ma and Dad. Junior was Leige's boy being raised by Matt and Nannie. He was Alma's brother. About one o'clock, there was the suddenness of a terrible commotion. Nannie sat up in bed. She shook Matt.

"Matt, get up."

He came to. Alert and for a split second, just waiting.

He heard the commotion. All the dogs from under the back porch were after something big. He heard their attacking yelps—same as when he took them after squirrels and rabbits.

Putting on his pants over the long underwear, he reached for the double-barreled shot gun and ran to the door. The moon drifted behind a cloud.

Then he heard the bone-chilling death cry of a dog that had been attacked by something that could pick it up and sling it back and forth, back and forth, back and forth.

"Oh, God." His dogs were all around in a circle up close to the back of the yard. He stayed on the porch. If he shot at the thing, he would kill some of those treasured hounds. If he didn't, the thing could kill the dogs.

He shot.

There was a scream that only a panther can make—a huge panther. It was a panther from up in the mountains. They were the most dangerous animals around.

This one was coming for the new calf under the floor with ol' Sookie. It had smelled the blood from the birth event and was coming for the calf.

Everything was quiet except the whimpering of a dog.

Nannie was beside him.

"I'm gonna save my dog. Nannie, build a fire."

"Matt, they's embers in the stove."

"Roll up one of yer paper bags and light it. I'm going up in that garden and get my dog."

She pulled out a brown poke from beside the icebox and rolled it tight, twisted the end, lifted the stove cap, and stuck it in, wiggling it.

"Hurry, hurry, woman."

She handed him the lighted poke and he went out. The moon had come out from behind the cloud, and it was as bright as first daylight.

He ran up the sloping garden to the fence. "Oh, God," he wailed.

There lay Princess. She was gashed open, her guts splayed out over her ribs, all smashed. She was whimpering.

Nannie was behind him.

Matt was working the guts back into a limp Princess.

"Matt, put her down, put her down."

Then everything stopped. The whole world stopped. Just the faint whimpering, Princess wheezing. They listened.

"Nannie, get my rifle."

She lifted her straight slip and ran back toward the house.

Matt commenced to cry. "What a goddamned world! What a poor pathetic event."

He was down bent over and could feel the blood and mess oozing through his fingers. He laid his head on Princess' head. He loved that dog. "goddamn world! goddamned panther!"

Then everything was still.

"Here's yer rifle, Matt."

"No need, Nannie. No need."

Matt cried. He cried for Princess and for so much unfairness of things that God seemed oblivious to. Directly, he got up. "Bring the shovel."

Nannie went back, moved a tub and picked up a pick and a shovel. She went back and together they dug a hole right there and put Princess in it.

"She'll be next to the little peach tree. Come on, Matt."

"You've got to get out of these clothes."

Nannie went to her trunk, reached way on top of the cabinet and pulled out two wine glasses.

"This is all I have of your mother's stuff from Lee County, Virginia."

"They're purty."

Poured two drinks.

They had communion.

Nobody had heard the commotion. If anyone had, they'd believed it to be somebody shooting somebody up in colored camp just across the branch.

Wherein N'Jenny Visits

N'Jenny was big and did washings. She went to the Owens', the Miller's, the Gibson's, and to the boarding house.

There she stood with a brown paper bag in her hand.

"Miss Charity, how you doin'?"

"I'm fine. Come in, come in."

"I brought you some greens. Here is poke salit, blackberry, and dandelion greens. The poke is good. How are you doing?"

Charity had never had a colored woman in her house. Did she say "sit down"? N'Jenny was the finest laundress in all of Tways. Jenny had four galvanized tubs. She had one tub for washing the clothes; the second for rinsing white laundry in lye water; a third for rinsing out the lye water; the fourth was for starching the white clothes then the colored clothes. Jenny knew exactly how much lye to put in how much water. And she made starch with no lumps. Smooth. Jenny had two stove irons and an electric iron.

"These greens are ready for cooking." She had half a bag full. "Put some strips of streak of lean and they's good and good for your constitution."

Charity had never heard of her "constitution". Where was it? Couldn't let her know that she didn't know about her "constitution".

"N'Jenny, thank you. James likes greens. I'll make some cornbread and some pinto beans."

Pinto beans were cooked at least twice a week and kept at all times. Pinto beans came in barrels to the A&P in Harlan. Pinto beans, buttery, filling, satisfying, the basis of the whole meal. Pinto beans, cornbread, and in the spring, greens were always on the table. You had other things, but pinto beans were the foundation of the mountain food chain.

"Wait, I'z got something, som'n else." She smiled and lumbered slowly out the back door. She picked up a little glass-covered bowl. She waddled back through the door. "I made you a 'nenner pud'n." And she held it out triumphantly. Charity was amazed. Bananas were a luxury! The funeral dish, banana pudding.

When somebody died and was laid out, two staples were necessary. Banana pudding and whiskey—often good moonshine. The most crucial thing on a banana pudding was the meringue. It had to stand in peaks. It had to swirl around on the top of the pudding and have peaks that were the right shade of tan. It was carried proudly to the kitchen of the place where the deceased would be mourned in the front room.

Sometimes the dead were kept up two days and two nights, calling for several puddings. Miz Brannon's pudding stood. Nannie Carter's pudding stood. But never, never had Charity seen a pudding so perfect, so standing, as this pudding.

"Jenny, oh, Jenny," she came toward Jenny. Jenny set the pudding on the table and enclosed Charity in her big arms.

"Oh, N'Jenny, I've never had—," her voice trailed off.

Big Jenny hugged the little white woman. She felt sorry for her lot. Jenny had nursed her own self through all her sorrows. Leaving folks in Alabama to come to Harlan to find a man whose bones she would rattle. Never finding a man with staying power. No little babies to nurse her big bosoms. Nobody to stay with her. She was huge. No man would have her. Jenny read too. She could read any Sears and Roebuck catalog ever placed before her. She could do crocheting, tadding, knitting, embroidery. But, her boat had fouled up in shallow water and she knew her days were numbered. She was an old, old woman. Fifty-two and "'bout dead". She hugged this little simple woman and they both cried, neither recognizing the complexity of the other.

"Charity, Charity, I'm hungry." Lois Jean stood in the doorway surveying the strange scene.

"Oh, Lois Jean, here's N'Jenny. Brought us some greens and pudding." Turning, "Jenny, do sit down". She couldn't—Jenny would break the chair.

"I can't sit. What you doing?"

"Well, I was about to bake an apple stack cake for James."

"Ohh," she rolled her eyes.

"Whyn't you let me take the recipe and I'll make it for you."

"No. That's in writing and you can't read."

"Yes, I can. I can read anything, and I can cook anything."

"Well, I declare. . ."

In Alabama, Jenny had been skinny. Then she learned to read. Then she found recipes written on envelopes and stuck in with other envelopes and kept in a kitchen cabinet between an almanac and a can of baking powder.

"Here, Jenny, take the recipe. It is precious. My sister gave me a copy of my mother's apple stack cake. It calls for dried apples. Mind you, dried apples. Read this." Jenny took the envelope and began. In a totally different voice:

Ida's Apple Stack Cake

3/4 cup lard (shortening)   1 tsp salt
1/2 cup sugar   1 tsp ginger
1 cup molasses   4 cups flour
3 eggs   1 cup buttermilk
1/2 tsp soda
2 tablespoons baking powder
Cream shortening and sugar. Mix well. Add eggs one at a time, beating after each addition. Combine flour, soda, baking powder, salt, and ginger. Add above ingredients alternately with buttermilk.
Beat until smooth. Roll or pat into [six] greased pans. About 3/8 inches thick. Bake in moderate oven [355 degrees] for 10-12 minutes.
Filling: Dried applies [about 3 cups]
1/2 tsp ginger and other spices [nutmeg]
Cook and sweeten apples. Combine ingredients. Mix well. Spread over each layer, stacking cakes on top of each other. Ageing makes cake more moist.

Jenny's voice was the voice of a well-educated person. A white voice. It sounded white. She enunciated every syllable. She read every word. Charity's eyes grew large; her hands dropped to her sides. "Where'd you learn that, Jenny? Who are you?"

Jenny replied, "I nose. I nose 'bout dried apples, dried peaches, dried pears. The onliest thing I's never dried is watermelon! Ha ha!" She picked up the recipe written on a little white card and lumbered out the door.

Charity walked over to the window, eased the shade back, peeped out and never moved until Jenny was out of sight.

Lois Jean was ready for oatmeal. Quaker oatmeal from the new A&P.

James was a little worried about Charity's doing so much trading at the A&P in Harlan. That could cause a falling out with the commissary. Vance

Owens could notice that Charity was taking money and not using scrip. She was buying more and more at the new A&P.

At the A&P, the cabbage was fresh. The pinto beans had fewer rocks. The A&P coffee came with flower seeds called Eight O' Clocks. There was jelly already made and jam and potatoes, onions, bananas, pears, and vinegar and rare small cans of sardines, dried prunes and raisins, mops and Duz and Rinso and P&G soaps and fine pork chops, country ham, streak of lean. Spaghetti and macaroni. Rumor had it that the Hunkies and Negroes up in Cumberland, Benham and Lynch had instigated these things. They ate macaroni like others ate pinto beans. If you took a recipe to the A&P, you could buy everything that went in it and come home and fix it!

She finished with breakfast. Fed Mickey Fowe a bottle. It was disgusting to see a woman breastfeeding a baby. Breasts were private things and not very good for much of anything. Why did James love to feel of breasts? He did. And she let him for she was no longer a virgin. She knew well the little pain, the tiny pain overridden by pure ecstacy, the first time he entered her tent. Sometime when she was moved to do it, she would read the Book of Ruth. Ruth had entered Boaz's tent! Ruth had dressed, put Evening in Paris on herself and lay at Boaz's feet.

She piled the dishes into the dishpan. A dishpan only improved with a few dents. It was one of the first things she bought when she and James set up housekeeping. It set on the enameled table that set under the window with curtains. On the other wall was the breakfast set. Table and four chairs.

She used a feed-sack dishcloth. Nannie had given her a whole feed sack cut up and hemmed on her fingers. Folded and ironed. They were in the drawer of the enameled table. That, and P&G soap, black electrical tape, scissors, and wire pliers. A place for everything and everything in its place. It didn't take long to clean the kitchen, her kitchen.

She had decided to take Mickey for her first showing to Miz Brannon's. The bones in Mickey Fowe's head had conformed and her head was round. She had that white hair and blue eyes.

Charity walked out the back door. It wasn't as steep as the front, and down the sloping hill to the dirt road. It was about 10:30. She left James sleeping. Getting ready for the night shift that went from about 3 to 11. He had worked graveyard, 12 to 8 a.m. Jim could do anything in the mines. He had even rigged up an apparatus to pump out water after a washout rain. Some said you could get electrocuted with that thing and made him turn it off. He slipped and used it.

Wherein the Chicken Lot Pays Off

They went around to the back of the house. Miz McCurg was hanging out clothes. "Miz McCurg," Ida sang out. "My settin' hen is under your porch."

"Help yourself, Idy. Just help yourself."

"Lois, go under the porch and tell me where the nest is."

Charity, holding the baby, stood nearby. Lois Jean scooted under the porch and came back with an egg.

"Lau, she's setting."

"Charity, you have Jim build you a lot. I know that Lurie Cloud is not raising hens. She's not doing anything. She will give Jim the fence. It's high. He and Arthur can take it down. Ted can dig yer holes. Get you a post hole digger." Of course, Ida Brannon knew how to make ideas become real productions.

"James' daddy has a post hole digger."

"You can go into the business now. I'll give you this hen. It's a project, honey. You've got a project. Let's go get your butter."

The chicken lot became a reality. James went to the Clouds; softened them up with a swig of his finest home brew. Most knew that he and Nannie Caddell Carter made some of the finest home brew in Tways. Indeed, her mash was the finest around. It was left under her bed to rise.

James had to pass his mother's house to get to the mines. He could take a shorter path, but they were in this project together. Peach brandy—of sorts. Sugar, peaches, and let them ferment. Then strain into jars. It made a few, precious few, pints of the finest, smoothest brandy in Harlan.

Who got it? Miz T.M. Gibson, Miz. Hall, Chief Miller, maybe one or two others. They paid the price and the women cooked with it, taking a swig every now and then. Happy women, happy, happy men. Swapping stories, rolling eyes. How good it was for cooking and drinking. Nothing like peach brandy on Saturday night.

Mr. Cloud's scripture was, "Keep 'em barefoot and pregnant." Lurie Cloud was "pg". Mr. Cloud was old, in his middle forties. James had given him three dollars in Tways scrip for the fencing.

"She's pregnant now!" James had told Charity when he came back with the fence and three brothers, Arthur, Ted, and August, to help him erect the chicken lot above the house on the hill. High fence it was. The boys took turns digging, stretching, nailing, drinking, cussing, and telling stories. Others gathered from upper camp and got into the spirit and the spirits. James brought out a pint of Nannie's finest.

N'Jenny passed her homemade potato chips. That woman had a set of knives that were razor blades. She cut the thinnest slices. Soaked them in cold pump water for an hour or longer. Hauled out a cast iron pan. Filled it with lard. Put in the potato slices and let them brown to gold or past gold. Drained them on a brown bag and salted them with a big copper salt shaker. She came out on the porch.

"Mr. Jim. Oh, Mr. Jim, I've got somethin for ye'all."

Jim ran down the steep hill over to the porch. "Aw, N'Jenny. Mityfine, mityfine. Can I slip into your front room?"

They went in the cool, dark front room.

"Here." He handed her the whiskey bottle. "Have a swig and when I go to Ma's, I'll bring you some."

He took the potatoes. All work stopped. The boys gathered in the almost finished lot. Sat down under a tree. They blessed the potato chips with, "Mityfine, mityfine. How's she do this?"

"Damn'd if I know. Let's ask Ted. Ted knows everything. Theodore F., how does Jenny from Alabama manage to produce a project such as this? And would it be feasible to manufacture such a product at the prestigious Berea College?"

Ted pondered for a minute, then, sounding like James, said, "Hell far, I don't know how the taters are made, and I don't care. But let's all stay in R.C. Tway mines and let slate fall on our asses and die coughing up our lungs! Shall we?"

August, handsome August. Black curly hair, strong cheekbones—"I'm not a goin' in. I'm not. I'm not."

August didn't read well. He couldn't play a guitar or a banjo. He could work a tambourine, though. And he could dance. He looked good in his clothes. But he couldn't read. He once told James something about his reading.

"Once I was reading the book. I was looking at the book in Ma's bedroom and I held it up to the mirror, close to the mirror. The words in that book look the same to me. In the mirror and just with my eyes. They are the same."

One day Jim took the book. Held it up to the mirror. It was all backwards. It was backward reading. It was scary. He quickly turned the huge book around and read.

"Better to reign in hell than serve in Heaven." The book was a leatherbound narrative poem with illustrations. Kept in the bottom of the trunk. The title was Paradise Lost.

Yeah, August had trouble reading.

"Jim," says August, "here we set under this tree, Jim, and say you are a rooster. What you going to do tonight?"

"I'm going to diddle every hen in this place." They rolled on the ground, laughing, drinking their brandy and eating the crisp fried potatoes. It was so good that it bore repeating.

"I'll diddle every hen in the place."

That set off everybody. All four rolled and whooped! When they could set up again, they all looked up. Then Jim said slowly, "If chickens don't have them big wing feathers, they can't fly."

They got up and began again. It was a Saturday. They worked all day. By late afternoon, there stood the finest chicken lot in all Tways. It even had a tiny hen house where the chickens could nest. Ted had done most of the architecture. He had noticed it at Berea.

They went out, gathered leaves, moss, and Ma gave off a badly worn feed sack. Jim got a yard gate at one of the empties in colored camp.

Jim and Arthur went to Miz McCurg's and got the hen. Carried the whole nest back up and, as Ted would later say, "They trimmed her wings and incorporated it into its new home. The hen adapted well."

The boys left and James went into the kitchen. "Now, Charity, there's your lot, and you can put the girls in the lot. They can play in the chicken lot."

"Yes, well it's alright, I guess." Never any praise. Never a fine word—"you've done well." Always she held back on praise. Never a complete out and out praise word of any kind. For reassurance, he came across the kitchen, put his arms around her, turned her around and kissed her, ran his hands under her breasts. She raised her face, eyes shut, and melted in his arms.

"Listen, Charity, I'm taking the boys to town. They's worked all day and we're going to the Green Parrot. And I'm setting them up. I'm wearing my white suit. I'm goin't to drink a drop or two. I'll be in before Chief closes the gates, not a minute sooner. I laid around here doing yer bidding and word's out that I'm 'under petticoat government'. Me, James, 'under petticoat government'. I've got to set things right. You know who told me that. Pa. Pa says that it's out at the commissary that I, James, I am 'under petticoat government'. Nothing is farther from the truth. See we are equal. You are by my side and I am by your side. I love you and I love my girls. But I can't be under petticoat government. A man has got to be a man. I won't get drunk, but I'll'drink."

"Oh, James, that's. . .that's. . ." her voice trailed off. Charity could not give approval. She understood, but she dared not be positive about anything. For one reason: if God, through Jesus, heard her give approval, He would take that good thing from her. She would lose it. That is the way it had always been. If God in Heaven, who listened in on everything, heard you approve of anything, anything, God would take it.

One of the Caddells had said that, "God dangles you over the pit and that you are tied around with a piece of string and He holds a pair of scissors in His right hand and ye know not the time He will cut you into everlasting perdition."

How could she tell James that it was fine, that she understood, that she loved him. It would be dangerous for God to hear her say a thing like that.

"Listen, James, I am going to put Lois Jean in bed with me. When you come in, not so drunk, eating with Arthur, August 'n Ted, telling stories, standing up to shake hands with all, you sleep on the Creton day bed. That way you'll not wake us up." She looked at him sweetly, turned, picked up the bucket. "I'll go to the pump and get you a bucket of water for your bath." He stood in the kitchen and pondered all these things in his heart.

Wherein It's Saturday Night in Harlan

"What'll you fine gentlemen have tonight?" The Green Parrot in Harlan was the place to be. Jim had on his white suit, tie, and fine leather shoes from Middlesboro. This really was his wedding outfit. Now going on five years old. Ted had on tan pants with a tan sweater that he got at Berea College. There was a church in Peoria, Illinois, that sent fine clothes to Berea for their students. August was in a navy blue suit with a white shirt. Arthur had decided not to come.

"Looks like you boys might be off to the Margie Grand. What ye have?"

James was driving. That made him in charge.

"I'll have the usual. I want that steak medium well. Fried potatoes. Are the beans watery or dry?"

"I can drain them for you, James."

"And I'll have a salad with everything and some dressing."

"I'll have the same," Ted said.

"I'll take the Hickey, Mr. Forrester," said August.

The "Hickey" was a hamburger on a plate with a large serving of mashed potatoes, pinto beans, and spaghetti covered with chili and a glass of water. The "Hickey" sold for fifteen cents.

What a feast. A glorious Saturday night feast. The service was quick; full house on Saturday night. Full house; full service. Jim was going in on the last of the steak, working it out so's the beans and salad and bread would all end at the same time, when something caught his eye.

Three tables down. He caught the back of a head. The back of a head that he could recognize anywhere. Nobody in Harlan had short, straight shiny hair as soft and shiny as hers. She was perfect. Not a flaw in her entire body. Tall, slender. Tonight she was there with Ola Collins and Russ. Of course, she had seen him come in. She knew that he was there. They were probably going to the Margie Grand. He finished his meal and it all worked out. Not a potato left, not a bean, not a scrap.

"You gents care for dessert? Tonight we have the finest banana pudding and pound cake."

"Naw, I don't care for any."

"Same."

"Same."

They knew that James was carrying a silver flask with his initials engraved on it. It was filled with fine whiskey. He had filled it to the top. And the brothers knew that they would be invited for a swig on the way home.

"Well, boys, let's go to the Margie Grand."

"I thought we was going to get a hair cut and play a little pool."

"Naw, let's go to the Margie Grand." He knew that his voice could be heard three tables away."

James paid the bill. The year was 1934 and their bill was under $5.00.

On the way out they stopped at Russ' table.

"Well, say, hello, Ola, Russ, Halley."

"Hello, yourself," said Halley.

"How's that baby, Jim?" Did she say Jim with a hint of sarcasm? Pain? What was it? "What's her name?" Of course, Halley had heard the story of Mickey Fowe.

Everybody in Tways who knew them, knew that Charity Carter had named her little baby girl Mickey Fowe after a mouse and somebody in the family. "Halley, come see her. She's a beauty—white hair and blue eyes."

He leaned over the table and looked her in the eye. "She's my girl." That's when he saw her eye for the first time. Halley's left eye was dark. She had layered on the powder. But he could see that it was dark. That son-of-a-bitch had hit her. He had blackened her eye. Everything grew quiet. She looked up at him.

"Well, I'm goin' to the Margie Grand; see you later. Good seeing you, Ola, Russ. Have a good evening."

His project had just become complicated. Arthur and Ted were waiting in the black shiny Durant that Jim kept locked up in one of a set of three adjoining garages out in McVeigh hollar. It was a beauty. Ted had asked to take it to Berea. Once again.

"Naw, Ted, what'd they think about a poor son of a poor coal miner coming in with a Durant. I don't believe I'd try that. 'It would not be practical,' to quote a line of yours."

August smiled, "Hand me a swig."

They parked up by the post office and walked down the street to the fantastic Margie Grand. They went into Margie Noe's Margie Grand. Being dark all day long, it was comfortable. The movie was just beginning. They passed the flask, taking tiny sips. Just August and Ted. Jim seemed engrossed in something else. Really he would never be able to tell a single thing about that movie, not the name, who acted, what happened.

They came out and headed up the road. They had to get back before Chief closed the gates and padlocked them. Of course, anybody could crawl over and come in, as many did. But the action of closing the gates prevented organizers, in their trucks, and other unsightly trash from coming into Tways. On Saturday night, Chief would accommodate the crowd who went to Harlan. He was known to draw the gates up but not padlock them. Anybody seeking mischief, but not serious enough to check, would think that they were locked.

The brothers sailed through. Jim, enjoying the sharp turn, came around the commissary; stopped dutifully and respectfully. Out came Chief, shining his flashlight.

"Jim, Ted, August, you boys have a good night."

He drove up the dirt road but didn't take the left to the garages.

"Jim, what's the matter? You forgot to turn in."

There was always, always a reason for not following habit. Habit dictated. If you were placing dynamite, you followed steps. If you were tending mash, you followed rules. If you were planting half-runner white beans, you followed rules. Not so much rules as steps. Get one thing out of step and it could turn into a disaster. Clyde Caddell said as often as he could, "They's order in the universe."

"No, boys. I'm going to drive you home." The road was narrow, wide enough for one car. If two met, and they seldom did, one got off the road on the steep side so as not to slide into the branch.

He drove slowly across the branch between the boarding house and Halley's, then shifted down, passing the Cloud's, the Young's, and the two empties. He came to Pa's and turned the car around. Bossy, standing under the floor, woke up when the car lights flashed, stood up, and, thinking it was morning time, mooed. The boys laughed. Jim cut the headlights off.

August, Ted got out. They leaned over.

"Thanks, Jim, good time. Thanks."

"Forgit it; it's nothing. Glad we got together. Let's do this again, soon."

He eased out of the holler with no lights. He knew every rock, tree, and position of the moon and stars. He could distinguish the dogs by their bark. He knew every house and who lived there.

Jim drifted into another world. His universe was R.C. Tway, and he loved it. His daddy had taken him into the R.C. Tway Coal Mine when he was a little boy. They lived close to the slate dump, and Matt entered the mines from the side above his house. The coal in Tways lay in a vein that curved around the mountain. Rich, black, bituminous coal. Jim remembered in vivid detail his initiation to Tway Coal Mine.

In the early days, he carried three buckets into the mines. Nannie would fix either a dinner bucket or a supper bucket. In the top would be choked out biscuits with slabs of pork chops or chicken or ham. There were several of these, and in the summer, beans in a little tin cup with a piece of waxed paper around it tied with string and, if it were available, a pear, a banana, but always a Moonpie or something sweet. In the bottom of the bucket would be water. He would fill the bottom of the bucket with water when he got to the mines.

As a little boy, Jim loved the cool, dark mines, the smooth floor. He went in and begged to stay. By sixteen he was drawing his own money. He had found his place. Nobody was better. He could skinny into smothering holes, carrying a piece of dynamite and a cap.

Matt knew he was good, as good as a jockey on a horse, or a doctor on a tonsil. He knew that what James did was skillful. At sixteen, in addition to shoveling and loading coal, he began to work with electricity and dynamite. By nineteen he could shoot any seam anywhere. He could run electricity anywhere, giving light to the darkest hole.

Pa taught him how to work with electricity when he was young. He took a piece of electrical wire, took the water bucket, stuck the wire into that bucket of water. "Now touch it, Jim. Touch the outside of the bucket. It will bite and it's gonna hold you 'til I take it out of the water. I want you to know how it feels so's you won't ever get electrocuted. It's just enough juice to hold your hand."

Jim had been in the mines doing spare work for free. Now he was being paid; he was, in the vernacular, "drawing". Now he had to learn to protect himself from the deadly water that often flooded the holes after a rain. He had to learn to protect himself.

Pa set the bucket on the banister, unscrewed the light from the front porch, took his knife, cut off the light, exposed the two wires. "Now, here she goes—repeat what yer a'going to do."

"Put my hand on the outside of the bucket—"

"Yeah."

"Yer gonna stick that juice line in the bucket and it's gonna bite the hell outter my hand."

"Oh, be sure to use the back of yer hand when testing so's your hand won't grab and hold you."

Gingerly, Jim laid the back of his hand against the outside of the bucket. Then he stuck his hand into the bucket.

"Daggum," Pa said. "Daggum, well I'll say. Jim, you are a special boy. God has created a special boy."

Jim was proud. Yes, proud. Juice could run through his body and he was unafraid. It wasn't pleasant by a long shot. But, he was unafraid of the jolt that it could deliver.

Nannie had slipped to the door. "Jim, put your other hand on yer Pa." He did.

All hell broke loose. The juice connected and James and Matt were feeling the current, 210, running through them.

Matt jerked the wire out of the bucket.

"Daggum, woman, you go find your place. Daggum, daggum it to hell."

Nannie bent double and laughed until pee ran down her leg.

Never mind that Pa had lost his composure. Pa. Head of the Carter boys, suddenly floundering. Not a pretty sight. He would need help in regaining his dignity.

Matt had slumped in the swing.

"Pa, thank you for the fine lesson." Jim felt the laugh commencing inside.

"Pa," he began, and the laugh exploded. He bent over. He laughed until tears come into his eyes.

Pa was put out; purely put out. Then Pa exploded. Nannie joined them and they all went into a laughing dance, a slapping knees, hugging and whooping. Just whooping.

Jim smiled, remembering the good time.

Wherein Sam Throws Out the Dishes

No lights came from the house he was looking for. He pulled up behind the coal pile and sat. It was coming up on eleven. That was when the first saucer sailed out the door, followed by a cup, followed by two plates. Sam had begun his Saturday night ritual. Get liquored-up-and-beat-up-yer-wife. Wake up the children every Saturday night.

Jim felt under the seat. There was his Smith and Wesson. He had never fired it at anyone, just target shooting. He had a good eye. Did he need it? He might. He opened the car door. Slid out.

Hell, he had forgotten that he was a wearing his good white suit. He took off his coat and turned up the starched cuffs of his shirt twice, slid his gun into the pants pocket, walked across the yard just as a third plate sailed out the door across the yard across the dirt road before crashing against a walnut tree. He heard Halley pleading.

"Don't throw out the dishes; we will need the dishes."

Jim bounded onto the porch, skipping the two steps. Sam was standing over her. She was sitting in a kitchen chair, holding both his wrists, pleading. "Don't hit me. Don't hit me! Please, please."

"Sam," Jim stood framed in the front door.

Sam did not budge. The only sound was a small click that every grown man feared. He turned around. His sharp face, utterly diabolical, his black curly hair, one curl trained to hang down in the middle of his forward. Not a big man. A drunk man. Drinking brought out the worst in him, but it also gave him courage. Energy necessary to beat this woman to show that he was not under any kind of petticoat government.

Sam had wanted to get out of the coal fields. He had been raised by good, God-fearing people who wanted him to carry the gospel. Sam had been saved and baptized into the Holiness Church. He was, some said, a good man who was lost. Also, if truth be told, Sam was a mama's boy, a pure, spoiled mama's boy. Sam could not stand on his own two feet except when he was beating Halley. He loved this beautiful woman. But liquor made him feel all the "slings and arrows of outrageous fortune," as Nannie was wont to say of unfortunates caught in their webs of circumstances.

The whole camp was surprised when Halley had married Sam. Yet that was the best that she could do. Sam came from a good Christian family. His parents had raised him lovingly.

Halley had driven her ducks to a bad pond, so talk went. They all remembered about four or five years ago when she quit school. Stayed home and wore her daddy's shirt out over her skirt when she scrubbed the front porch. Then she went to London, Kentucky, to stay with her grandma.

Talk was that Sam and Halley's daddy would drive to London to see her. Then Sam and Halley came back married. And Halley had Bonnie. Dark hair, brown eyes—Sam's eyes were green. They were green eyes. The baby had brown eyes. Her hair was black and straight like her mother's.

Sam stood. Then said, "You son-of-a-bitch. Halley never said, but we all know, don't we Jim."

He was drunk.

Jim's first blow landed straight into his nose. The next against the side of his head. He didn't feel the third.

Halley sat, didn't move. Everything was quiet. Jim went to the little white enameled table, picked up the water bucket half filled and threw it over him. He never stirred.

He went over to Halley. She sat there, head in her hands.

"Bonnie is not my child. You know it and I know it. Bonnie's dad is Daniel, grandson of a big wig who so impressed you that you took off your dime store panties and sang, 'ho dommie diddle dommie, diddle dommie do'." He continued. "My child carries the 'mark of the beast'. When I'm accused, I can always check. The first time I held Bonnie, I checked.

"I know." She was completely defeated. She looked up. Her lip was puffed up. She opened her hand, and there was a tooth, a front tooth gone.

"Oh God, Oh God, Jim. Oh God."

He reached for her. She stood up. He pulled her close; she lifted her head. He smoothed her hair out of her eyes. Kissed her on the forehead.

They heard a noise. There stood C.C. in the doorway.

"You folks need any help?"

"Yeah, C.C. Bring this bastard around and make sure he gets to bed. I'm going to get this stuff together in the yard and kitchen." He went out to pick up the broken dishes in the moonlight.

He got in after midnight. He could move as silently as a snake in a chicken yard. He slid off his pants, tucked them behind the Creton daybed, unbuttoned his shirt, and slid down on the little narrow bed. Sometimes you pay a big price to escape petticoat government.

Wherein Charity Attends the Services in Harlan

Charity got up early Sunday, dressed both children, put on her wedding dress, fed them breakfast, and began the two-mile walk to the big Harlan Baptist Church. Dr. W. J. Bolt was pastor of this large, red brick edifice in the city of Harlan.

Harlan County, named in 1819 for Major Silas Harlan, born in Virginia, 1752. Silas Harlan came to Kentucky in 1774. Built Harlan Station, seven miles south of Harrodsberg on Salt River, 1778. Commanded spies, 1779, in Illinois, campaign of Gen. George R. Clark, who said: "He was one of the bravest soldiers that ever fought by my side." Killed in 1782 at the battle of Blue Licks while commanding his detachment. Buried at Blue Licks.

The courthouse at Harlan was burned in reprisal for the burning of Lee County, Virginia Courthouse, October, 1863. County records were saved in the clerk's office nearby. Charity remembered that history lesson, those names, those dates with pride. A little learning is not a dangerous thing. It could be used to impress others.

She carried Mickey Fowe, wrapped in a white shawl with fringe, wearing a white baby dress with tiny pink rosebuds across the smocked front. She had on a little baby bonnet with white satin ribbons tied in a bow under her little chin. The bones had knitted well and merged into a perfect little round head covered with white hair. Mickey Fowe's hair had come from Charity. The doctor who had delivered Charity described her hair as "goose down yellow". She always smiled. Why, Mickey Fowe looked just like her. And Mickey Fowe was a beautiful baby.

Lois Jean was skipping down the road, singing, "ho dommie diddle dommie, diddle dommie do…" James had bought her a green crepe dress. A green crepe dress with tiny pink, felt roses across the front and tied in back.

Charity had combed her hair around her fingers to make curls. She had on lace-up white shoes.

It was a lovely sight, and some window shades moved as she walked through lower camp. She went past the shack. Nobody came out. Most everybody was home sleeping it off. Everything was coming down Sunday morning. Some just rolled in bed. Some rolled in ecstasy, some in pain, gingerly touching burning eyes, lips, and bleeding noses. Some were building fires, some fixing biscuits, some taking out chicken, cleaned dressed, ready to fry for Sunday dinner.

Charity got through the gates when the Millers came by in their car. Mr. Miller worked in the commissary. Mr. Miller was a gentleman, a fine, upstanding gentleman. They had Diane and Diane's little brother Ernest, and they lived next to the Owens in a well-furnished four-room house.

"Charity, get in." Mr. Miller got out, came around and opened the door.

"Lau, Mr. Miller." She hesitated.

"Get in, get in," he urged.

"Let me in the back."

"No, Lois Jean can ride back there." She slid in by Miz Miller.

"Oh, let me see Mickey Fowe," Everybody in Tways on both sides of the branch and in lower camp knew that Charity Moses Carter had named her baby girl after a mouse and a relative who had fought for the North.

She passed the baby over to Miz Miller, who took off her bonnet. Mickey Fowe opened those baby blue eyes and smiled. Nannie Graham had told Charity that when a baby under three months old smiled, it really wasn't a smile; it was a poot.

Oh God, she hoped that Mickey was not pooting. Just smiling. She hoped that she didn't smell up the car. How embarrassing. She was uncomfortable.

"Lovely child, lovely child."

"There's the new kindergarten." They were past Baby Jones' little store, the only store in Harlan that stayed open on the Sabbath selling penny candy to children who slipped out and walked to the store using their "offerings" for candy.

"Yes, I understand that it has a load of children who turn six after December."

"Why, Miz Miller?"

"Because children who turn six after December can't go into the first grade. They go to primer class first. So, by going to kindergarten, they can go into the first grade and not lose a year."

"When did this one open, Mrs. Miller?" Miz Miller was from a totally different culture than Charity.

"Well, I'd say a few months back. They had to close down the one in Harlan."

"Yes, I know."

Everybody knew. The headmaster had a Princeton education, had come to Harlan, and had begun a fine little school. Only to fall prey to narcotics. It was during prohibition and a man of his nature needed something. He started going to sleep and sleeping while the children were left to their own actions. They ran him out of Harlan. Charity made a mental note.

They arrived at the huge church. Mr. Miller let the ladies out. Miz Miller held Diane's and Ernest's hands. She swooped into Sunday School, Charity following her. Charity went to the nursery first and handed the baby to a young woman wearing a smock and with painted fingernails.

"Oh, sweet, sweet baby," she cooed.

Charity handed her a bottle of formula. The formula was from Dr. Tye's drug store. She was proud of the boiled water formula, the clean diaper, and the bib.

"Oh, my, you are certainly prepared."

"Yes, I am. Take good care of this baby. If she cries, don't feed her until 11 o'clock. She is on schedule." She turned and walked away with Lois Jean.

"Well, I'll declare. Well, I'll declare," exclaimed Emily Dickenson Jones. She was helping in the nursery. "Well, I never."

Charity went to the door marked five-year-olds. Lois was only four. Why not take her into the five-year-old children's room and tell them she was five. Then she could go to the first grade when she was five and a half and not lose a year. There was a very good reason why she could not increase Lois' age. She was a virgin when she married James L. Carter, but Lois was born exactly ten months after they had been married in Middlesboro.

Ten months—she frequently paused even now and counted that on her fingers. She would bend down her thumb on her left hand and say "May to June" before going to the index finger and saying "June to July". James had tried to show her that she could bend her thumb and say "May to June", bend her index finger and say "July". But she insisted on her way, even if they both came out on exactly the same finger. No shortcuts when things were that close. She dearly remembered that Ida and Charity's sisters, Girtie, Mary, and Nannie, had all counted because Lois Jean had been born close.

So she took her to the six-year-olds. "How old is your little girl?" This spoken by a town girl. That meant that she went to Harlan High School.

That she went by the drug store, sat in a booth and coyly drank R.C. Cola or Coca Cola through a straw. Wore sweaters and wool skirts. Her mother had a maid. This girl was in training to become a teacher or a nurse or a secretary until God sent her a heavenly suited man who did not work in a coal mine, one who could play basketball at the University of Kentucky and later own a coal mine.

Charity was so relieved that she had never been in her house doing any maid services. Here in the hall they were on equal footing. Charity with her fine bone structure, slender, in the silk stockings and slippers, could pass as a sophisticate. When it came down to it, Charity was proud. She had been proud all her life. Aloof, never learning to swim. Standing back and observing, observing, observing. She looked at the petite little doll of a woman standing there and said, "She is. . . She is. . ." God was watching her. God was in heaven with her book open writing down her sins. Lying was a sin.

"She was four in March."

"Oh, let me help you. Here is where this pretty young lady goes. Here with Miz Whitcome."

She was talking and leading them down the hall. "Four-year-olds" on the door. She opened it. And inside was an amazing room. Rugs, big soft rugs, little tables with a cutout for a teacher to sit in, low chairs that fit little bottoms, and little feet could reach the floor.

On an easel was a flannel board. Miz Whitcome had just begun the most amazing story about "Little Moses in the bullrushes". She had pictures, and as she introduced little Moses, who was in a basket, she stuck the basket in the blue water on the flannel board.

Lois Jean was led to a chair in a trance. She sat down at the table. The story continued: a princess in a big chair and wearing a crown on her head took the baby home. The crown had real gold, real shiny gold. After a story, they were served juice and cookies that Miz Whitcome or somebody had baked.

But the biggest shock was yet to come. Miz Whitcome and another big girl lined them up and took them out in the hall. All of this was under the floor. Lois Jean knew this because she heard music above her. They lined them up, walked down the hall and stood in line. Into the room they went, one at a time. What for? Maybe Jesus was in that room.

Maybe Moses was in there. Everybody came out all right, it appeared. It came her turn. The pretty girl led her in. The first thing she saw was a big bowl setting on the floor. A big shiny white bowl with a lid setting on the floor.

"Gotamiteysword. . ."

"What honey?"

"Gotamiteysword."

"Here, honey, let's pull down your panties and let you pee."

"Where's the pee bucket?"

"No, sit here."

"Peeing in a bowl, I'm peeing in a bowl."

No wiping. She jumped up, pulled up her panties. Then it commenced to rain in the bowl. Rain hard. Making large sounds.

"Ok." And out they went.

"Did she wash her little, precious hands?" asked Miz Whitcome.

"Yes," said the town girl, but really she had not.

Wherein James Attends to His Soul

Charity got home from church to find James gone.

She looked behind the kitchen door. The rifle was gone. He would come in with a rabbit, she hoped. She refused to eat squirrel or, God forbid, opossum as some did—possum and sweet potatoes did not suit her.

Jim had awakened early. At first he couldn't remember why he felt suddenly despondent, tired, not really a hangover, but something like it. Affairs needed to be sorted out. A good excuse to go after a rabbit. If he got one, he would skin and dress it at Ma's, let the pack of dogs eat the entrails. That was part of their training. Matt Carter had a prize pack of hunting hounds. He bragged that they had better lineage than his boys. Princess had been his prize dog.

James slowly roused himself, went to the kitchen, poured a little water into the wash pan, splashed it over his face. Made coffee, found a cold biscuit. Put on pants and a shirt, picked up his gun from behind the door and stepped out into the glorious morning.

He decided to go up colored camp, above the houses. Changed his mind and walked up the upper white camp, following the branch so's not to be ensnared into talking by somebody having an early smoke. His spirits began to pick up.

All the flora and fauna dew pearled. The sky was cobalt blue, not a cloud. There was the house. He went out behind the house where the dogs lay under the porch. Naw, he wouldn't take them. He needed not to be encumbered by anything, no dogs, no folks, no Charity, no kids. He needed to be alone with his spirit. He needed to talk to himself about himself. Folks called that praying. Well, maybe it was praying. When he was off alone with nobody around, he could go into a part of himself that gave ideas he had never dreamed about. Answers came, ideas formed, sentences formed. A man needed off by himself with nobody around. He had been climbing for a good while when he turned around and looked back.

Tways had totally disappeared. It had rained a little on the tin roofs, and now with all the wet on the gardens, trees were hidden in the cloud forming in the valley. That cloud had risen above the camp except for a place or two where chimney smoke came through. Oh, God, great merciful God, what a sight. He stood perfectly still. Did not move until he could see the little houses again. He climbed higher. Sat down on a rock and just waited. A rabbit would be out directly.

"Say it, just say it: I'm changing. Events are changing me! Why did I do it? Why?" He spoke aloud. She had represented beauty and innocence. In the hospital, under that white sheet in that white bed, she was vulnerable. Beautiful. He did not know her name. He had been visiting the hospital. A whole bunch of great women ran that hospital. It was a good place to visit. There was always a miner with some part of his body gone recovering there, and it was always a great meeting place.

Carrie Forsyth, charming, taking charge. Carrie had told Jim that her name was Charity. She was lying there, eyes closed, as he looked in from the hall. She was asleep. He would never forget what Carrie had said to him. "Jim, she's a virgin," she laughed. "She's a twenty-two year old virgin." She had swept into the room to make this announcement. Jim remembered his color rising. He left, only to come back a day or two later.

He married her. He knew now that he had gathered up everything he had liked in every woman he had ever met, including his mother, and infused these traits into Charity. He had assigned them to her in that minute that he stood looking at her from the door. He didn't know her last name. Just Charity.

A few months later, they had gone to Middlesboro, she in her dress with the puff sleeves and gored skirt, he in his white suit, and been married. Rev. Reeves married them, with his wife and daughter as witnesses. They had hidden the license under the front seat of the Durant, and James had gone to the night shift all in the same day. Charity had gone back to work at J.J. Newberry's.

Why? Why had he acted in such haste? Jim was twenty-seven.

"I was ready to settle down."

Suddenly his eye caught a rabbit. He sat still. Sure enough, out came seven little ones. Most he had ever seen at one time.

Jim had been in charge of his life. Calling the shots. Well liked. Respected for what he could do in the mines and outside. He knew about the inside of Tways mines, and he liked that. He knew when a timber was bad and needed to be replaced or when a place needed to be timbered. He didn't need a bird; he didn't even need the blue light, although he had carried it for Pa. He blended with the mountain of coal. He blended into the mountain. Respectful and unafraid.

Pa had been in the hole when the dynamite had not been placed correctly. A piece of slate had angled down. It only broke his back, but it bowed him over forever.

He vowed never to go back into that mine. He moved to R.C. Tway Coal Company, bringing Bill, Leige, James, Ted, and Arthur. Later he moved to the shack at the driftmouth to answer the phone and take care of the dynamite, and the boys would all work at the mines. It was a good life.

Matt's folks had come in from Virginia. Often when a man needed to move from the farms and plantations, he left the family and became prodigal. Jim wondered what his great, great relative had done to get from Lee County, Virginia to Buck Creek near Williamsburg, Kentucky.

What did he really think about Halley? There was a part of him that— there was a part. . . he could not finish that thought. He could not see the answer. He had known Halley since she came into the camp. She was a beauty; well, not a beauty in the sense that Helen at the boarding house was a beauty. Halley was pleasingly formed and passionate. Even now he could feel the glow of her kiss. How did he feel about Halley?

What did he intend to do about Charity? She loved him in her own way. It stopped there. She could not say, "I love you." Why couldn't she run her fingers down his body and say, "I love you." She never slipped up behind him to kiss his neck. She never hugged him.

Charity had guarded her virginity too well. But why? Every woman in the world, he believed, had a little Eve in them. Just as every man a little Adam. Love was natural. He loved women. He loved Ma; he loved his sisters; he loved Miz. Brannon; he loved Aunt Ella. He enjoyed the company of good women.

Charity was a good woman. But, not all the way. Something was. . . his mind wouldn't let him go there. Charity was a good woman.

But Charity was a totally different case. Had he been influenced by the fact that some called her the Virgin Charity? She was untouched. He knew that for sure. He had expected her to begin with a kiss and take that kiss somewhere. She didn't kiss. She was intense like eating a red juicy melon is intense. But it never began with a kiss. It began "in medias res" and went from there.

He loved the Saturday night ritual, the Green Parrot, the movie, a drink or two and home. It was a wonderful ritual. Would this ritual go? Would a wife and two little girls change his rituals?

Jim Brannon played the horses; Matt Carter took Nannie to the courthouse to hear bloody dramatic trials. They walked to town together. Sam had his ritual—get drunk and beat up Halley. Some just slept, ate, and slept. They had nothing they wanted, nothing. That was the sin. Not to want anything. The next step was to do nothing. Has nothing, wants nothing, does nothing. There were many a man and woman sitting in a porch swing or in a rocking chair in that shape. That was the sin. He suddenly felt the weight lift. Just then a rabbit ran out and sat down not twenty feet from him. Jim smiled. Shot it. Picked it up and headed home.

"James, I'll fry the rabbit. You tend to the children."

"Where are they?"

"Lois Jean is with somebody called Miz Piertison and Shirley in the chicken lot. They are not real. Mickey's in her bed."

"Charity, do you worry that Lois sees people not there. Ma says…"

"Don't' tell me that. Who's your mother to know?" She didn't want Jim even talking to his Ma. Didn't scripture say, "Thus a man shall leave his mother and cleave to his wife?" It was time to begin your own life. Move forward; don't look back. Charity wanted more than anything to be a new woman with nobody knowing about her toes, her terrible toes. Her father's death—the typhoid from the spring. The nights of going to bed with maybe a baked sweet potato and piece of bread. The days of lying in the bed sick with the flu and Otis dead and in bed with his mother for more than three days. The endless moves from one mining camp to the next, following Millard. She wanted a fresh start. She didn't want anything from her past. Nothing. She wanted nothing from her past. Running sheets and pillowcases through the big machines and having them completely ironed. Losing her precious mom twice, once to Bill Smith and next to Lee Haynes, whose car, rounding a curve, had hit her when she was coming home from church, and Charity could hear the peroxide boiling as they poured it over Ida's wounds. She heard it even now in bad dreams.

Life had changed when Charity had married James. And now her chicken business was thriving. And her Duke's mixture bag was filling up. Of course, most of that was in scrip. She sold mostly to the colored camp. Folks would let her know that they would be wanting a chicken for Sunday dinner, or two if they were having company.

She would heat the kettle, and she and Lois Jean would go in and chase a Rhode Island Red or Plymouth Rock around until they had it cornered. Jim went often and, with scissors, cut the feathers—gently, gently so's they would not fly out of the chicken yard. The colored people bought chickens. Some wanted that skinny leg with the toes attached. When they first started coming by with orders, she couldn't believe that people actually ate the toes. It made her gorge rise.

Wherein there is a Birthday Party
with Epiphanies

"Happy Birthday to you
Happy Birthday to you
Happy Birthday, Lois Jean
Happy Birthday to you."

It was Lois' birthday; she would remember this one forever.

She had been out in the chicken lot with Shirley and Miz. Piertison, who lived in the chicken lot. They had moved in when the chicken lot was built. Miz. Piertison was telling her as to how she and Shirley should try to crack an egg like Charity could. That was another thing. In the chicken lot, she could call Charity "Charity", but in the house she had to call her "Mother". Sometimes she forgot, and if Charity wanted to, she spanked her on the leg with the egg turner. If Daddy was there, he would tell Charity not to do that.

Miz. Piertison told her and Shirley to slip out an egg, take it over to the side of the hen houses, and crack it on a rock. "See if you can make a crack, not mash it. Make a crack and gently pull the egg apart and out will come the yolk—the yellow part—like a round, yellow ball."

Lois Jean reached under the old, warm hen, got an egg, squatted down so no one could see her, and cracked the egg. Nothing happened. A little harder; nothing happened. She smacked it hard; it mashed. The yoke ran into the white. She knew she could crack an egg so that the yolk would not get mixed up in the white. A second egg. A fifth egg. All running together. Several chickens had gathered round. Charity looked out the window. Something wasn't natural. She dropped the dipper back in the water bucket and ran. "Lau, don't let anything happen to her." Opened the gate, screaming, "Lois Jean, Lois Jean." Chickens scattered, and she saw the biggest mess and at least thirty cents melting before her eyes.

She jerked her up, dragging her out of the pen, down the slope, into the kitchen, snatching the silverware drawer open. No egg turner. Then she saw it in the skillet on the stove. She grabbed it and began spanking her on the backs of her legs. Spanking, spanking.

Lois danced in pain. She hit Lois Jean in time to what she was chanting: "Never, never, never suck your thumb. And never, never, never call me "Charity". And never, never, never…"

Lois Jean was screaming. Charity was screaming. Suddenly the whipping stopped. There were whelps on Lois Jean's legs, and her legs were slick with grease.

"Let's go outside." She took her out on the front porch. "No, somebody will see me." She went to the back porch. "Oh, God, what have I done? Why, why?" That was the way Millard had beaten her, except with a belt. "Why did I let go like that? Why did I?" She had actually enjoyed that feeling. She began to cry. "I don't believe that this happened."

N'Jenny saw her. Charity had never been in Jenny's house, and never planned to go.

"Charity, are you'ens. . . ?"

"Fine. We're fine, Jenny. We are just fine, Jenny."

"Come sit on the porch. Come on, Charity."

Charity walked over, sat down in a chair, and began to cry. "Jenny, I. . . Jenny, I spanked her."

Jenny looked at Lois' legs. "Charity, since it's her birthday, could she have a little while here with me?"

Well, what nerve. Then she heard herself saying, "Why yes, Jenny, yes. Let me clean her up a little."

She went back into the kitchen. She heard Mickey crying. She set her out of her bed.

Lois Jean was snubbing.

"Stop that. Stop and you can go to Jenny's."

She bathed her face in the cool pump water. The whelps were swelling. She ran her hands over the whelps. Why? Dressed her, combed her hair, and made Shirley Temple curls.

"Go see Jenny."

Down the path to Jenny's.

"Come in, honey." Jenny took her hand and led her into the house. In the front room was a sofa with beautiful pillows bearing embroidered flowers.

A table with books and magazines on a little shelf under the table. The Bible, and a Sears Roebuck catalog. A radio. And a teeny-tiny piano in a little box with buttons.

Jenny picked it up and pulled it apart and commenced singing, "Happy Birthday to you." Lois stood perfectly still. Never had she heard such beautiful sounds.

Jenny says, "This is an accordion. It is mine. I can play it. You could too with just a little practice. It's like a piano. It can make beautiful sounds." She played and sang,

> *"Iiiiiii knows*
> *Iiiiiii knows*
> *Iiiiiii knows*
> *Iiiiiii knows*
> *I knows my name's written there."*

"Let's sing it." Together they began and after two tries, their voices rose and fell in perfect unity.

Occasionally, there was a snub, but all in all it was a great song.

"Here, let's look at the catalog. I'll show you things that make music. This is a guitar, a banjo. Your daddy plays these. He really can play these. Now this. This here is a "pianer". That's what your grandpa calls it. Your pa can play the "pianer" better than anybody. And when he plays, even I can dance. I dance out in the yard so's the whole floor won't come down." She laughed and Lois Jean laughed.

"Honey, come here. Sit on this lap."

She felt the whelps on her legs, but didn't say a thing. "Now, let's go into Jenny's kitchen and sees what we have."

She pulled out a cane chair, put the big Sears catalog on it, and set her on the chair. With movements that flowed, she produced a choked out biscuit. Jenny had a square dish that was raised on a stick-like glass thing, and it was filled with stuff. A honey dish with honey and a honeycomb.

"That's a piece that stood all my life on my mammy's table in Alabama that a Miz Carter had on her table in the big house where my mammy was born. That's right. She was a Carter, and I've never mentioned that to anyone here." She lifted the lid.

"What's that?"

"Honeycomb, honey." She leaned back and laughed. "Here, let's open the biscuit, drizzle the honey on the biscuit, drizzle, drizzle…" Then sunshine streamed in, catching the honey, and the honey turned all amber and shiny.

"We can write your name in the plate. Let it drizzle down. Write it—not print it. Here, let's write your name." As Jenny moved her hand, the name "Lois" appeared in the swirls of honey.

"You a special little girl, Lois. I see you playing Adam and Eve—a pinning them leaves together with hawthorne. I see you, precious little girl. You are centered with blessings. With the blessings of sweet Jesus." She looked at the child and loved her.

"Jesus will send his angel to tend you. To tend your body and soul." The honey ran in a tiny thread. "Jesus will bless you and your little sister and your daddy. Jesus, oh, sweet Jesus, give her the spirit, the spirit never let harm come to her. May she increase in wisdom and stature and in favor with God and man. Amen. I have given you a lifetime blessing, and it will stay with you, precious." Lois ate the biscuit, with the honey. And then Jenny showed her how to chew the comb.

Later they came back to the front room. There stood Charity on the porch with Mickey.

"Come on, Lois Jean, it's time for you to go."

"Come in, Miz Charity."

"No, I don't have time for that. Come on."

Out she went, and Charity turned, never saying more. Jenny watched. "Oh, Jesus. Help that child—them children—to keep the spirit. The Holy Spirit." She went into the kitchen and put the lid back on the honey dish.

The three girls walked a few steps and were on the dirt road. She looked up at her house, her three-room shotgun house with the tin roof and two porches. The pink roses from the rose bush that covered the lower part of the bank were full of early buds.

"Wait, Mother, wait. Jenny has a present for me. I've got to go get it." Lois Jean ran along the road, back to Jenny's. Charity scarcely heard.

"Jenny, Jenny, I forgot my present."

"Yes, you did, honey, and Jenny made it just for you. Here."

She held out a tiny box wrapped in colored paper, tied with a red satin ribbon. Miz Gibson had given it to her.

Jenny said, "Prepare yourself to open a present. Sit down. Sit up straight. Turn the gift slowly. Comment on how lovely the boxed gift looks, saying, 'This is a beautifully wrapped gift.'" She had learned that from Miz. Gibson. Miz. Gibson was a Virginia Lady whom T.M. Gibson had swept off her feet, and they had come to Harlan. They lived in a huge house with indoor plumbing and a telephone. Their place had a graveled driveway and a rich man's magic gate. When a visitor or anyone drove down the drive, there was a rope hanging from above the gate. Pull on this rope and the gate would swing open. Jenny gathered clothes from the Gibson's. She was the wash woman. Miz Gibson often threw away things that a body would desire. Such was the case with the birthday gift.

Lois Jean sat down, put her knees together, picked up the box.

"This is a wrapped, gift," she said.

"This is a beautifully wrapped gift," Jenny said.

"This is a beautifully wrapped gift," Lois said.

"Yes, honey, it is a beautifully wrapped gift. Now, slowly pull the string."

Lois Jean did. It loosened silkily, and the bow melted into a heap in her lap. She lifted the lid, and there was a little gold cross on a gold chain. She had never seen anything like that.

"Keep it on, honey; keep it on. It's a talisman." That's what Miz Gibson had said. Jenny had walked that word home. "Here, let me put it on you. It's solid. It's solid. It was meant for my neck, but mine's too fat. It's your talisman."

She hugged Jenny and Jenny hugged back. It was nice to hug back. Daddy hugged back. Mickey was learning how to.

"Oh, Jenny. . ."

"Aunt Jenny."

"Oh, Aunt Jenny, I love you."

Jenny commenced crying. "Oh, honey, oh, honey. Oh that you were mine. Oh, that only you were mine." They hugged.

"Bye, Aunt Jenny, bye."

Neither knew, but it would be the last hug that Jenny would ever give Lois Jean.

She ran down to the road, box and ribbon in hand.

Ran up into the yard and slowed down coming up the front steps. She stopped midway up, felt the cross. Sat down, remembering the little piano. She turned around. Thrust her legs through the step opening, lifted her fingers to the step above, and began to "play the piano." She sang.

> "I nose, I nose, I nose my name's writ on there.
> I nose, I nose I nose my name's writ on there."

She sang it over and over. Playing the imaginary piano. Head back, lips rounded around "nose". Clear, happy sound.

Jim had been to the store and to the gasoline station, parked the car in McVeigh holler, and was carrying groceries in when he came upon the sight and sound. He walked up to the bottom of the steps and stopped. She was his. She belonged to him from a virgin woman. He loved her like he had loved a prize dog, a good prized dog, only more. Her little voice rose in the song that Jenny sang washing clothes. He stood still. Then it hit him. He wanted her and Mickey to have a piano. In colored camp a family owned a piano. That man's first name was Washington. It was Washington Lincoln Carter. He said that when Lincoln freed the slaves that the former slaves on the plantations took their names from the folks that had owned them. That had happened during the Civil War. Washington Lincoln Carter had a piano. James wanted a piano. He went around to the back porch.

"Charity, go look on the front porch. Lois Jean is playing the piano. I believe it means something." She dried her hands on her apron and went to the door. Out on the porch. Lois Jean had changed tunes:

> "Ho, dommie diddle domanie,
> Diddle dommie do.
> Ho, Ho, Ho (nodding with each word and swaying)
> Ho, Ho, Ho, short jerkey."

Lois Jean was jazzing. She was jazzing. He would teach her to love the real thing. Her'n Mickey.

"Charity, I'm going to the Cumberland Valley Music Company and buy a piano. They can cut me each pay day until it's paid for."

"Well, that will take care of Ted, I guess."

"A man's got to take care of his girls." He came into the kitchen, took out the pinto beans, potatoes, flour, meal, lard, P&G soap, and handed her a box of chocolate covered cherries.

"James! How and where'd you get these?"

"I won the punch board. I'm good. I've done it more than once."

"Well, this is my first box."

He looked at her.

"Not now, that's a bedtime thing." She smiled.

He helped her put up the groceries. Oiled the screen door in the kitchen. Tightened the screws on the chair that slid under the table with the stenciled Dutch flowers in the muted pastels in the corners from the McComb Supply. He reached for a biscuit, sat down, poured some strained honey from Miz McVeigh's, and ate it.

All at once, no Lois Jean. He ran to the porch. She was gone. Charity ran to the chicken lot, both calling frantically. Not at Jenny's. No, not across the branch to the boarding house. Nobody had seen her. He ran to the Smith's. Geneva, Thelma, nobody had seen her. He called. Charity called. Hearts racing. They yelled upon school house hill—nothing. Then he started to lower camp. Past Miz Brannon's. The ladies at the pump. There, Vesti yelled at him. Vesti was about ten or twelve years old.

"Jim, Jim. I saw her going toward the garage."

"The garage. Oh, God in heaven. Let her be at the garage."

Charity was standing by Miz. Brannon's, holding Mickey. He ran. She ran behind him. He ran ahead, past the spring to the three garages where he and Jim Brannon and Uncle Tom Carter kept their cars. Two Fords and a Durant. All black. All cars were black. The only car color in Tways. Then he saw her. She was trying to unlock the garage.

His relief swung into rage. He unfastened the sterling silver belt buckle. It slid through the loops. He bent it double. Buckle in hand, he walked up behind her and hit her below the knees. She turned and started screaming and running. He was behind her, hitting every step. Ann Ramey peeped out—Jim Carter a whipping his girl. "It's just startin', honey," she whispered. She opened the door to the front porch. He was past her now, Charity with the baby. Doing nothing. Nothing she could do.

He whipped her legs again, again. They came to the pump. Her legs were red again and he looked and one had opened up.

The women stopped talking.

He stopped. Lois Jean ran ahead screaming. He let her run.

Then he came to himself. He picked her up, pulled out a white handkerchief.

"Blow."

She was snubbing. He ran his hands along her leg.

"God, I promise you, I will never lay a hand on any child of mine—no matter what. I promise."

"Blow." He wiped her face and his eyes.

When he got home, he set her down. Knelt in front of Charity.

"I promise to God and you that I will never lay a hand on any child of mine. Before God."

"Get up, James. You look silly. That child deserved it."

He got up and slowly looked at her. He went out on the front porch. Pulled out the Duke's mixture bag and rolled one. He could feel a rearrangement of priorities.

There was something about this woman that he did not understand. He had been attracted to her by her looks. He prided himself on knowing women, beyond the Biblical sense. He couldn't connect to her except on one level or maybe two. She loved him, this he knew, but in her own way. No sitting down like some and sharing a cigarette and a smile and afterglow, a long sweet kiss. . . . Then there was the woman with the house and the two girls. Charity was clean as a pin in her house. Lois Jean and Mickey clean. She was even clean in the garden and with the chickens. She was the finest. But. . . he ground out his cigarette and kicked it off the porch. Never would he spank any child of his again. Tomorrow to fresh woods and pastures new.

Wherein a Real Piano
Is Delivered to the Shotgun House

The legs healed. James remembered his promise and delivered. He dressed for Saturday. This time he went by himself. Went straight to the Cumberland Valley Music Company and presented himself.

"I'd like to buy a piano. Mind if I try it out?"

"You're Jim Carter; your daddy is Matt; and your mother is Nannie."

"That's correct."

"Yeah, we sit in the same place at the trials as your parents. I am Charlie John, Murm's boy. Yeah, we've eaten together at the Green Parrot. I've been here about eight years. It's a good place to work. No mines for me. I understand you're the best Tways has when it comes to dynamite and electricity."

"Much obliged." He nodded. "Much obliged."

"You want to try one?"

"No, I want to try several," he grinned. "This is for Lois Jean and Mickey Fowe. I want the best."

"Well, set right down and help yourself."

He did. He played his version of "Amazing Grace" with a bass that nobody had ever been able to do but him. Deep rolling bass "...how sweet the sound that saved a wretch like me." Everybody in the store stopped what they were doing and gathered around.

"Jim, play 'Blue Eyes'."

"Play 'First Night I Come Home Drunk and I can be...'"

"Can you hum a few bars?" He played. He played.

"Here, let me try a smaller one than this."

"Anyone you want! Anyone you want!"

He saw a smaller piano, warm honey colored. He sat down.

"Play 'Jesus Loves Me'," piped up a little voice.

"Ok, if you'll sing it."

"I will."

"Stand him on the bench so's we can see." The place was packed. Charlie John moved up to carry the tune. Little voice trailing. . .

"Jesus loves me this I know," letting the little voice go ahead and just trailing along behind. Some of the women commenced borrowing handker-chiefs.

Suddenly Jim stopped.

"I want this one."

"Oh, go on. . ."

"Naw, that's enough. That'll do."He told Charlie John that he could cut him $5.00 a month until the piano was paid for. Signed the paper and went home. No pool. No Green Parrot. A piano for his girls. And Mickey and Lois Jean increased in wisdom and stature and in favor with God and Daddy.

Wherein James and Charity Give a Party

James and Charity were holding open house. They had prepared for months, beginning with Charity taking fine clay silt from the branch that ran through the Garden of Eden, adding water until it was the same as paint, and painting the walls. It dried flat and creamy. There was one bad feature about it. If a body rubbed up against it, a body came away creamy looking. Miz. Brannon told her that she should go to the McComb Supply and get some calcimine. "You mix it with water and it won't rub off. " Charity did, and it worked.

She borrowed Miz. Brannon's curtain stretchers and took down the lace curtains, washed the coal dust out, gently pushed the delicate hems and sides onto the short, straight pins. They dried very quickly. She cleaned the window panes with vinegar and newspaper—Charity was glad that Jim Brannon played the horses. Miz. Brannon kept a stack of newspapers. Everybody saved brown bags neatly folded, waiting for further use. One of the best uses of brown paper bags was to put unripe peaches in them for overnight or a day to make them soften up. N'Jenny had started that. She said they had peach trees in Alabama and that if you got in a hurry for a peach, that was the trick. Says, "If'en you want a splendid dish of peaches and cream early on, place them peaches in a paper bag and place it on the cabinet for a day or two." She would close her eyes, lean her head back, and repeat the same words.

Charity's house was spotless. The windows shining, curtains standing out in starched attention, jelly jars hidden behind four real glasses, floors polished, front porch painted with colored oak enamel. And a whole bank of pink roses in full bloom.

Even the toilet was ready. Charity had sprinkled lime in and around and turned the Sears and Roebuck catalog over to display the front cover. James had torn off the back cover and ripped out the index before realizing his mistake. Now he had to hunt for what he wanted to look at rather than turning to the index, and it would be six months before a new one would be ready. Charity loved to remind him of his mistake. Charity reminded him often of his mistakes and shortcomings. Nannie had often said, "You need to build up your husband and children; don't tear them down." Then she would close her eyes and lift her head, intoning, "Train up a child in the way he should go and when he is old, he will not depart from it." But nobody had bothered to show Nannie the concordance so she could not cite it.

Everyone was waiting. The Fourth of July fell on a Friday. For most that meant a three-day holiday. This was a festival that came once a year. Almost as good as Christmas. Some of the more prosperous businesses in Harlan put out flags.

Charity had ice cream bowls and James had borrowed some fancy dishes from Uncle Tom Becker. Charity had never seen anything like them. They were clear and somewhat heavy. Oblong, and turned up all around the edge. Uncle Tom said they were Sunday dishes. His had come from a drug store in Alabama. He had worked in the back for Dr. Holloway, who was the druggist, and had over the years carried away twelve. He liked the feel of the dish in his hand. That cream was going nowhere except on that dish.

With the help of Jenny and Uncle Tom, Jim had concocted chocolate sauce and strawberry sauce. Jenny had come up with a new one, sugar maple sauce, but the best was melted marshmallows. She allowed nobody to see the making of that sauce and would carry that secret recipe to her grave.

All was ready. All the relatives were coming except Leige and Irene. Ora and Ruth, along with Alma and Junior, who now lived with Nannie and Matt, were coming; Bill, Lenny, and their two girls; Ted, August and Eva, Arthur and his wife. Then the Carters in lower camp. Uncle Tom Carter, Matt's brother's boy, Aunt Ella and theirs, Leithe, Tom, Gerald, Roland, Captola and Florence—her twin could not come; she had stumbled into the boiling lye water in the backyard and died. Aunt Ella had taken to the bed and scarcely ever got up to raise the shades in the bedroom. George and Octava, beautiful Octava, black hair, perfect complexion, and fine figure. Bill had done well. He was the bookkeeper in Stymen, Virginia. All envied him.

And always there were those who came from around who were not family. They usually arrived with firecrackers from Bell County and a bottle that allowed them to stand in the yard where their party was.

And to make matters more exciting, Jenny had opened her house with

Uncle Tom and others from colored camp. After dark, all mingled in a glorious, glorious celebration.

The older ones came first, claiming seating in places of honor. The rocking chairs. Jim had borrowed two of Jenny's for his Ma and Pa. Pa's back had never straightened out from the cave-in years ago; he walked stooped and used the cane. Ma was in good shape. Tom and Ella were important enough to have the swing. They would be the first to go if Ella had one of her spells. She was doing better. Of course, there would be the perfunctory visit by Russ Collins and Ola and Chief Miller might show up. Depended on how the place was running.

Jim was ready. He had the reputation of throwing a good party. Out came good liquor, drunk discreetly. Out came the banjo. Out came the songs. Out came the foot-stomping dancing. Out came the invited and the good times rolled. If the Fourth of July happened not to have a full moon, then a fire was built just across the road next to the Garden of Eden, so's not to disturb the garden. Folks would toss firecrackers into the fire, and it sounded like the Fourth of July. There would be at least twenty to forty or more, counting Jenny's yard, his yard, and the fire below the hill. It was a party!

The first arrived shortly after twelve noon. Charity had just finished dinner, the middle meal. First breakfast, then dinner, and last, supper. She had done a sandwich deal for dinner, bologna sandwiches with crisp fried potatoes and iced cold lemonade and tea. Tea for the older ones, lemonade for Lois Jean and Mickey Fowe.

Ted, who was at Berea College, was holding court on the front porch. "We have always been here. We never came on a boat to New York. We have lived in these mountains since before the Revolution in 1776. We came here from Virginia. The Carters from Lee County, Virginia, went to Whitley County and set up farms. So did the Moses and Cox families. We farmed, fished, built a cabin or house, set up a county seat. We did that until these mines opened. Then some families left the farms and came to the mines to make money. Why? Well, I'm beginning to believe that we would have been better off on the farms. The only thing that is better here is the Fourth of July."

At that moment, in came Pa and Ma through the kitchen door. Pa would have to leave by that same door or he would come upon bad luck. And he couldn't afford too much more bad luck. They went to the front porch and sat in the rocking chairs.

"Gramma, Gramma, open up yer pocketbook." Nannie always carried two things, an umbrella and a big pocketbook with her crochet needle and thread and something for the children.

"Come sit on Ma's lap." Lois Jean and Mickey Fowe climbed up on the ample lap. "Give gramma a kiss." They kissed her, knowing what came next. She reached into the big bag and out came two pieces of wrapped candies. If you pulled the little piece of paper sticking out on either end, the magic began opening the whole piece. Charity stood in the bedroom, peeping out from behind the lace curtains. She had never had candy like this when she was a little girl. And they would get it on their pinafores. She appeared on the front porch.

"Miz Carter, I don't want them to have that candy. It will make them sick. She took it out of Lois Jean's and Mickey's hands and put it in her apron pocket. Everything stopped. No one said a thing.

"Sure, Charity, sure. Here, hug Gramma." They did.

Charity swooped into the kitchen and pulled the little papers, put the candy in her mouth and leaned against the wall to let it melt.

Grandma reached back into her reticule and pulled out two tiny pieces of corn candy. "This is better. It produces no evidences." Everybody roared with laughter. The party had begun.

Soon couples began to arrive. The women walked up the steps, appearing slowly, sporting outfits that they had planned for a year. Chiffon, silk, some in sleeveless white pleated dresses with sailor collars, just topping their heels, one in hose, perfume and even manicured fingernails.

Aunt Ella came dressed in black from head to foot. She was still in grief. Not quite a year since the accident. No makeup on that beautiful face, a sweet sadness. Uncle Tom in a white linen suit, white shirt and a red, white and blue tie. How did he do it? In the winter, Uncle Tom wore a cashmere overcoat. He was certainly the best dressed man in Tways, maybe the best dressed in Harlan County.

People came and continued to come. They sat and talked. Who was "pg" and who had moved on, who had married and when the baby was coming. (A close observer could see fingers moving.) Who had died and if they had been buried in the family plot up on Wolf Creek or Buck Creek or Harlan. By three o'clock, out came the walnut ice cream, the R.C. Colas, Moon Pies, and, surprise, a pound cake that Jenny had added. Charity was in the kitchen, putting out the ice cream and the pound cake for the adults and the ice cream for the children. As one finished, she washed the "Sunday plates" and refilled them.

About four o'clock, she pulled out her own surprises. She put a dipper or two of walnut ice cream, then chocolate, maple, or strawberry syrup on top and then a red maraschino cherry on the top of that. Charity had seen her first maraschino cherry at Ide and Homer Clodfelter's house when she worked for Ide. She had taken some of her chicken money and slipped and bought three jars of cherries at the A&P and hidden them.

Well, everybody was amazed when the ice cream arrived adorned; adorned with red candied cherries. It would date time. "Well," folks would say, "it was the time Charity served cherries on that ice cream that Octava got pg." Or, "Well, it was the time that Charity put them cherries on the walnut ice cream that the mine cave-in happened."

Octava and George, who was Uncle John's younger brother, had settled in the swing. She was beautiful—too beautiful. She looked like a China doll. Chiffon dress the same color as her eyes. Little pearl buttons from the top to the bottom. Hair and nails perfectly done. And laughing. She laughed at anything George said and wouldn't let him out of her sight. If he told a joke, she laughed and laughed and laughed. She took little bites of the ice cream and licked the cold spoon with her pink tongue, staring at him all the while. Every man there watched that little drama play out. And some said that George blushed.

Jim got his guitar and they sang several songs:

> *"Down by the Barnyard He Stumbled"*
> *"Beautiful, Beautiful Blue (or Brown) Eyes"*
> *"Barber Allen"*
> *"Old Joe Clark"*
> *"Camp Town Races"*
> *"Give Me that Ol' Time Religion"*
> *"Life is Like a Mountain Railroad"*
> *"Cripple Creek"*

Octava, soprano, Ora with the alto, George with the tenor, and Arthur with amazing bass. They stood together, heads almost touching, and sang. Octava knew the words to all the songs. If the others did not know a phrase, they hummed their part along; humming, letting her sweet voice fill the porch and spill across the road and down the hill and up the mountain.

Pa was the first to move. "Oh, God, oh God, it's an owl, and before the sundown. That's the worst it can be." Matt knew and practiced every superstition in the book. He knew why his back was broken in a cave-in. On that day, he had allowed Nannie to enter the driftmouth of the mines.

"Matt Carter, don't be throwing cold water on this party with your superstition," said Nannie. Matt knew and practiced every superstition in the book. He knew why his back had been mashed. On that day, he had allowed Nannie into the driftmouth of the mines. She had fixed fried chicken and wanted him to meet her.

"Here, Matt. Pinch this and throw it over yer shoulder. It may undo the owl." That was Ella. She practiced superstition now. "I heard the owl before sunset about a week before the baby…" Her voice trailed off.

The colored folks were in full swing at Jenny's. The sun was going down and firecrackers and guns were going off all through the Tway Mining Camp. The Fourth of July was in full swing.

Then came Lois Jean. Charity had done little curls all over her head. She was wearing a pinafore, a red pinafore with white rick rack and lace-up shoes. Jim took his guitar, Charity helped clear a fine place, and Jim commenced a Kentucky Breakdown. Lois curtsied and began to dance, to dance, to dance, feet flying. People started clapping. They were with her. They liked it. They loved it. Jim played. Suddenly, up the steps appeared Uncle Tom Becker. He was dressed in white with a red satin tie and a straw hat. He looked mighty fine. He had a juice harp. "Let's do one, Jim, that little feet can move to." Not a moment's hesitation.

"Ok, girl. Here's an Irish jig." She danced. Hands on hips, she did the damndest dance that anybody had ever seen. A little girl, feet flying. Heel to toe. An Irish jig. Where?

Charity had seen Lois and Miz Piertison and Shirley up in the chicken lot a dancing. She had gone up and taught her what she had learned at the Pine Mountain Settlement School. The students did a Maypole dance and wound long ribbons around it. Charity had changed it just a little and Lois Jean danced the wild, wonderful version.

Uncle Tom put his harp in his pocket, stood behind the little girl, took both her hands and let her twirl. She looked at him. He smiled and they both danced. Everybody danced; the fireworks went off; the moon came up; car horns blew. Oh, God, transported to another world! Ecstasy. When it stopped, everybody looked around as if they had returned from another land.

"Well, I never," one breathless one kept repeating. "Time for watermelon. It's time for melon." Jenny came through the house with a butcher knife, ready to cut. The watermelon needed to be plugged by the oldest man who "pronounced it". "Pronounced" meant it was ripe for eating. Pa was gone. Uncle Tom did the honors.

Suddenly there was a child on the dynamite box. It was Mickey Fowe.

She had something to do. Lois Jean had been working with Mickey Fowe, and they had a surprise. Little Mickey was going to do a trick.

Charity and Jim were in the kitchen with Jenny and the melons from Alabama. But uncles, aunts, neighbors and friends knew how to oblige a tiny cotton top who needed a little praise.

She had on a blue pinafore, solid with white rick rack. "Lau, ain't she a purty thang."

She was fumbling in her pocket.

"Set her up on the Atlas box so's we can see the trick."

Mickey pulled a little wilted something out of her pocket. Lois Jean was standing to her side.

"Stretch it, Mickey Fowe, stretch it."

Lois had been going through the second drawer of the chifforobe when she had come upon a little package, a tiny little package. She had pushed the drawer back in, closed the door, and just made it to the daybed undiscovered. She had slipped off to the chicken yard and Shirley and Miz Piertison had managed to get it open. It was easy after you made the first little break in the package. Out came a white balloon. It stretched and stretched. Then she had showed it to Mickey.

"You can stretch it, honey."

She did, and Lois stood up and then pulled on the balloon. It stretched and stretched. Mickey Fowe put it above her head and it stretched as wide as her arms and Lois clapped. Her trick.

Mickey stood on the Atlas Dynamite box and slowly began to stretch the creamy/white balloon. She lifted her arms above her head and pulled, her arms wide apart. Not many were paying attention, but someone happened to notice. Some standing close got still.

"Look at that."

It was a long slender balloon.

"Oh, my God, look at that."

"Is that what I think it is?"

"I've never seen one in light, have you?"

Suddenly, someone clapped. They commenced to clap.

Mickey Fowe held the balloon below her knees and everybody clapped. Then back up over her head.

"Now, blow it up! Blow it up!"

She began. Nothing happened. She handed it to Lois. Lois did another stretch.

Mickey commenced. They had practiced with the balloon and it was long, long, and flexible. Mickey put it in her mouth and began to blow. It began to fill up, growing longer and longer, but never any rounder than a fine cucumber.

Folks began to laugh and clap and clap and laugh. The balloon was bigger and longer. It was long.

Ora came over to where Mickey Fowe stood. Jim's sister, the beautiful quiet Ora. "Here, honey, let Aunt Ora make you a crown." She took the balloon and wrapped it around Mickey's head and twisted it in back.

Mickey then put one little foot out, pulled out her skirt, and curtised to all. Tears ran down their cheeks. Word had reached the kitchen. What to do? Jim and Charity could never let on that they were embarrassed. What to do?

They went out on the porch, Jim on one side and Charity on the other. They laughed and Jim pronounced, "Let him who is innocent blow the next balloon." Perfect. It was the perfect touch. Charity wiped her eyes with her apron.

They all ate watermelon.

It was late. The boys set off fireworks below the road. Lois and Mickey Fowe found laps and got heads rubbed to sleep. Folks sat, moving gently in the swing. Some in the yard pulled silver flasks, some bottles, and passed them around.

Arthur found Jim. "We're going, Jim, if I'm going to work graveyard for you."

Jim had asked Arthur to take his place so he could be at the house for the party. Arthur had obliged. He was younger than Jim. He was handsome and couldn't make up his mind what he wanted to do. The coal mine was a good place to get things worked out. Once a man got over the fear of that dark, once he understood there were "rooms", and once he realized that he needed to know how to survive, the dread of the mines left him, at least at Tways.

R.C. Tway was two miles from Harlan. Tways was state of the art. It was a tiny, complete community that boasted families working together. Town was accessible. The culture was town culture. Folks went to town. Folks read, saw movies, subscribed to the newspaper. Women, and some men, read the Bible, Shakespeare, Milton, and some would read *Trail of the Lonesome Pine*. Harlan was uptown and R.C. Tway was two miles from Harlan.

But Arthur couldn't make up his mind to stay in—to be dedicated to mining. There were Bill and Lennie over in Stymen. Bill was the bookkeeper. They had two girls. The belief was that girls were not as valuable as boys. Girls were necessary or at least a girl was necessary to a man. Certainly

Nannie Carter had been necessary for her boys. But Bill had girls. James had girls. A household needed boys.

Arthur wanted a boy! What else did he need? He loved baseball, and he could pitch. On Sundays he would go down across the road to where planes landed, The Sizemore Farm. The cows were put up and planes landed in wonderful air shows. Before the planes landed, there would be a baseball game. Men came from Coxton, Lynch, Kinver, Mary Hellen, Wallins Creek, came to play ball. They brought their own bats and gloves and balls. Women came with children. There were picnics and gossip. Warm spring, hot summer, even in fall. The boys played out their game, chewed tobacco, cussed on the mound, looking around for children. Children were the prize. In the mountains children were prized above everything. Nothing in the world like a baby coming on, except those few who saw it as another mouth to feed, but that was seldom.

Arthur pondered these things. He had plans. He planned to go this Sunday and pitch. He had a fast ball. Others who had come in from as far as New York and Chicago saw that Arthur Carter was good and talented. He needed to settle on, either staying with his family and the mines or letting go, and dedicating himself to baseball. Nothing in the world felt as good as a cheering crowd.

These thoughts went through his head every day, every night, but he couldn't let go. He loved his wife, and he wanted a family

"Much obliged, Arthur," Jim was saying. "I am much obliged for you taking this shift for me. Buy something nice with it." They both laughed. One shift wouldn't buy too much "nice".

"But you know I don't want for much. I could live on this hill with Charity and these two little girls for the rest of my life."

"Yeah, I know. It is a hard thing to take a chance."

"Yeah, a hard thing, but with your talent on that field"—-here his voice trailed off.

They were standing with hands on the banister rail looking out across the road to the mountain. Moon was full. A full Fourth of July moon. Folks were settling down, children dozing, some eating just one more slice of melon, smoking one more cigarette, taking one more swig from a bottle. Occasionally a cracker or a gun went off.

"Well, I gotta go."

"Thanks, brother."

Suddenly Arthur grabbed him and hugged him. "It's been a party."

Jim stood, finishing his smoke.

It was late. Shift change, graveyard shift, would begin soon. Jim loved working the graveyard shift. Sleep in the morning, rise late. He loved graveyard shift.

Later that night Charity surprised him. No, she shocked him. This was a new Charity. The party over, lying in bed, she flirted; she spoke softly; she was gentle. She whispered, "I love you," over and over again. Even her tone of voice was low and lovely. He had never, ever seen this side of this woman. He was surprised and pleased. They curled into a lover's knot and slept.

Wherein Arthur Takes Jim's Place

Then somebody was knocking on the kitchen door. Loud. Insistent, pounding on the door. Jim jumped too. He was wide awake.

"Jim, Jim, it's C.C. Open the door." Jim reached for his pants, pulling them on, not missing a step, opening the door.

"Jim, there's been a cave-in. They's been a fall. Git yer shoes." Jim put on shoes—no socks—no shirt, grabbed two sticks of dynamite and three caps, never missing a step, grabbed his carbide light and ran.

He ran across the branch, up through the white upper camp, past the Cloud's, past the Young's, past the empties, past Pa's, up through the backyard, up the hill, heart pounding, lungs pumping. He was operating outside his body. He was above himself, seeing himself run, run, run.

"It's not bad. It's not bad. Maybe a broken arm, leg. It's not bad. God, Jesus, don't let it be bad. Not Arthur. God, don't let it be bad. I'll never. I'll never. . ."

He saw the clump of twinkling lights outside the driftmouth. That was odd. Why were they standing around? They had Arthur out. Arthur was telling them what had happened. On he ran in the moonlight. Off up toward Bird Eye, he heard a panther scream. He ran in slow motion. Once he leaned against a tree and caught his breath.

Far below he heard C.C. breaking through brush and cursing. On he went. He heard the men yelling. What were they saying?

"Jim, Jim, take your time."

"Take your time. Take your time."

The men were yelling to him to take his time. Why? Why? Why were men telling him to take his time? Arthur needed him. Arthur needed him. Arthur. . . Arthur didn't need him. Why wouldn't Arthur need him? He stopped still, didn't move. He heard himself breathing. He saw the full moon.

He heard frogs, the one's near the branches. He heard a dog—whose dog? He started running.

"Where is he?" Three tried to grab him.

"Every minute counts. Don't hold me."

"Jim, listen, Jim listen. He's dead. Arthur's dead. He's mashed and we can't get him out."

Jim sagged to the ground. He was outside his body again. He saw the whole scene from above, entered his body, stood up and quietly announced.

"Yes, we'll get him out."

"Whyn't you go look? Jim, he's a few feet from here. The slate came down in the driftmouth."

Gotamity. In the driftmouth. The driftmouth; that was not possible.

"Yeah, the driftmouth. Arthur must have just come into the driftmouth. It was shift change. We'd been working down in that new cut that you blowed yesterday, and we heard something fall—not near us. It was a big fall, though. We climbed up to the track and pushed for the car; nothing happened. We could hear stuff, but the car didn't come; so we walked."

One was handing Jim a bottle; he passed it by.

"We commenced crawling 'til we could walk a little. We came on up, not hearing nothing. We came to the driftmouth and it was almost blocked. That's when we saw Arthur. He's back there, a few feet. He's dead, Jim. He's dead. You have to squeeze in on the right side. That's the thickest piece of slate I've ever seen. I've never seen anything like it. You ready?"

Somebody had put a jacket on him. Suddenly he was in charge. "Boys, get a jack hammer."

"Won't work—wait 'til you see."

Back the miners went. Light shift for the holiday. They squeezed through the side of the driftmouth, moving their bodies up to fit wider places, scraping back to the other side, then sliding down to stand up.

Jim's eyes searched for Arthur. There were his feet, his legs. . .

Then he saw—there was Arthur's face—his two eyes laying down on his cheeks. Jim got down on his knees, crawled up as close as he could and with both palms gently, gently, pushed the eyes back into his head; but he couldn't close the lids; he needed more skin. That's when he saw the slate. Arthur's forehead was there and his black curly hair was there, but the back of his head was under tons and tons of slate.

He knew what had to be done. And he had it with him.

"Boy's, I'm goin' to get my brother out. If you will help me drill. They found the auger, the breast plates, and began to drill, taking time and going between layers.

"Jim, this is touchy. Hit's touchy."

"I know. Drill."

"How much you goin' to do?"

"Just a little so's we can move him."

"Jim, we can move him now."

"No, he needs his brain."

"Jim, think."

"No, he needs his head." They drilled. Nobody spoke.

Ma would not be able to handle this. Knowing Ma, she would have to examine her boy's whole body.

"Jim, C.C.'s called the funeral home in Harlan. They'll do the body."

"Not in here, they won't. I'll blow this out so's we can take him out."

"No, whyn't we take him out and walk through to the tipple side; the ambulance can meet us there. We can pull him out."

"No, that would hurt him too much. I want the slate lifted off his head. He needs his head. He needs his head." This time he drank from the proffered bottle.

"Boys, let me set the dynamite. I can do it. Arthur needs his head, boys." He was crying. They left him to set the sticks. He did. Came out, walking backward pulling the wire, set it down, cut it loose from the roll.

"Git out, completely outside. They did. He was yelling from habit.

"Fire in the hole." It blew, then settled. They all came back in.

Jim was already there. Lifting pieces of slate off of Arthur. The pieces were the right size to lift. Dynamite had been set to blow the slate back. It cracked but stayed in place.

Besides the seven workers with him, others had gathered at the drift-mouth.

Jim knelt down, lifting pieces, lifting pieces, working gently. Suddenly he stopped. He knew that there would be his head, flat between the rocks, no brain left, just a wide, wide, blood stain, nothing to indicate a thought, nothing left to propel a baseball or even to walk his legs, nothing, no Arthur.

Ma was not to know. For the first time, he thought of Arthur's wife. He took off his jacket, laid it over Arthur, went back to the front. They had the stretcher.

"He's loose."

The men lifted him slowly and laid him on the stretcher. The mining car would not move. The electricity was out.

"Jim, connect the juice."

He did and time began again.

They would bury him at Mountain Ash. The Carters had their own graveyard in Mountain Ash near Williamsburg, Kentucky.

Anderson and Laws did a fine job on Arthur. They wanted to throw out the eyes, but Jim stood by and made them put them back. Ted tried to stay but couldn't . Leige and Bill stood outside and smoked. Nobody could move Jim.

He helped button Arthur's white shirt. He put his own linen handkerchief in his coat pocket. When he went through Arthur's pants pocket; he had found a baseball! Arthur Carter carried a baseball all the time. It was in Jim's pocket. He'd ripped his pants a little getting it in his pocket.

"Well, Jim, what do you think?" asked Mr. Anderson. Don't he look natural?"

The mark of any good undertaker was to make a body look natural, and he had done a good job. He nodded toward the door. Two men came in.

"Now, what we do is sink his head, what's left of it, down into the piller so's Nannie won't catch nothing. Jim lifted. Arthur was stiff. They laid him in the casket. Mr. Anderson straightened him out and Arthur looked like he was asleep.

"Jim, go home and sleep. You've been up a long time. We can take it from here."

"OK, boys. But let me have a little time with Arthur by myself. I want to—have a little time."

"Sure, Jim."

He stood looking at his brother. Stuck his hands into his pocket. He had forgotten the ball. He pulled it out of his pocket. Put it back in his pocket— then took it out. He lifted up one of the cold stiff hands and placed it under it, but the fingers wouldn't close. They had already formed. He took it out, opened the casket, took his knife, opened the pocket a little and slid in the baseball—tears running down his cheeks.

"Jim, Jim, what ye doing?"

"I was just looking at my brother for the last time."

He turned and walked out.

On the day of the funeral Nannie went to the funeral home to ride behind the hearse. She slowly climbed the steps and went into the dimly lit room. Nannie asked to be left alone with Arthur. "Arthur, this is Mother. I believe that you are seeing everything and hearing everything that I am saying. Your body is presentable. I want to connect my soul to your soul. I want to feel your spirit, not your ghost, visit me. I want to lay you to rest, but I want you to visit often. You're welcome to visit me and your Pa anyway you desire. I suppose that you are still around that driftmouth somewhere.

Arthur, son, you have some unfinished business. Take care of James up there. James has been and is the linchpin. Knows how to work that mine. You should have been doing something else. You should have had the opportunity to play that ball game that you loved.

Son, I know that you will be here to guide us, to help us, to inspire us. Arthur, visit Matt and Jim." Suddenly, she reached into the casket. Ran her hands behind his head. "I thought so. But, I also know it didn't hurt, you didn't feel it. Arthur, son, if this is true, give me a sign. As was Jesus, you'll be around these parts for three days and three nights. Son, give us a sign."

Mr. Anderson sent Billy Ray to look in on Miz Carter. "Go see that she's all right, son."

Mr. Anderson had seen it all. He stood in silent reverie. He was still in shock from last week. Last week they had picked up old Mr. George W. Hogge from his farm up above Lynch. He owned enough land that connected to the mines, but wouldn't let go of one inch, not one inch. Him and his boys had barbed wire around the whole blooming acreage, and he would not be talked out of one inch.

The slick talkers buying up for the big boys—the absentee land owners who didn't care one iota about anything but money and living high. Not putting a damned thing back for another generation. These boys had tried to buy Mr. Hogge's land, but nothing doing. He had timber and coal, but nobody would take the coal while he or any of his boys were alive. He had that fixed in his will. The land would stand with no "invasive action being taken to remove coal or trees". He made them put that in for 100 years in perpetuity.

He was fortunate enough to have a bunch of strong boys. They all had rifles and carried pistols. Nobody could get up to the porch for the dogs and the boys. The rumor was out that one of the sweet talkers had come on his property and never returned. When he was questioned about the missing person, he shook his head slowly, "Hit's been a bad year for panthers. I heerd 'bout a man in Tways whose best dog was killed. Boys, hit's no place to be out adder dark."

He raised enough fine smoking tobacco to keep him and his boys in 'bacca and was working on making snuff. His family had been on the land since before the Revolutionary War.

George W. Hogge had died from the Lock Jaw. It was hard to believe that a nail, a rusty old nail, could kill a grown man. He had been moving a new toilet. They had dug the hole and were going to lift the old structure over the new hole, when the side that he was carrying slipped. He reached to grab hold and where it had been pulled from the foundation was a nail. It went through his foot—his entire foot—and the boys had to pull him loose.

Lily cleaned it. First P&G, then alcohol, then iodine. She had taken her fingers and worked the iodine in well and wrapped it up in a clean piece of sheet. He put on his sock and his shoe, rolled down his pants leg and finished the toilet.

A week later, the foot had commenced swelling. A week after that he was dead.

Bill Laws, who worked on the body, had never seen a red streak so far up a leg before.

The boys brought in his burying clothes, and Bill and his daddy had worked getting them on him. In fact, they called in a woman to work on the back of the coat so's it would go all around him. They had him laid out well. Called the family in. Family grieved and were comforted by "how good Pappy looked."

That's when Marcell, the middle one and strange, got the idea. "Let's take him out and take his picture. He's never looked this good," says Marcell.

"Gotamity, no," says Luther. "Ma'd kill us."

"Well, she don't haf to know 'bout it."

"Don't he look natural?" Marcell was persuasive. All five brothers went over to open the casket. Pa was clean, even under his fingernails. Hair combed. Even a hint of a smile on his face.

"Go down to that place where the newspaper is. Get the man from the Enterprise to come up here now. Get the Kodak. Tell him we's keeping it 'til we get a picher. If he don't want his place burned down—tell him, 'at once'."

Two people came from the paper. The boys had the old man up, out in the backyard. They had carried him to the door. Then down the back steps under the clothesline where the limp towels hung. There they waited.

The men from the Enterprise stopped and then didn't move. Sober faces appropriate for the occasion.

"Now, look here," said Marcell. "We each want a picher of Pa—we'll take the cameras 'til the pichers is ready. No offense. We jest want the pichers of Pa 'cause he does look good."

"Boys, we'll do the best that we can possibly do. But we'd like to have it for the paper."

"Nothing doin'; hit's fer us." Marcell.

Luther and Abraham Lincoln Hogge, his younger brothers, both hit their hips—they were packing and ready.

"Not over this dead body. We don't want to make no showing. They're for us alone; they will honor Pa. We will give them to Ma. Got that boys?"

"Yes, we got that." They took pictures on two cameras. "Well, boys, we'll get them to you."

Mr. George W. Hogge was stiff and held up well. They put him back in the box and shut the lid.

Bill Laws believed that it was smooth sailing. But, no.

A few hours later, in came Lily. She hadn't cried a single tear since he had died. George W. Hogge was the best man on this earth. They had stepped over the broom when she was fifteen years old and lived in love, having healthy progeny since. God had richly blessed her and now she was bereft. Totally bereft. She came up and her boys surrounded her. They hadn't said a word about the surprise that they had for their little Mother. Abraham went over and opened the casket. "Gotamity." Pa's neck was broke and he'd turned black and other stuff was wrong.

Luther, Marcell, Melvin, Chester, and Abraham Lincoln gathered around. "Set Ma down and get Mr. Laws back. Don't let Ma see him in this condition." Bill Laws came. Speaking in low, soothing tones, he said, "Miz Hogge, yer boys had never seen their daddy looking so good. His suit and all. They took him out and took his picture. They should be ready by the last of the week. If you'll sit right here, I'll spruce on him some and then you can have your viewing. The Lord's presence is in the room."

Upon hearing this, the boys jumped. All stood up. Bill continued, "Now boys, take yer Mother down to the Green Parrot and eat some of their meat-loaf and sweet potatoes. Get some banana pudding and iced tea. Then, Miz Hogge, return for your private viewing."

She stood up, lowered her black veil. Her boys surrounded her, and off they went to the Green Parrot. When they returned, sure enough, Mr. Hogge was ready for the viewing. He was taken to the family cemetery on their farm and buried. Lily did fine until it came time to throw on the first shovel of dirt. Then she took on. She wailed; she fainted; they put ammonia under her nose. She refused to leave. So she and her boys stayed the night sitting in straight chairs, wrapped in quilts. Neighbors brought food and others sat and talked the night long. Lily would doze off, come to, cry, and doze off. They sang; they told stories of others who had departed. They visited other graves. Two days later, Luther and Marcell announced, "Hit's time to go home."

Now, here was Nannie Caddell Carter, rubbing what was left of Arthur's

head that Mr. Anderson had worked so hard on. He was one of the finest cos-
motologists around. He could make a whole face, front or back, if necessary.

This woman was not going to mess up his work.

Someone called down to Williamsburg and some relatives opened a
grave at Mountain Ash, near the Carter farm.

Folks from Tways loaned their cars or drove their cars to the graveside
service on Sunday afternoon at Mountain Ash. They got up way before daylight, dressed and left before seven. They would be after midnight getting
back in. Charity decided not to go.

Jim drove Arthur's car with Arthur's family.

Charity had pressed Jim's dark wool suit. She starched his shirt with the
French cuffs. Charity got out his felt hat. He refused his summer straw. She
had waxed his shoes, and he was carrying two white linen handkerchiefs.

"Charity, whyn't you going?" Jim asked her.

"James, I can't take Lois Jean and Mickey Fowe on a trip like that."

"Yes, you can."

"Well, I don't like funerals. I don't want to see any of them grieving. It
reminds me of my mother." Jim went without her.

Wherein Lily of the Valley Smokes for Jim

"What I need is a good long drink of some pure shine." That was the idea that rolled through Jim's brain, early Saturday morning, the 18th of July. I need some good sunshine. Some shine." He rolled over and looked at the clock. Six o'clock in the morning. Nobody'd be out this time of day. He got up, went to the kitchen. Better not try to build a fire. Wake up some. He slipped out the back door, sat down on the porch, and pulled on work shoes.

What a day. Sun had not come up over the mountains yet. Everything was bathed in silvery mist. Couldn't see ten feet in front of you. What a sight. Walking in a tiny silver bubble. Why you could walk upon a panther—that's what Ted from Berea called it. A panther, and not see it. As he moved forward, the bubble moved with him. He stretched out his arm, full length. "Two lengths and I couldn't see the ends of my fingers." He crossed the road, went down the side of the hill, skirted the Garden of Eden. Didn't want to step on the tomatoes or beans. He began to climb; it was steep. Here were poplar trees, high as the sky; here were hemlocks. He thought of old Socrates. Ma said she wouldn't risk even a touch of a hemlock tree. He looked down in his bubble. There were jack-in-the-pulpits and heart leaf. He stood for a minute in perfect silence. "No church could give a man this feeling." God was there in the trees, in the jack-in-the pulpit, in the silvery silence.

But where was Arthur? Suddenly he was washed in grief. The presence of the Almighty was gone. He was standing in a silvery bubble all alone. There it was. He knew it was there, but he couldn't see it. Covered with bushes, like little Moses in the bulrushes.

He knew that it was here because he had found the three rocks. He put his hand forward, still in the silvery bubble. There were dead tree limbs; he pulled back and there was the still. Copper shining, little drops trickling.

One thing that could be said for Shine Smith was he knew how to operate a still. His stuff was smooth. He told nobody what his recipe was, and even the boys from Lexington bragged on it.

Shine averaged about four gallons in about eight runs. He wasn't greedy. He went for quality. Jim ran his hands along the ground—under the little fire hole. Faintly warm. He smiled. He had come upon Shine about two years ago when he had come over to pick up a few walnuts for Saturday night chocolate fudge that Charity made. He had smelled fire and moved toward it. That's when he found Shine Smith.

Shine was a runt of a man with wild blue eyes that darted. His hair was wild, wouldn't lay in a part, just stood around on his head. He wore denim with boots that laced up and he tucked his pants leg into them. He wore a mine jacket and a brown felt hat all the time. He was seldom seen anywhere in a crowd. He was nervous. Never able to settle into a drink, a smoke, a talk. A body wondered how'd he slow down long enough to get two kids here. Jim chuckled at that.

Shine had been hurt somewhere, somehow. And he was always darting around. Never able to ponder the moment. Never able to sit and socialize in the mines, in the commissary, in the church, or in the bed. He was disconnected and just couldn't connect to anything except this still. This fine moonshine still. Why, this shine was so fine that Miz Hall, Miz Elmer Hall, had been slipped a pint. Shine had never seen Miz Hall, nor been in her house. So, one day he had poured a little into a pint bottle. He collected bottles for such, and had spit on the back of the bottle and rubbed it 'til it shined in the sunshine and swore to himself to take it to Miz Elmer Hall at her house. And he did. Or, he said he did. The Halls were not a part of Tways; they lived on the side of the road on small acreage with an inside toilet and a telephone. Very few ever had seen inside the Hall's. They didn't seem to go to the Green Parrot, the Margie Grand, or the First Baptist Church.

Well, now wher'd Shine put his shine? He had several holes and places he stuck it. Jim had improved the still immensely. He had borrowed copper tubing that coiled for a better run. He had tightened up the apparatus so's it didn't cover all that space. He had told Shine to stay away from anything metal. Several enameled pans, blue ware, had disappeared from his and Shine's house.

Theirs was a clean, safe-to-drink operation. Ma prized it for toddies for those who had flu and colds. One tablespoon of shine, honey to taste, and one-half cup hot water spooned down a child would cure pneumonia.

Well, the bubble had disappeared; the sun came down in shafts, seldom finding the verdant floor of the woods. Jim came out of his reverie and got serious. He searched around and found nothing. Then a shaft of light hit bright sun and landed on the spot just in front of his foot. He looked up. There in the hemlock tree hung a toe sack. One that Irish potatoes come in.

He shinnied up the tree to find two quarts of fine stuff. Two quart jars. He took it off the tree limb, lowered it as far as he could. Wouldn't work. He held out the sack and twisted it. Wrapped the rope round his arm, shinnied down. Took out one quart.

Shinnied back up and hung it up. He picked up the quart.

That's when he heard the sound. Looked round. A whinny sound. Then dead silence. There it was again. Then out come a little wobbly puppy, wiggling toward him. It was a hound puppy. It couldn't be more than a few days old. He picked it up; put it in his jacket pocket; and walked home.

He slid the shine under the edge of the porch and went to Pa's with the pup. It was about ten o'clock. Lois Jean had stayed the night with Ruth and Alma at Pa's and Ma's. They would be having breakfast. He'd just have a few biscuits, honey, maybe some pork chops and eggs to add on.

What would Charity think? We'll, he'd just say that he wanted Lois Jean home. All in all it had been a great day.

He dropped off the puppy, picked up Lois Jean, and was on his way back. Matt had given him a pint of honey with the comb. He had put it in the righthand pocket of his jacket. Lois Jean skipped along beside him.

"Lois Jean Carter, I feel like Jack. You know about Jack. Jack does everything and it works out. It works out. Jack goes huntin', sees a flock of ducks settin' on a limb, takes his rifle, shoots down the limb, it spreads apart and snaps 'round them ducks' legs; and he saws off the limb and brings twenty-five, no thirty, ducks home."

"Oh, tell me more."

"No let's sing." And he began

> "Ho, Ho, Ho Dommie, diddle dommie
> Diddle, dommie do . . . ."

She joined in; they had passed the two empties, the Young's, and were in front of the Cloud's. Lurie Cloud was out on the porch sitting in a rocking chair.

"Good morning, Miz Cloud." Lurie Cloud was seldom referred to as Miz Cloud. She was seldom referred to at all. She was not accepted. When the women had come together at the pump, at a given time, generally around ten, she knew never to go. She saw herself as fat and dumb. She was not accepted. After all, the Clouds did some strange things.

For one thing, humpbacked White Horse Harry Cloud didn't work. He had been in a serious mine accident and didn't work. He stayed inside, never coming out on the porch. Never going to the commissary. They were looked after by folks who gave them leftovers. Summer, fall, winter, and spring. Coloreds and whites took what they didn't eat and didn't wear and gave it to Lurie and Whitehorse. They were dirt poor.

When Lurie smiled, she showed all rotten teeth. And she had up and had a baby. "The baby," Miz Brannon said, "was a 'change of life' baby." It was embarrassing to think about them two having a baby.

With all the rats, chiggers, bed bugs, over-running toilets around that house, could anybody find the pleasure to have a baby? They had.

"Jim, Jim Carter, come see the baby. Come up here and see my purty little girl."

"Well," he thought. "Just to humor her." Lois Jean slipped her hand into Daddy's hand. Jim felt in his pocket. A quarter in scrip. Up he went.

"Wanna see what she can do?" asked Lurie.

She took out a bag of Duke's Mixture, poured some loose tobacco in the little white paper, and rolled and licked it with one hand.

"Do you have a match on you?"

"Yes."

"Do you maybe have a quarter on you?"

"Why, yeah."

"Do you want to see Lily of the Valley smoke it?"

"Gotamighty, gotamightysword," he whispered reverently, then glanced at Lois.

He looked at the tiny baby doll in her arms. "She's twenty months old. Lookee. Lookee at her." Her head was round with chestnut fuzz on top, but what struck him were the blue veins up both her temples. She was lying there like a little sick dog. "Lily, wake up. Wake up, Lily. They's folks to see ye. Let's smoke a quarter's worth."

He couldn't move.

She roused the sleeping baby and, after taking two draws to see that it was lit, she stuck it in Lily of the Valley's mouth. The little girl roused. Opened her eyes. Drew in on the cigarette.

"Smoke, purty thing. Smoke for the folks." She did. "Do hit again, honey."

Suddenly, Lily was fully awake. She sat up and drew again and yet a third time. Lurie took a draw and then another one.

Lily began to cry, then scream.

Lurie threw back her head, laughing and giving her another draw.

The window shade raddled some. Jim said politely, "Thank you."

Went down the steps. No more singing. The song was gone.

Wherein Lois Jean Learns about the Jesus Cards

Lois had gone out to the toilet and while sitting there, decided to go visit Thelma and Geneva. She pulled up her jummers and strolled across the backyard and into Thelma and Geneva's kitchen. Every house in Tways said a lot about what was important to the inhabitants. Theirs was no different. They went to the Holiness Church. Nobody in Tways had a kitchen that had Sunday School cards strung all the way around the ceiling. Every Sunday at Sunday School the girls were given two cards, not much bigger than playing cards with pictures from the Bible. And they were in the order of events:

Abraham about to kill his own boy, Isaac

Moses in the bulrushes

Moses parting the water

Moses with a lot of grasshoppers

Moses with Pharoah trying to get a cold drink, but it was blood

Moses carrying two pieces of slate with numbers, just numbers on the two—Miz Shine says they were Roman navels, the ten Roman navels. Then on down the line were:

Jesus being baptized and a white bird over his head

Jesus knocking at somebody's door, wearing a pink nightgown

Jesus on the cross

Jesus with the pink robe open, showing his heart

Jesus rising up to heaven

Thelma and Geneva were eating breakfast and Thelma was crying because Geneva had used the last of the Pet cream on her oatmeal. She had put butter first, then the cream and sugar. Thelma didn't have any cream for hers and she was crying as she shook and shook the can over the bowl.

Geneva said, "Why'en you ask Jesus for some blood for your oats?"

Thelma jumped up, ran out the door to the back porch, and puked, or tried to puke. Lois Jean felt bad.

"How many cards do you have up there?"

"Well," said Geneva, "We have one for each Sunday and they's fifty-two Sundays in a year. And we've been here about three years. It's about 52 + 52 + 52. Cause we don't miss a Sunday, and we get two each Sunday so that's 104 a year 'cept we don't put up two of the same kind every week. We put up just one. We keep ones we like down here. My favorite is Jesus knocking at the door. Now looky here." She opened up the drawer in the tin-top table like Lois had at her house and pulled out the card. "It's Jesus and He's knocking on the door. See?" Lois Jean bent over, their heads touching. There was Jesus in the pink gown. Geneva said to call it a "robe". There was Jesus in the robe standing before the door, and pink roses just like hers in her yard were growing up and over the top of the door.

"Look closely." She had heard her mother, who had heard her preacher, who had heard his teacher from Illinois say "closely". Some said he was a sissy. Anybody who didn't work in the mines was just half a man. Real men worked, smoked, drank, and cussed, but not around a woman or children.

"Look closely. There is no door knob. The door has to be opened from the inside. Jesus can't open the door from the outside. It opens only from the inside."

Thelma quietly put her spoon down, looked around the kitchen and noted, "I'm damned tired of this shit." She hissed. "I'm very damned tired of…" Miz Shine appeared. Reached for the P&G and soaped up her dish rag, grabbed Thelma by her arm, lifted her in one swoop over to the dishpan, and washed out her mouth while Thelma screamed, choked and begged for mercy.

Then Miz Shine said, "And tonight it's castor oil for you."

Lois Jean loved visiting at Thelma and Geneva's.

Wherein Charity, N'Jenny, Ida, and Nell Go for Water

Charity had gone early to the pump—the pump in lower camp where roads not much more than paths T-boned. This road went back to the garages, where the McVeigh's house sat back in a vale, with Ann and Fat Sheehan's house on the left side and the end of school house hill on the other side.

There was a fine spring of water at the very bottom of school house hill and a body could plant one foot on the hill and the other on the side of the road, swing his face near the smooth rocks, and open his mouth and drink glorious mountain spring water with not a hint of sulfur.

Charity had slipped a time or two on her way to the garage, pulled up her dress skirt above her knees, planted one foot on the road, the other on the mountain side, and drunk and drunk and drunk.Charity liked this lower pump. It was early in the morning. She had on her apron over her dress and had a reason to be at the pump. She was out of water. Who was that coming up the road?

She turned her back. That way she had the upper hand. She could decide to be surprised or be silent and leave. She didn't like to lose control of her choices by engaging in too much talk with anybody. Charity believed in dressing, even for the pump. Combing her hair. Standing before a mirror and primping. Looking in the long mirror, admiring herself down to her bow legs.

She changed clothes to come to the pump or go to the commissary. Her hair was always just right, the part straight. Nose powdered. And it could be said that she carried herself well. She was said to be proud. She felt like she was better than some of the others.

She accomplished this feeling by not running around, not laughing real loud, by not engaging in too much talk. She had a strange reserve. She didn't tell dirty stories. As a young woman in the swing, no boy ever dared lay a hand on her knee to start something. She was cool, aloof, and scared of the strange feeling of inadequacy.

She never told about her family, her beginnings. She had no history and she was ashamed of poverty. What she had was a body, good bone structure, fine delicate features, smooth satin skin. With a man who provided, good furniture, children who showed no evidence of any deformity, she counted her blessings, naming them one by one. She was humming and pumping the bucket full.

"Good morning, Charity."

"Why, good morning yourself, Jenny."

Jenny had lumbered up the road, carrying a basket of laundry from Miz T.M. Gibson's. Shirts, delicate dresses, underwear and white linen handkerchiefs with an ornate "G" finely embroidered in the corner.

Word was out that Miz Gibson had "been a board." Been "a board" meant that she had gone back to Ireland on a boat and brought back lots of linen goods. Seems like the Irish liked linen about as much as they did potatoes. Truth is, they had more linen then they did potatoes. They let their potatoes rot. Lazy, good for nothing. Irony was, the very ones who spoke of this had ancestors there that they knew nothing of. All that went through Charity's mind just gazing at the handkerchief.

"I don't know how long I can keep this up," Jenny lamented. "I can't sit down. I has to keep walking." Charity had never thought of that. If Jenny sat down in the road, it would take a bunch of people to get her up. But Charity didn't let on that she was thinking that. Charity was enjoying the idea that just darted through her mind. She could not only sit down, she could jump into a tearing run full speed and outrun anybody. Even Millard. She started laughing out loud.

"It ain't funny, Charity."

"Oh, no, no, Jenny. I was thinking about running. Running away from Millard, my little runt of a brother. When my daddy died, he took over as head of the family. And when we didn't do his will, he'd take off that brown leather belt with that buckle, fold it in half and whip us. Sometimes with the leather fold and sometimes, if he was mad, with the buckle end. Well, last month or so, I was at my sister Mary's, and we were talking about the election. He asked me how I was going to vote. I told him I was free, white, and 21, means I can vote anyway I want to. Millard said that James had two votes, mine and his'n. I told Millard I was going to vote for Franklin Delano Roosevelt. I wanted a New Deal.

He raises up, takes off his belt at Mary's, my sister's, table and I look him in the eye and says, 'You are a fool, Millard Moses, you fool. I'm through with you and your little ignorant wife, Bessie. Come on if you think you can whip me. I can out run you, you fool, I can, I can.' He jumped for me, and I took off. He ran; I ran. I outran him a good quarter of a mile, circled back. He waited with Bessie 'til he had to leave to make the night shift. I hate him. That little dried up gone-to-seed fool." She was losing herself.

"Charity, Charity." It was Ida.

She caught up with herself, turned, smiled. "Miz Brannon, I come to see and hear whatever's going on." Then came Nell Farmer and finally Novella Haynes, Mr. Haynes' lovely, lovely daughter, pretty as Ora and Ruth.

"Have you'all heard about what's happening two doors up from the Owens'?" It was Nell. Nell Farmer had a spine. Nell stood up to anybody and spoke her mind. Nell was Ola's sister. Ola and Nannie, Charity's sister, had gone out dancing on Saturday nights. Nannie often wore Charity's wedding dress.

"Seems that the house is rented to Harlan's most famous whore." She continued, "They have put out that ol' street walker in Harlan. Seems that some of our men have seen fit to take up a little donation to put her in business, pay the light bill, the rent, give her money for—you know what."

"Theylaume."

"Oh, sweet Jesus."

"What are you saying?"

Jenny said, "I need a drink of water bad." They all looked at each other. How? They all had buckets. How? Jenny couldn't bend over to get her mouth under the spigot.

"Oh," said Jenny, "here, pump me a drink." She reached into her pocket and handed out what looked a little like a biscuit cutter without the red wooden top.

"It's a collapsible cup; see here." She stuck her thumbs down in the center and pushed down. A cup formed.

"Did you bring that from Alabama, Jenny?" That from Nell.

"Yes, I did."

"Did you stand down at the commissary, Jenny?"

"Yes, I did."

They all hushed. It was Jenny's story.

"Well, word came that colored girls wuz needed to marry colored men— colored men in Tways. Colored men would go out on Saturday night to get liquored up, take pills, fight, have cock fights, use straight razors, stay out 'til

Sunday night and not be fit to work come Monday. So's it was made up that what they needed was a good woman. They come in and rounded up forty of us, put us on the train, and brought us to Tways.

I was big, but then I could fit on a double seat and they took me.

When we got to Tways, I remember fixing my hair and stuff. They stood us in a line down at the commissary. We faced a line of men who didn't have a woman, and there was a bunch of men. A long bunch of men. At first, they just stood there shuffling from one foot to the other. Then one broke loose and trotted over to a pretty woman. Others followed until I was the only one left standing there. My best friend went off with her man. Everyone of them had a man except me. I was left standing. That's when Captain T.M. Gibson came up to me, said, 'What's yer name?' I said, 'Jenny.' He said, 'Jenny, we going to put you up here on a pallet on the porch for awhile. Would you like a cold R.C. and a Moonpie?'

'No, thank you. Just a cup of water, if'n you have it.'

He said, 'I'm sorry, we don't have water here for drinking except for the white folks. I'm going get you a cold R.C.' And he did. I said, 'Does anybody need shirts and white laundry done?' He said, 'Sit right here,' and I found out later that he went to his wife and Miz Elmer Hall. Miz Hall comes to the porch with Miz Gibson. They look me over. Then Miz. Hall says, 'You find this woman a place to stay, T.M., even if it is your bedroom.'"

They all laughed and laughed 'til they wiped their eyes on their aprons.

"Go on," said Nell, who loved a good story.

"Well, that's when I moved into what is really white camp. Miz Gibson or Miz Hall had the doors fixed for me and helped me get stuff I needed, and later on my cousin brought my stuff here. And here I am."

"Oh, laume." That from Ida.

"Oh, Sweet Jesus." That from Nell.

Nothing from Charity.

"Oh, one thing you must know. 'Bout a week later after this story went through the mines, a man shows up at my door with a beautiful woman. Uncle Tom Becker. It turns out the woman is his niece, Johnny Warren, and a teacher at the Rosenwall Colored School in Harlan. They made the sweetest talks. They welcomed me; they told me about the school activities, about Georgetown, and explained rules. Same as we had in Alabama; except y'all don't have any colored facilities here in this camp."

"Jenny, we don't have white facilities," said Nell.

They all laughed.

Then Jenny made a statement:

"I don't feel like I'm colored, and I don't feel like I'm white, living where I live and doing what I do; I feel like I'm Jenny. I love Charity's two little girls."

"Oh, my goodness," said Miz. Brannon. "I've got to run." And she picked up her bucket and left. "Charity, don't forget footwashing," Ida called back. The others followed suit. After everyone was gone, Jenny took a long time drinking water from a collapsible cup.

Wherein Charity Prepares for the Foot Washing

Charity continued taking the girls to the First Baptist Church. It gave her an important way of "making a showing". That was the commandment that she followed religiously. Thou shalt make a showing of thyself, thy children, and of whatsoever thou wearest or whatsoever thou eatest. That is what worked. Her furniture made a showing; her chickens made a showing. She had Rhode Island Reds, Plymouth Rocks, and White Leghorns. They were pleased to be Charity's chickens and pleased to lay eggs for her.

Her children made a showing. They were smart, clean, pretty little girls who set her off very well. Furthermore, James was a real catch. He showed her off. He supplied the means. She loved that man in her own way and own good time, paying him for his name, his security, and taking cash from his pockets that she went through as often as she could.

She allowed nothing to "bring disgrace," nothing. She often said at the pump, "I'd rather see one of mine dead than have it bring disgrace on me."

The girls were dressed in Sunday clothes and went to Harlan Baptist Church. Most of the time they rode with Mr. and Miz Miller, Diane, and her little brother Ernest. Mr. Haynes and Mr. Miller were very significant to everyone in Tways. People would line up at the commissary to be waited on, and they were waited on two at a time, Mr. Miller waiting on one and Mr. Haynes on the other. It was a nice way to get groceries.

Walk up the dozen or so wide concrete steps to the porch with the round iron, black railings. Children could wrap themselves all around the cool rail in summer and the freezing one in winter. Enter the huge store sporting coffered ceilings, big fans, fine wooden cases that held goods, fine cold shelves holding meat. A body could stand up inside the meat storage wooden cabinets. On the other side were goods for making dresses, buttons, thread, rick rack, and an array of scissors. Then there were parasols, umbrellas, fans, stockings, and socks. The commissary didn't sell underclothes. Panties were purchased at Newberries. While one was waiting, he or she could get an R.C. and a Moonpie and let others' mouths water as he ate it. There were mining buckets hanging high up, carbide lights, cans of carbide, and barrels of beans and rice.

The stock market crash in 1930 had little effect on the coal miners. The government sent in food supplies. One of the finest was cheese in a wooden box. Folks would swap money for that cheese. It was better than that round, dried out wheel cheese that Mr. Miller and Mr. Haynes would cut from. This cheese could melt in your mouth. It melted on the top and went through the macaroni. It laid soft and supple on toast in the oven. It would rise up, turning dark brown and growing crisp, allowing picking of that crust and anticipation of the creamy texture coming into an eager, almost drooling mouth. Some said "better than sin". August got the Carter's cheese. None of them would ever stand in a line to get cheese from the government. They waited for the poor to get in line; get it; and then sell it for U.S. dollars. No scrip. It had to be U.S. Dollars. August didn't mind this transaction a bit. Franklin Delano Roosevelt was looking out for them all. FDR and others in Frankfort, Kentucky.

Now, the most worrisome thing was coming up. The foot washing.

Uncle Milt Farmer from up on Bird Eye Rock, no less, had begun a Wednesday night prayer meeting up at the school house. Uncle Milt refused to declare any denomination.

"It's God's church—the church of God without no drinking pisen and handlin' snakes. It's the Holy Spirit that you can feel in your souls as well as yer bodies. Feel free to shout if you are so moved. But we are following Jesus the Nazarene."

Not a man would show up. Women's stuff. But the miners in various ways had supported his efforts. Went in together, got him a pulpit and two chairs that could be pulled out onto the stage in the other room of the two-room school house that was for fourth through eighth graders. Big boys and girls. It was nice to have that setup. That room had box suppers to raise funds; it had programs and the Christmas play; and now it would hold church on Wednesday nights.

But a foot washing. "To humble the proud and to see Jesus through something as humble as washing your neighbor's foot."

There was a run on towels and new enameled wash pans at the commissary. Miz Brannon said she would not buy a towel, that her bleached cow-feed sack was good enough. "In fact, Jesus didn't use no towel from J. J.

Newberry's. He was more likely to use a feedsack his mother had found in the stable and took home as a souvenir."

Charity thought to herself, "That feedsack won't make a showing." She pranced down to the commissary and purchased herself a pink towel. But then there was the secret, the one that she could not escape. What was she going to do?

When Charity was a little girl, her daddy went to Proctor Commissary or maybe somewhere in Williamsburg and came home carrying two pairs of red shoes for Charity and Little Nannie girl. They hugged him, smothered him with kisses, and put the shoes on bare feet. Never, never had that sight been seen—blood red shoes.

Alas, they were too short and her toes scrounged up in the ends and dirt got under the sore toes. Nobody could get Charity to give up her red shoes. She put them under her side of the bed. Nobody touched them. She hopped along, everybody laughing.

That was the year she was big enough to drop half-runner white beans. Charity was born December 29, 1907. She had a younger sister and several older sisters and brothers so she had to fight to get anything. She even learned to stick out her tongue to catch every drop of oatmeal or soup beans. Out flicked that tongue. She would place the spoon or the piece of cornbread on it.

From somewhere, somehow, she turned up with a pink silk parasol. Some said that Millard had slipped out to the carnival and brought it back. Some said that Grandma Moses swapped butter for it—unlikely. But there she stood in the hot sunshine, head of yellow hair, face as fair as fair could be, with red shoes and pink parasol, ready to plant half-runner whites on Good Friday.

The others laughed. She paid them no mind. Went up and down the rows, carefully dropping three white beans into each hill. "One for me, one for you, and one for the teenie weenie bird." It was a sight.

The toes were badly infected. Both toenails came off. Ide wrapped the toes in salve. Charity wouldn't go without her red shoes. After a month or two, the shoes softened up some. But two ugly, thick, gray and black nails grew back. It was said that one of the preachers on Wolf Creek preached about the sin of wearing sin. He said, "Sin was short-sleeved dresses, painted mouths, hair cooked under a machine, and red shoes."

Never ever did Charity have red shoes again. Nor did anyone buy red shoes. God had never forgiven her. Back came her sin over and over. Now it would be seen by the whole world. Her deformed, black, thick toenails. She was going to pray for guidance. The children were in the chicken lot with Miz Piertison and Shirley and the chickens. She knelt down by the table and prayed: "Oh, Lord, what can I do about these toes that you have burdened me with? Lord, I don't want to be embarrassed. Either send me the miracle of perfect toes by Wednesday night or let me hide them successfully. In Jesus name, Amen."

She raised up, feeling a load off of her mind, although she had not the faintest notion of why. Tuesday went by. No answer. She got up early Wednesday, passed through the middle room. There was Lois Jean, pajama sleeve pulled down over her thumb and pinned with a huge safety pin to keep her from sucking that thumb. They had done everything, castor oil on the thumb, red pepper—she got in her eyes—spanking. But it happened while she was sleeping that she sucked that thumb. Suddenly, Charity knew exactly what she was going to do about her toes.

Wherein Murm Johnson Gets a Radio and Goes to the Foot Washing

Murm kept a piece of red teaberry chewing gum in her mouth to expel the nervous energy. If she tired of it, she put it on the post of the rocking chair or on the bedpost. There were several pieces in both places and if somebody came along and wanted to chew her gum, they'd sure as hell better put it back when they were finished with it.

Murm was a survivor and an innovator; everybody watched from afar as she equipped her house with the radio. She lived close to the Gibson's, and one day she was passing by when Mr. T.M. walked out the front door and down the beautiful front walk, grass lawn on both sides, white petunias edging the walk.

"Murm, you want you a radio?"

"Oh, Lord, yes, I'd take it right now."

"It's big. Who can carry it?"

"Me, that's who."

"No, it is big."

"Ol' Murm can carry it. I'll wade around to the back and pack it home."

"Murm, you can't do that."

"Yes, I can, Mr. T.M. Jest you watch."

This woman had more energy, a small muscular woman with kinky hair and no interest in the beautiful at all.

Round to the back of the house she came, up to the back door.

"I won't come in. Jest help me get it onto my back."

"How's Rube?"

"Aw, he ain't so good. TB will kill him, I guess."

That's why they lived back in the field across the other side of the camp and that's why their kids were not in school and that's why she had to do it all. Her boys helped her garden and she had pigs and collected slop for her pigs. They had a cow and folks from Harlan Baptist Church helped them. Her children were good. They left home but never their parents. One or two of the boys were already settled in Harlan.

Truth was, the doctors had told her Rube didn't have TB; he had emphysema, but TB was easier to say.

"Hey're, put it on my back."

"No, I'll get somebody; yell for your boys."

"I'll yell, but put it on my back. I can carry the thang, thank you."

T.M. was tired of it all.

"It won't play."

"We'll see about that."

She stood at the back door and yelled so she could be heard from one side of the mountain to the other.

"Famous, oh Famous, oh Fame," calling voice riding up and down the scale in her own familiar tune.

She heard a whistle.

"Brang the rig."

She never missed a step. Knees bent and staggering and taking teency, eency steps.

T.M. and Miz Gibson never moved from the window. Soon Famous showed up. The rig was two automobile tires joined by the axel springs from the car and 2x4s from the first toilet forming the bottom and sides. Then a steering wheel was mounted where the tongue of a wagon might be. One son pushed and the other steered.

Famous showed up with Hen, and they took the radio and laid it down in the back of the rig and covered it with a dirty quilt.

"Well, what's wrong with the radio?"

"Not one thing, boys. It's good as new. I don't think it's ever been played."

She climbed up onto the little bench and steered; the other two pushed the rig. She loved riding along, being pushed by her children.

When she got to the yard, she hollered, "Oh, Rube; hey're, Rube; come hey're; see's what we got."

Rube appeared, robust and grinning, pulling up his overall strap. Looking round, then feigning weakness and falling into his rocking chair.

"Nobody's looking, Rube."

"Never can tell. Ye can't get careless or ye'll blow yer cover. Never take chances. What ye got, ol' Lady?" He looked at her lovingly and thought how they had made a good life together and both loved it. Folks would die if they saw what he, what they had. They had everything. They went through the castoffs of others. They went behind stores in Harlan. Bowers, Quality Shop, Dr. Tye's Drugstore, McComb Supply. They scrounged and lived well. He knew that many folks set out extra, knowing that poor old Murm would come by with Famous and Hen and carry it off. Left a good feeling, knowing that you were helping somebody worse off than you were.

Rube collected everything. He had a large collection of buttons, pennies, pins, shoe strings, tools, nails, and paper. Paper was hard to come by. Most got groceries, carrying them in feed sacks or tow sacks that heavy-duty goods were shipped in. But he managed to have paper bags and a small supply of Harlan Daily Enterprises. He had broken china and fans from every source, churches, funeral homes, and places of business. His prize, though, was a turtle, a weird turtle that Murm had found near Miz Elmer Hall's. One of their finest pieces. It was a turtle with green and bright pink on its back. It was about five inches across the back and alive when she brought it in.

One day Rube was in bed. He kept the turtle by the bed in a big wooden bread bowl that Murm used every morning to make biscuits. She'd place the turtle in the bed until breakfast was over, then put the little turtle back in the bowl. Rube was lying there with his eyes half closed when the little teency turtle commenced to move down his chest. He was propped up on his pillows and looked down. Suddenly words formed and a beautiful scene appeared. Palm trees, blue ocean, pink sun, and it was Myrtle Beach. Jesus was visiting him. Oh, God. He was dying. That brought him to. He yelled at everybody and all came, all nine.

"Murm, look here. Git in bed. Lookee." Murm squinted her eyes. All the pieces moved together, and it said "Myrtle Beach". Famous, Ruby, Henry, and the others looked at the turtle's back.

"Now we could charge. . . ," began Murm.

"No, it's our secret. Nobody must know about this. Stand up 'round the bed. Raise yer hands and repeat: 'I'll never tell, so help me God.'"

They did.

Today they were blessed with a radio. A real fine radio that didn't work.

"Rube, put this in your brain pan. If you got a good radio that won't play even when the juice hits it, what's the matter with it?" Back he came. "It needs an earl."

"Can you and the boys do it?"

"Yeah, we kin. First we got to put up a pole. Tallest pole we kin find. Next, I got to find electric whar and a little hickey that screws onto the house, an enamel plate through to the radio."

The project was underway. Rube had a store of poles ranging from fence size to telephone pole size. He selected one. Then he went back to bed.

"Murm, get the young'uns together; dig a hole four or five feet down; fill it with river rock; put dirt around it." That from ol' Rube from the bed.She did. Everyone in the family worked with everyone else. It was like a hive of bees except Rube was the king bee. And they all loved and appreciated the other one. One had an idea; the others helped bring it to fruition. It was a fine, loving family.

Before hot sun had hit the meadow, the pole was in place. The smallest climber shinnied up the pole and followed out instructions called out from the bed, to Murm, to the child. That done, they unrolled the fine wire, retrieved from the mine where it had been thrown out, back to the porch through the window to the radio that stood in the front room.Out of bed came ol' Rube, who took over. He was as fine as any surgeon with a body.

"Pliers." Slapped into his hand.

"Screw driver."

"Needle." Murm obliged.

"Flashlight."

"Little finger." A little finger appeared.

"Mash it."

Then he tinkered more.

"Done." They all laughed.

"What day is it?" They all thought. Time flowed in necessary activities not activated by a calendar. Each day brought on what was needed for that day. Rube had turned on the radio. He was getting static. Lots of static. What was wrong? Then he thought of the dial and knobs. He squatted down, twisted a few, and suddenly the room was filled with blue grass.

"Oh, God. Oh, God."

Up he got, grabbed Murm, and they began to dance. The children stood around slack jawed; never had they seen anything like it. Never. Then Rube went over, grabbed his little girl, and said, "Put yur little feet on my big feet." She did. They danced. The morning glories bloomed....

Word was out that Rube's and Murm's radio was the finest and could get Nashville, Tennessee. That had happened several months ago and Saturday nights they would tune it loud. On Saturday night, Nell Farmer, Maxie Carter, Russ Collins and Ola could stand out on their respective back porches and hear the words being sung by folks in Pineville, Kentucky. That's how good that radio was.

Wherein Lois Jean Is Almost Saved
at the Foot Washing

Charity put on the one pair of silk hose that she owned, packed up the white enameled wash pan and the pink towel. She would take Lois to prayer meeting.

Days were still long, and today was beautiful.

Supper was served early that warm summer night. Dishes washed, table cleaned, floor swept, fire dying out in the cook stove. Charity even swept the back porch, pausing to look up to where tall trees met evening sky.

Then, it was time to get dressed. Each woman dressed carefully, knowing that she would be judged on her appearance. "Judge not that ye be not judged." But that would not prevent another from passing judgment. It was better and certainly more entertaining to judge. It was, in fact, an all-consuming pastime, and it was free.

Tonight was judgment time, ranging from who had thought of the best setup—the enameled pan for instance—towel, or feed sack. Miz McCurg could let down her long hair from its knot and dry everybody's feet with her hair!

Then there was how much makeup. Some felt it was a sin and only "who-ers painted themselves up". Yet, everyone needed a little help from Cody and Tangee, and very few disdained rouge and permanents.

A foot washing could expose you. It called for delicate understanding of just how prepared and devout you must appear. Not overly prepared. Just the right actions. Charity was taking Lois Jean. All of the women would take their children. Not nursing children—God forbid that Lurie Cloud would show up with that little thing. Lurie was well aware of the rules.

Supper was finished. Charity stood a long time in front of the mirror, adjusting makeup, putting hair in place, setting blond waves deep just above her beautiful forehead. She got the pan and towel. It had been discussed at the pump and decided that they would carry pans with the towel folded and tucked in the pan.

"Go get the pan and bring it to me, Lois Jean." She tried both arms; decided the left was better. Pulled up to her breast or under her arm. The towel might slide out. The pan would go over her left breast but a little to the side.

Then, there were the stockings, the silk stockings. She had them stuck down her dress in the middle of her cotton brassiere. Garters and all. Above her Duke's mixture bag of bills. Busy place, she smiled. Real busy place. She had decided on this action since she would run her stockings wearing them up the hill in the dark. But how to put them on. She could slip in the other room and put them on.

"Come on, Lois Jean."

They were going to walk up the mountain from the lower camp side. The side with the little path. She could have gone out the back door and up the hill, but she needed to be doing what everyone else was doing—only better. Everybody would be watching her just as she was watching everybody. Yes, it was judgment day and time to make a showing. Others were starting out; some were at the base of the mountain.

There was a yellow clay bank worn into a sloping path that would accommodate those going to school from both upper camp and lower camp. Others joined in. People she had not seen in a long time. Murm Johnson; Miz McVeigh and three of her beautiful daughters; Miz McCurg; Maxie with little Vinnie; Miz Haynes with Novella; Miz Brannon with Frankie, Jewel and Virginia; Nell Farmer and, lo and behold, Aunt Ella Carter with Florence and Captola.

"Watch out for snakes," they frequently called out.

The place was covered with frogs. They didn't mess with snakes too much. Some carried a stick kept on the porch. You could do much with a stick—find a tomato, scrape a puppy out from under the floor if it had gotten lost behind a chimney, beat off snakes or whip a child—"spare the rod, spoil the child." Up they climbed, talking, laughing softly in the summer air, a little nervous about the ceremony.

Murm was chewing and even popping that red Teaberry gum. Maxie, walked with little Vinnie. Little Vinnie was spoiled. She clung to her mother's skirt and was bashful. The other children were up ahead, catching lightning bugs, squeezing out the lights and putting the light on their finger-nails and waving them.

They all paused; halfway up the mountain there was a little shelf of dirt, smooth as a table. They all turned round to survey the little tin-roofed houses with lights on the front porches spilling out into front yards.

"You know, that is a sight as beautiful as a painted picture. We are fortunate to have a small camp of mainly good neighbors." Ella Carter had joined them. She had put down her detective story and joined in the foot washing. Cappie and Florence were with her. It had been some time since the baby, Florence's twin, had fallen in the lye water, but she still grieved. "She has bad dreams," said Tom Carter.

Here she was appreciating Tways and loving, caring neighbors. By now it had gone dark. The moon would be up soon. A full moon. The sky was still light and stars faintly seen. No air stirred. Then they began the steep climb up to the flat, wide-open playground and the two-room school.

Uncle Milt from up on Bird Eye Rock had walked down alone. None of his people had ventured down. They stayed on that mountain, sending men to the store about once every three or four weeks. They were completely self-sufficient. They raised their chickens and hogs. They made candles for light. They made their coffins for burial and filled them with apples that often lasted right through until spring. They dried beans and turned late fall cabbage upside down and buried it deep so that it would last months. They wore homespun with aprons over it. These folks could sing shaped notes. They made salves for sores and shine for colds and fevers.

Here stood Uncle Milt. The room was ablaze with light. He had picked the lock, pulled the handle on the juice box on the porch, and lights were on. His guitar and Bible were there. The small, wiry fellow was gracious. "Come in, come into the Lord's House. Come in one and all." "One and all" was said at the circus. He had to have been to the circus. Where else could one hear "one and all".

Charity and Lois Jean sat down in desks. George Washington's picture hung above the blackboard. There was a stage with a teacher's desk. There were the ABC's above the blackboard and down both sides of the room in print and script. There was a water bucket on a little table with a dipper in it. The desks were nailed to the floor to keep the rows straight. And in the room was that familiar smell from the banana oil on the floors and the pencil shavings.

"Let's git started. Find a place and be seated."

Suddenly Charity remembered her stockings. She had to put on the stockings so no one could see her toes and pass judgment.

"Excuse me, Miz Brannon."

"Of course, Charity."

Uncle Milt began. "Let's stand and greet each other with either a handshake or a hug. Begin." He gave them ample time. "Now, hit's nice that you'ens er here. The spirit is here. Let's sing *Amazing Grace.*"

After several songs, an announcement, a prayer, the scripture, Uncle Milt began the sermon. "We need, 'uh huh', to feel the spirit, 'uh huh', moving in us, 'uh huh'. We need the spirit, 'uh huh'. We, 'uh huh', need to love and to 'uh huh', forgive others as, 'uh huh', Jesus forgives us, 'uh huh'."

Murm was the first to jump and begin clapping her hands and speaking in tongues. She was in the aisle, her shoulders jerking, eyes closed, and dancing from one foot to the other.

She was joined by Ann Ramey, who spoke a sentence that would be used at all the services: "Scheek-a-ma-shilo, give-it-to-Cylo."She had her hands cupped in front of her and her eyes shut. She bent over her friend and touched her hands. Up jumped Cleo and commenced shouting and speaking in the tongues. Uncle Milt droned on. The others sat still.

The frenzy released the evil forces from their bodies, and everybody loved and forgave everybody else. They were crying and clapping their hands. The old devil, Satan, had been released from their bodies, and there in its place was sweetness and light. There was love and kindred feeling. The room was bathed in the splendor of the Holy Spirit. Uncle Milt had invited Jesus, and Jesus had delivered the Holy Spirit.

Lois Jean had been caught up. She felt the spirit.

Uncle Milt reached for his guitar and began strumming. "Just as I am, without one plea, but that thy blood was shed for me. . . I come, I come."

Then, strumming softly, he says, "If you need the saving grace, come on down, kneel down. Ask Jesus to wash your sins away; to make you whole. Come on down."

It was the "altar call". When a sinner stepped out in the aisle, all eyes would turn to follow the sinner. The sinner would come to the altar and fall on her knees and pray for forgiveness of sins and newness of life. After an appropriate time, she would rise in a newness of life and be welcomed into the church of the living God.

This simple ritual worked. Women's lives changed. They gave up smoking, drinking, cursing, and settled firmly into their true colors. They had a place. They became part of the community of believers and followed the teachings of the church.

Men were embarrassed and put off by this ritual. A real man did not make a showing of weaknesses. So they continued in their sins. Men joined a church and when asked what church would give them a letter, they would name a non-existent church or one that had burned up. This side step had its problems, for the joiner then had to profess his faith and be baptized. Many did that, especially in larger churches.

So the altar call floated out and no one moved. "Come on down," Uncle Milt begged. "Come on."Lois Jean stepped out into the aisle and went forward before Charity could reach to stop her.

"Kneel down and ask God to forgive you of your sins and stay there until you are moved by the Holy Spirit," Uncle Milt instructed, "and pray for her that God will cleanse her and give her newness of walk."

Lois Jean knelt down and stayed there. Minutes passed. She was waiting on the Holy Spirit to come. He didn't come. Nothing happened. Outside a whippoorwill sang, frogs croaked, owls hooted. It was late. Lois Jean was tired, but she stayed there, waiting for the arrival of the Holy Spirit as she waited for Santa Claus. What was to be done? It was quiet. They had all waited at least fifteen minutes, and some were ready for the foot washing. Miz Brannon began to sing. "Just as I am, without one plea, but that thy blood was shed for me." She moved out into the aisle. Others joined in. She went down to the altar and lifted up Lois Jean, who looked around and rubbed her eyes.

Charity stood still. As she came down the aisle, Ann Ramey put her hand on the child's head. Cleo did the same. Nell kissed her on the cheek. Murm passed her a piece of gum from her pocket. When she got to Charity, Charity smiled, leaned over her and said, "If you embarrass me like this again, I will spank the living daylights out of you." Lois Jean just smiled and put the gum in her mouth. What a nice Holy Spirit. She felt warm and connected to everyone and just a little sleepy.

"Now," said Uncle Milt, "we are ready. Face the one acrost the aisle from you. Set the pan in the floor, and we have two buckets of water. I'll come by and put the water in the pan; you bend over and warsh the feet of the person acrost the aisle. Kneel down and warsh the foot. Then, place it on yer knee and dry it. Then the other foot. I'll be reading scripture whilst you do that. Don't say a thing. Just gently warsh that foot, then the other foot."

The women slid down on their knees and, in an amazing night quietness, sweetly observed the ritual. Miz Haynes didn't say a thing about washing Charity's foot with a silk stocking on it. Uncle Milt's voice reading about how Jesus, born in a manger, crucified, dead, and buried, rose from the grave and is on the right hand of God. The night was sweet with a pause from all that was mean, bitter, violent, demeaning. When the ritual was over, he reached for his guitar and sang.

"Shall we gather at the river, the beautiful, the beautiful river. Gather at the banks of the river that flows by the throne of God."

They prayed, went out into the fresh night air, the full moon. Not very much was said. Everyone had been moved by that simple service, and there had been stirrings in the souls beyond conscious thoughts.

Wherein Jenny Dies
and Is Prepared for the Journey Home

Jenny started before the sun was up. Fried her bacon, put in eggs, opened a cold lard biscuit, and fixed coffee. Ate. Tidied up her house and began the walk to pick up the Gibson's laundry. Miz Gibson would have the dirty shirts, dresses, and underclothes down by the big gate that swung open. There was a rope that Jenny pulled and the big gate opened as wide as the road opened to the driveway. She moved slowly through the camp.

R.C. Tway was a beautiful little camp. Most of the yards had fruit trees or maple trees or a hemlock. Some had an old tire whitewashed with eight o'clocks from the seeds on the side of a package of Eight o'Clock coffee from the A&P in Harlan. Every house had a front porch swing. Some had rocking chairs. Most families had a dog that slept "nunder the floor" and knew when somebody foreign came up the steps to come out and bite him. Bad dogs were chained during the day and let loose at night. All the dogs were familiar with Jenny; they never moved when she lumbered by.

It was cool. Jenny was carrying a fan from the Anderson Laws Funeral Home with a picture of the Last Supper on it. Down she went, past the Miller's, past the Owen's, past the shack, turned to the right and up the road to pick up the shirts and whites.

She bent over, and when she raised up, her head was swimming. She fanned a little and started back. It was still early. It would be awhile before the night shift would be coming home.

Back up the road. Vesti McCurg was cutting kindling, her back to Jenny. There was Maxie coming out of the toilet. She didn't see Jenny, who turned by Miz Brannon's and past the Mitchell's. The next house would be the Smith's, then the Carter's, then hers.

She got to that place in the road that Lois Jean, Charity, and Jim called the Garden of Eden and the garden that Jim and Charity put out every year.

She looked below the road. Set the clothes down. "What a beautiful place." She was at the edge of the road. Took one step forward and began floating through the air. She floated weightless above the Garden of Eden—slowly, slowly, rising to the throne of God.

Charity got up, built the fire, fixed breakfast, started the washing machine. Children got up, dressed, ate breakfast. They went up to visit with Shirley and Miz Piertison and to get the eggs. Mickey held the basket and Lois Jean felt under the warm hens that were trying to set. Today they gathered eight eggs.

"Go down to the Garden of Eden and get me some green tomatoes. Today we're going to have us some fried green tomatoes." She handed Lois Jean a brown paper bag to put the tomatoes in. "Watch out for snakes."

Out she went, down the steps to the road. That's when she saw the basket of shirts and whites. Nobody near it. She started down the well-worn path to the garden. That's when she saw Jenny. Jenny was laying face down, one side resting against a huge tree.

"Jenny, Jenny. Hello, Jenny." Jenny did not speak. She was sound asleep. There was something not right. She dropped the bag, ran back, "Mother! Mother! Mother!"

Charity grabbed the rifle behind the door. It was a snake. She ran down the steps.

"It's Jenny. Jenny's asleep. She's asleep and won't wake up."

Charity ran, saw the laundry and then Jenny. "Go, go sit on the porch in the swing. You and Mickey sit in the swing. Don't move until I get back."

She ran toward the boarding house, yelling, "Help, help." By the time she was mounting the steps, C.C. had stepped out.

"What's wrong, Charity?"

"It's Jenny. She's dead. Rolled down close to the Garden of Eden."

"Just a minute. Let me get my gun."

Out stepped Helen. She was simply beautiful. She had on a bathrobe.

"Hello, Charity. You say Jenny's dead?"

"Yes, she's dead."

"Well, we need to let upper camp know so's they can take care of one of their own."

"No, she belongs to all of us. We need help from upper and lower. James can help. She has been a saint, and I don't care what color she is, she's with God in paradise."

"Yes, I'm sure, but in the meantime, we have to bury her."

"Get James from the mines."

"I'll call the driftmouth." Helen had taken charge.

Away she swished in a china blue silk robe with a fringed tie with the technicolored dragon on the back.

The night shift was just coming out. Uncle Tom and Jim got the word together.

"How and where can we bury her?" Tom asked.

"She's over the road by the garden, the one down over the hill."

"No place to bury her that I know about." Resthaven was for whites only. "What are we going to do?"

"Get a truck, get her in it and. . ." James' voice trailed off.

"Yeah, get a truck, wrap her in a sheet. Get her bedspread, wrap her in it, tie strips around it."

"Put her in the truck and take her. . ." voice trailed off.

"Jim, let's do the first part first. I'll get the boys. She belongs to us."

"Tom, Ma will help wash."

"No, Jim, no washing—not time. Wrap her up and bury her somewhere tonight. Providence will provide, Jim. Providence will provide."

Word spread fast. The boys from upper camp, including ol' drunk Lemon, came. They surveyed her.

Jim thought of the ice wagon, but they needed a truck.

"Don't ol' Mr. McVeigh have a truck?" someone asked.

McComb Supply had three trucks. A call was made from the shack to Harlan. Jim volunteered to drive his car down, leave it, pick up the truck, a handcart, and a flat with rollers. Tom went with him and drove his car back to Tways.

Women had arrived to care for their own. Miz Becker took the chenille bedspread with the bouquet in the center from Jenny's bed. Spread it out and suggested that they tie a strip around her head to close her mouth. Then cut a hole where the bouquet was, slip it over her head, and bury her.

"Won't work. Nain't gonna work. She got to be wrapped proper. Round her body, crossing her head."

"She ain't gonna roll nowhere."

"Jesus, Mary, and Joseph, what us gonna do?" says Lemon, nursing his drink and enjoying the idea of stepping out of the ordinary. He imagined this party could go on for maybe a day and a night, if things worked out. Lemon liked to observe. A death was the highest form of suffering. You could gaze at the deceased and whisper, "Have mercy," or you could take a small edifying drink of good shine and whisper, "Have mercy," or see a woman that set you off and slowly shake your head and groan, "Have mercy". Lemon's ability to grieve was down to a fine art. He did better than any other person in R.C. Tways with "Have mercy". Furthermore, anybody else trying out or practicing, "Have mercy" was put down with a fierce, "You shed yo moaf." He meant it.

When Miz Becker arrived, she took over, carrying white sheets. She stood on the road and directed the boys step by step.

"Spread out the sheet. Fully. Don't worry about things underneath. Take the second sheet and spread over her just as she is. Now straighten her out so's she is lying flat. The tree has her stopped. Flatten her out, but make sure that she is on the edge of the sheet." They followed directions. So far they had not touched weight.

"Now, shoulder to shoulder, five of you line up with two hands about midback and roll her over on the sheet, face down." When they did, Jenny groaned, air rushing out of her mouth. The boys ran, and Lemon screamed.

"Get yourselves back here," Miz Becker called. "Now, she's not alive. She just had air stored up. She's gone to Jesus." Upon hearing that, Lemon murmered, "Have mercy," and resumed his station.

They rolled her onto the sheet, brought it up on her back, slipped the second one so it overlapped, and rolled her back against the tree. She was covered completely. "Now, Jim, can we put a pulley and rope on her?"

"Who's got rope?" asks Jim.

"They's steel cable at the driftmouth rolled up. We could borrow that and the stuff we use to drag out the boys when they're trapped."

"Yeah." He pitched his car keys into the knot of boys. "Go get my car, drive it up past Ma's. Run up to the driftmouth; bring all the cable and pulleys in the dynamite box there by the shack. Boy's, half a hour at most."

They ran.

In the meantime, Jim found a tree on the other side of the rode below Shine Smith's house. Walked around the walnut tree. Crossed the road, looked down at the huge pile of Jenny.

"We're goin to need some boards. Roll her up on the boards."

He thought a minute. "Lemon. . ."

"Mr. Jim, ol' Lemon can't do nothing. He's sick."

"No, he's drunk, but he can go take them boards off the top of Jenny's front porch railing. Pull out the nails and bring them here."

"You go wis ol' Lemon, Mr. Jim."

They went off to get the boards. Charity, Lois Jean and Mickey were on the front porch watching wide-eyed.

Jim came up on his back porch, got the claw hammer, and he and Lemon took the whole top railing of smooth boards—two from the ends and four from the front—but leaving those on either side of the steps. They were not as long as Jenny. Back they went, laid them down ready for use. The boys returned with the steel cable. They began clearing of all the weeds, rocks, a smooth path.

Jim and Uncle Tom stood over Jenny while the boys worked the cable under her. Planks lying on the cable, they worked until they had her body on the planks and sent two up the hill to work the pulley. The rest pushed on Jenny while the two moved the lever, and slowly, very slowly, Jenny moved up the hill. It was late afternoon when they finally got her up to the road.

The truck was backed up.

"We are going to lift her, boys," said Jim. "Ma knows levitation, and here's how it works. We all, everybody who can touch her, gets up close and we all get two arms up to the elbows under her. On the count of five, eyes closed for the lift, we fly her up. If you can't believe this, you don't try it. I have seen chairs walk across a floor and little women lift a heavy man from a sitting position. Believe that we can lift Jenny into the truck and we can do it."

Jenny flew to the back of the truck, then fell back to the ground. When she touched the back of the truck, her body did not clear the back.

"Ok, this time we need the best men, the biggest, the youngest to get under her and push. When we lift, you'ens run under her and push. Four volunteered, and it worked.

Light and easy, they remembered long afterward, all working in unison, light and easy. Jenny was in the McComb Supply Truck with the back gate in place.

Where were they going to take her? Not to Alabama. She wouldn't last. Not to the Resthaven. They had folks hired to watch the place. Not to a mountaintop. Where?

Jim had driven the truck into Jenny's backyard, and the boys were sitting on the front porch. The women from upper colored camp were arriving with huge plates and bowls of fried chicken, corn on the cob, cole slaw, green beans, cornbread, ice cold tea, and several banana puddings.

Voices low, "Have mercy," whispered Lemon. Charity sent plates and spoons. So did the boarding house. Jenny was a beloved woman.

Jim knew one thing. Politics had to be kept out of it. Politics couldn't get into it. Folks could be killed. He sat next to Uncle Tom. "We need to finish this thing as soon as we can."

"Jim, we can't git her to that excuse of a cemetery up on the mountain. She's too big to handle. No truck can get there."

"I know. Listen. What I'm about to say is between you and me. No questions. They's a place below Harlan called Loyall. They's a cemetery down there up on a hill, but that spills down over the side of the mountain. It's almost full. Some of them stones goes back aways, into the last century. Now they's a rough road. Well, it's not really a road. But the truck could go up there. There's nothing. I've been back there in a car. Now, we wait 'til dark. We dig the hole, we put Jenny in it. We lay some rocks and brush on top."

"Jim, if it would go that way."

"Tom, never was there a better woman than Jenny. I believe the Creator—the same that created her will help a bunch of willing boys to bury her. We will be ok."

"Yes, Jim, we will walk in grace."

"Tom, what's grace?"

"A gift. Grace is a gift. An unmerited gift."

Word spread that there was a plan that called for just the boys. Boys who were working night shift. All would be over by eleven. The plan was not divulged.

They ate and talked. The afternoon breeze came up. Women came and went through her things and passed them out. Miz Becker took her books. Dresses could be cut up for quilts. Her utensils and furniture were scattered throughout upper camp. Jim took the large washing tub. The women scrubbed the floor and the back porch and pulled the door shut.

Finally, it was dark and the first of several cars went out, not all at once, and immediately pulled off the road to wait outside the gates for the truck. Chief Miller opened the gates.

Out they went, down the paved road. Through Harlan's main street. Not all together in one long car van. A few driving through and waiting on the other side of town. On down the paved road, round Moo Cow Curve, down to Loyall.

The whole world was asleep. They took the sharp curve to the left and after about a quarter of a mile, Jim stopped the truck, got out. Came back, put it in low and straddled the path, not even a road. Boys followed, leaving doors open so's not to make a noise. Several had sticks and pushed them in front.

"Everybody, stop." It was Jim. "Stand still. Look up, get your bearings, let your eyes get adjusted. Get the picks and shovels, and let's move."

"Do they's be anything heh?"

"Like what?"

"Haints."

"I don't think so."

Some stomped around upon a little bank just above the path.

"Heh et is."

They began to circle and break up into groups and two standing almost against the back of the other two. They began taking out the dirt.

"This sho'nuff mo easier than fo'lef," referring to Tway's coal at the mines.

"You waits 'til we hid uh roc."

"I sho' will. I sho' will."

On they went. The dirt was soft with very few rocks. The others took turns. The hole was up to their knees, then deeper.

"Boys, when we git her in, we got to put pressure on the top so's nothing can smell her and take her up."

"Gotamity, Jim."

"I brought some kerosene. We going to pore it over her. That'll keep things away."

One moaned, "Does we haf ta?"

Tom explained, "Jenny's in paradise. Her body bound her. She was a prisoner in that body. She never had the joy of a dance, a man, a baby. She was a prisoner. If'en Jenny is seeing us, she would say, 'Pour the kerosene on me; let me return to dust, not have my bones dug up and scattered.'"

"I bleeve," says a voice.

"So does I," another.

They dug on into the night. Owls hooted and dogs barked, but mostly everything was quiet with a little cool breeze.

Finally, Uncle Tom was lowered. He had to reach up, never touching the top edge. "How far away is my hand?" One leaned over and felt along the edge. He lay on his stomach and found the tips of Tom's fingers.

"Alright," he pronounced.

Jim put the flat that they used to deliver pianos on the ground. It would not help. Nowhere to roll it. Neither would the handcart.

"We've got to lift her, boys."

"On our shoulders. They carries ice on they's shoulders. We carries Jenny."

And they did. Two went before, down on their hands and knees, and brushed away anything in the newly established path. Two in front took pocket knives as sharp as razors and cut polk weeds and saw briars, moved rocks and made the way smooth.

Then there was the open grave.

"I's guiden feets," one volunteered.

He reached out to the first man and put his hands around his ankles. "Move where I pulls yo feets."

Slowly, slowly. There they were on the upper side of the open grave. They lowered her. "Roll her in."

There was an unearthly sound of that body hitting the bottom of the grave. Not a word was spoken as Jim poured a gallon of kerosene over Jenny. They put the dirt in. Then everyone was to get bushes, rocks, and put them on top of the grave.

It was all a success, a real success. They hugged and slapped backs.

Suddenly a strange voice nearby. "Well done, though good and faithful. Well done."

Total silence.

"It's me, Joe, Frank's boy, Joe. I've just broke out, and I need a ride to Tways. I know yer secret and ye've got to help."

"Come down here," Jim yelled.

He did. Still in prison garb. Nobody moved or said a thing. Joe stood in the dark.

Uncle Tom stepped up. "Don't nobody speak cepen me. Now, Joe, I'm the only one you are about to hear. This is the plan. First of all, I want Lemon to go into action. Now, Joe, we will take you up colored camp, put you in clothes and turn you loose. Or we can give you some of ours and drop you off here. They's a train close, I think. James?"

"Yeah."

"Lemon, you in place?"

The answer came in a low moan of utter fear of—"Oh, sweet Jesus, don't, oh, please, God, don't."

"Don't speak, Lemon. Lemon's got his blade at your neck, Joe. All he has to do is begin. I give the word."

It was perfectly still. Not a leaf moved.

"Get me to them rails, please, Tom."

Tom said to the crowd, "Boys, I need a shirt, pants, and belt." They were handed to him.

Jim spoke, "I'm taking the truck back to McComb Supply. I'll drop him off at the depot. He can go first class. Now, Tom, drive my car and follow me. We'll drop him off at the first crossing that we come to or at Harlan." The plan was whirling into action.

"Before we go, let's gather and pray," says Tom.

"Oh, Lord, we lift up our eyes unto these hills from whence cometh our strength. Our strength comes fromThee. Take Jenny with our recommendations. Take what was imperfect and perfect it. Take the old and bathe her in the newness of thy love. In Jesus name, Amen."

Nobody moved. Who was Uncle Tom Becker? How did he learn the art of communing so easily with God?

"Oh, yes, Father. Take this stupid white trash and show him just enough of hell that he may decide to change before it is too late. Amen."

"Come on, boys; it's time for the night shift."

Wherein Dee Dee, Tilman, Spookum, and Gipsy Mae Move into Jenny's House

Life settled down nicely. Nothing of the death and burial was ever discussed at the commissary. James told Charity never to breathe it, even to Ida Brannon. Not to discuss it, even with his folks. Nobody. Just forget it. He told her about Joe Young showing up.

She told him about Lurie Cloud's baby dying. The company furnished a tiny white casket, and its funeral was to be the next day. There was a place up near Bird Eye Rock. No, she didn't plan to go. Nobody from lower camp was going. Jim knew that Ma would go. So much had happened since the Fourth of July. Arthur, Jenny, and the baby. Why not somebody like Joe Young or Lemon? Why the good ones?

Charity looked out the kitchen window and was surprised to see someone moving in. Out of a car. Stuff out of a car. Nothing else. When did they put the furniture in? Who was it?

She picked up her bucket and started to the pump across from the boarding house. She walked down the backyard path to the road. Out came the woman. Charity was shy about speaking first. "Hello," says a bleached blonde woman wearing bright red lipstick and chewing hard on a piece of gum. And it was not ten o'clock.

"Hello. I'm Della—Dee Dee to my friends," she winked. Suddenly three little undernourished children ran out of the house. "This is Tilman; this is Spookum; and this is Gypsy Mae." They were all from different daddys—it seemed to Charity.

"Do you have chillurn?"

"Yes, I have two girls."

"Oh, good. I want to leave Tilman and Spookum and Gypsy Mae with you long enough to get my stuff moved in. That ok? They've not eat breakfast."

"Well, we have had breakfast. Take them over across the branch to the boarding house. Miz Amics will give them all breakfast."

Charity was walking toward the pump in determination. She was not going to start anything with Dee Dee. Later in the day she went to the pump in lower camp.

"Who is Dee Dee?" Ida and Charity were standing at the pump with Nell and Maxie. Nell knew.

"She's the one who Vance, T.M., and others I won't mention moved into that vacant house three doors up from Vance's and set her up, if you know what I mean. Everything was quiet until she brought in them kids, and there was trouble on the border. She's a street walker. Run out of Bell County. Come in here under cover of night. Moved in three doors up from Miz Owens, it seems. A day or two later Miz Owens cooked her something. Ola says she even made pimento cheese sandwiches and cut off the edges. I don't know that for sure. When she got back from her visit, she informed Vance that 'that trash had to go.' I'm quoting her very words. Miz Owens told me that she went into the house and that there was a bed in the front room with a purple silk spread, candles, artificial flowers, and a singing canary in the corner. And a victrola playing music. Do you get my meaning?"

"Why did Jenny die?"

"Ohlau, honey. Charity, don't cry. Jenny's with our Lord." This from Miz Brannon.

"That kerosene smell not going to be so good in heaven."

"What you say?"

"I didn't say nothing." I said, 'She'd be a scene in heaven'." Charity had slipped up. She'd never do it again.

"Charity, whyn't you move into lower camp? If that street walker and them three little kids are going to worry you, whyn't you move into lower camp?"

Charity couldn't answer that. She pumped the water, picked up the bucket, and started past Miz Brannon's, up the road, thinking of Jenny in that hole covered with kerosene. No, she wouldn't smell in heaven. No, she would have a new body. She was now in Heaven enjoying a new, slim body. Was it white or brown? Neither. It was Jenny. Just Jenny. With no imperfections. Jenny's body was whole and wonderful, and she was so light she could fly—without wings. She felt sorry for the angels having to molt with the seasons. And the feathers would be a foot or longer. Who would clean up after them? Why, the ones who had just barely made it to heaven. They'd be the ones sweeping, cleaning, and, maybe, making fans with them feathers. . .

What in the world? She stood perfectly still, not even putting the bucket down. The front porch was full. There was that strumpet in her swing. She had her children with her and Lois Jean and Mickey and they were eating. They had bowls and spoons. She started running.

"Hello, Charity," called Dee Dee. "Come on up. We're having breakfast. Lois Jean invited Tilman, Spookum, and Gypsy Mae to come over and eat. We was on the porch, and she said, 'You'ens come over and eat'."

Charity knew that was a lie. She didn't allow Lois Jean to say "you'ens" for "you all."

"We came, and I fixed us all a bowl of oatmeal. She showed me where you keep it." Dee Dee was smiling. She had on a white dotted swiss dress and slippers. Hair set, nails painted blood red.

"I looked in on yer man. He's sleeping the sleep of the dead." She giggled.

This was too much. What was she going to do? She went into the kitchen, put the water on the tin-topped table. On the stove was an enameled pot with oatmeal in it and the spoon left in the pot. Charity never left the spoon in the pot. Suddenly something flew over her. Something took possession.

Grabbing a piece of kindling laying by the cook stove—a piece of board that she had found at Jenny's—she went to the front porch, grabbed Lois Jean by the arm, and began to hit her legs, again and again. Her bowl of oatmeal lay spilled on the porch.

Charity was in a world of her own. Although she was whipping Lois Jean, it felt like she was hitting Dee Dee and she hit harder and harder, dragging her screaming toward the kitchen.

Suddenly she felt her arm stopped in midair.

"Stop it." James was there. "Stop it. Don't touch her again." He took the long stick of kindling out of her hand. "Charity, what are you doing?" She stood still, Lois Jean crying. The others gathered in the front room. Suddenly Dee Dee was standing in Charity's kitchen, giggling.

"You ain't got your pants on. Them's fine legs you got."

He looked down. "You go home. Take them brats and go home. As you can tell, yer not welcomed here. When you need a meal, go over to the boarding house and let C.C. service you."

She said not one word. Gathered her little brood and went out the back door. The whole house was in total disruption. He went in, put on his pants, came back out, buckling his belt.

"Fix me breakfast and clean up this house," he demanded.

He picked up Lois Jean, put her on his lap. Turned her so that he could see if skin was broken. Whelps, but no broken places.

"You ok, honey? You ok? You're Daddy's girl and I love you."

Charity had come back into the room.

"James, don't you hug her like that. That's not right. In fact, it's plain dirty. We had a family up on Wolf Creek that carried on like this and the daddy had a baby by his own girl. And she had them little sheepy eyes..."

He gently put Lois Jean down.

"Sit down, Charity."

"Don't try to tell me what to do, James Carter."

"Sit down." He stood up.

Strangely, she felt a certain euphoria at being ordered around.

"Sit down and listen to me. You are in charge of raising these two little girls, but you are not going to hurt them. I know how it feels to hit someone when you're mad. I did it to her. Now, there's something about you that I don't know about. There's a part of you that is not the woman I thought you were. I don't like you when you behave like this. I don't know you. Right now there is a woman in this kitchen that I don't really know. A woman who says damned ugly, vicious things. And does damned ugly, vicious acts. Charity, don't let this crazy woman out again or I'll kill her. Keep her locked up somewhere. You can spank these girls, but don't you ever beat them. Fix my breakfast."

He walked out of the kitchen, went out on the porch for a smoke. She followed him out.

"I can outrun you, James. I can outrun you."

Later that day she called to Lois Jean.

"Lois, I'm gonna give you a nickel for me, one for you, and one for Mickey. Go buy us some candy. Lois, you are going to the store by yourself and buy us some candy."

She handed over the 15 cents in scrip and said, "Go straight to the store. Get me a Nickel Loaf, you penny candy, and Mickey penny candy. Five pieces for you, five for Mickey, and don't let them cheat you either. Don't talk to strangers; don't go into the shack; and be back as soon as you can."

"No, wait. I'm going as far as the pump. Come on." James was sleeping.

Lois Jean had never been so far away from Charity. Down the road she skipped. Charity behind her. Past the Garden of Eden, round the curve. Down the road past Miz Brannon's, past houses with women sweeping the porches, the yards, children out playing. The ice wagon with Butchell coming toward her, pulled by two horses. She knew the women; they all came for water, but she had not seen them in their yards, on the porches before. On she went by herself. She had made the trip with her mother and her baby sister, but not alone.

She got to the store. Big steps. She went to the side with the rail. There was a line of people.

"Hey, you're Jim's girl. What's yer name?"

"Lois Jean."

"What ye buying?"

"Candy."

"Folks, this is Lois Jean; she's buying candy. Let her by."

"Go ahead, honey."

"Go on, go on."

Up she went—and word spread. Buying candy. "Anythang else? Let me see yer money."

She showed them her money. And they passed the word along.

"Buying candy."

She was looking at a man in a white shirt. A tie and black garters on his arms. It was Mr. Haynes.

"What ye want, little girl?" He smiled at her.

"Penny candy and a loaf."

He was back in a minute with a brown paper bag. Took the money, gave her the bag, and she was out of the store.

"What'd ye git?" Charity asked.

Lois wanted Charity to be happy and not mad. She wanted to give her mother what made her happy so she would say something good. Something happy, like, "We have six fresh eggs today and you didn't break a one." Or. . . she couldn't think of another thing. But she didn't want another stinging, awful, beating. It was a beating. She'd do anything to try to please so she would not get a beating.

"What'd ye git?"

She handed her the brown bag. Charity peeped in.

"Well, you got it."

"Can we eat one now?"

"No, we are going to get to the house and eat it in the kitchen with the doors shut."

"Here's one for you and one for Mickey. B.B. bats and vanilla drops." She set the Nickel Loaf aside, savoring it.

"One for you, one for me, one for Mickey."

Lois Jean had five pieces; Mickey had five pieces, including a strawberry

B.B. bat, and Charity had the Nickel Loaf. Charity planned to eat Mickey's candy.

"Well, there's a piece extra. How about that—ol' Lee Haynes gave you an extra piece."

Still, Lois Jean had five pieces.

They were in the kitchen, and it was before dinner.

"Let's eat one," said Charity.

She opened the Nickel Loaf, broke it in half and took a bite. Nothing in the world was as soothing as a piece of candy, a bar of candy, a Nickel Loaf. She chewed it, savoring every particle of sweetness—the coconut, marshmallow, mixing with the chocolate covering everything. She closed her eyes and chewed slowly until the texture was that of honey, holding the moment as long as she could until she just had to swallow it. She sat there for a moment in perfect stillness, eyes shut, rocked in the satisfaction that there was more to come.

Lois Jean was eating a vanilla drop and Mickey was licking the B.B. bat. Charity opened her eyes and broke off another bite of the candy bar. Something. . . what was it? A worm. A worm. A white worm was in her candy. She didn't move. It was a piece of a worm in her candy. She stared at it. It seemed like the front half of the white worm was gone.

She got her knife, dug out the worm, mashed it between her fingers, checked it carefully, and ate the rest. She sat there savoring the moment. Clean kitchen, two children, James; she touched her breast—money. Real money from the chickens. She was fairly well off. If everything would just hold together. If she didn't lose anything—she went into the front room. The piano. It was there. That was a big project. The piano was there, but Lois Jean continued to play piano on the steps. Time to get that project underway.

At the pump Maxie had said that Lois Jean was too young to start lessons. Let her come to the piano on her own when she was ready. To Charity, Lois needed discipline. The discipline of Miss Kay Adams. She went back to the kitchen and announced, "Lois Jean, you are going to take piano lessons." Lois Jean had chocolate from the vanilla drops all around her mouth. Mickey was licking the B.B. bat.

"That's enough of that candy. It will spoil your appetite." She learned that phrase at the Pine Mountain Settlement School. They said—Miss Pettit and Miz Aundi said "spoil your appetite."

"Here, put it up and wash your faces." Not a single protest. They climbed down and washed around their mouths.

"Lois Jean, you are going to take piano lessons."

Wherein Tilman Gets a Haircut

Life at Jenny's ol' house seemed to have settled in. Dee Dee did take Tilman, Spookum, and Gypsy Mae over to Miz Amics and C.C. paid for her meals "until her stove comes in." Truth be known, there was no stove, no table, no bed. Just a radio and what the children had on their backs. Miz Amics said it was a shame and that something had to be done. C.C. went to Vance Owens.

Seeing Vance Owens meant going into his office. That was an accomplishment. When anybody came to get groceries—meaning a miner, his wife, his child, his relative—he presented the yellow scrip card and Vance would ask, "How much?" Then, if "that much" had been worked out, the miner, his wife, his child, or his relatives could draw that amount. All this was done at the scrip window. And, if the amount was not there, everybody in line knew it. It was thought to be disgraceful to be short. Ida Brannon was never short. Nell Farmer and Charity were never short. Nobody went into the office unless invited.

C.C. went into the office when he wanted to. He wanted to today. He had to help Dee Dee get a stove and a bed. He knocked on the door just left of the scrip window.

"Who is it?"

"Me, C.C."

"You sound like an Indian. Me, Vance. Come in, C.C."

C.C. went into the Tway commissary office. Well organized, gray bound ledgers with orange trim holding records of each miner stood in alphabetical rows. New scrip cards, sharpened pencils. But Vance used a pen with a sharp point and did exquisite numbers, enjoying the flourishes when he stroked a "4" or crossed a "t".

"What's on yer mind, big boy?"

"It's Dee Dee. She's moved them three brats into Jenny's ol' house and is sleeping on the floor on a quilt that Miz Amics gave her. Now you can imagine how comfortable that's going to be for some. If you get my drift."

"Didn't Jenny leave some stuff?"

"That was all passed out the day she died."

"By the way, where'd they take her?"

"Back to Alabama. Her folks took her back."

"Now, let me think on this awhile. I'll come up with something."

"You'd better. Yer the one who felt sorry for Dee Dee. Yer the one who wanted her helped."

"Yes, I know."

"Well, it ain't perfect, yet."

"Close the door on yer way out. I'll give it thought."

The line had backed down the steps. Vance went to the toilet before he came back.

"If it's not one thing, it's another."

Three days later things came to a head. It was about nine o'clock. James had come in, bathed in the tub, eaten, and gone to bed. Charity had fixed his breakfast, cleaned the kitchen, and gone to the pump. She was in the kitchen when she heard Dee Dee's unmistakable voice.

"You'ens playing school?"

"Yes, we are."

"Well, isn't that purty."

"How's it purty? What's purty?" Lois asked.

"That means it is nice." Dee Dee was working to sound like a movie star. Movie stars didn't say "hit's"; they said, "it is."

"Well, I'm going to the store; be right back; so let Tilman, Spookum, and Gypsy Mae be in your class." The two little boys and little girl came up the steps to the front porch.

She was gone in a flash. "Tell Charity I'll be back directly."

Lois Jean began school. She had the blackboard, chalk, and some of the Jesus cards that Thelma and Geneva had given her. She had a tablet and a box of bad crayons.

"I am the teacher. You are in the second grade. Gypsy Mae is in the first grade, and Mickey is in primer class."

Spookum began to cry. "I don't like school. I don't like second grade. I'm hungry."

Charity stood listening to them.

"I'm hungry too." Gypsy Mae was crying.

Tilman just sat staring out into space. Then he asked, "Is your mother a hoe'er? Does she hoe the street?"

"My mother is a hoe'er."

Spookum and Gypsy Mae stopped crying.

"Is yo mama a hoe'er?"

"Yeh, my mama's a hoe'er. We have the best beans and tomatoes. My daddy's a hoe'er, too."

"God damn," says Tilman, very interested.

"Yeah, they both hoe'ers. I'm a little hoe'er too." They all began to laugh as the boys rolled and laughed.

Charity bent double laughing. The children began playing, heads close together, extending school to cowboys and Indians to Shirley and Miz Piertison.

"P'like I'm a cowboy. And p'like I get drunk."

Here Tilman threw himself on the porch, rolling in agony.

"And p'like I drive you to the hospital."

"And p'like I go in and kill the doctor," said Spookum.

"And p'like I ride my horse up the hill."

"And p'like Shirley lets you feed the chickens."

"And p'like I roll a cigarette for Shirley."

"And p'like I sing a song on the radio." Tilman had a stick in his hand for a microphone. He tilted back his head and out rolled the sweetest voice. "In Dixie Land where I was born early on one frosty morn, look awaaay, look awaaay, look away, Dixie Land." Then he began to yodel—really yodel. Charity came to the door and listened. The others stopped playing and listened. Nobody moved.

Never had Charity heard a voice like Tilman's voice.

"Ok, p'like I'm the leader—everybody sing." Tilman was in another world. He was bringing pleasure to all around him. They had all stopped and were in his thrall. And Tilman liked it all. He felt good.

"Down by the barnyard he stumbled"—here his voice stumbled—"fell down by the door. The very next words that he uttered, 'I'll never get drunk no more'——beautiful, beautiful brown eyes, beautiful, beautiful brown eyes, beautiful, beautiful brooooown eyyyyes. . ." The note was high and he held it forever. "I'll never get drunk no more."

They all applauded.

"P'like I'm Dee Dee," says Gypsy Mae.

Gypsy put out her hip, one hand on that hip and the other above her ear. "Woncher com over and see me," eyes rolling, "sometime?"

Tilman and Spookum rolled on the front porch.

Charity came out on the porch. She had peanut butter and jelly on breakfast biscuits. And apples.

"P'like I'm the waitress and give you some dinner." She smiled; she liked what she was doing. It felt good.

Charity needed more water for the washing machine. She had done the whites and the colored and now the work clothes were running. Next came the rinse. Some did two rinses. Since the children were playing, she would run over to the pump by the boarding house.

This time she took two buckets. Wouldn't fill them clear to the top, leave room for walking. There stood Helen. Beautiful Helen of Troy—whatever that meant. She had on the robe with the dragon on the back. Bent over. She was bent plumb over.

They laume, Helen was brushing her teeth and spittin' water.

"Helen! Oh! I didn't mean to scare you."

"Oh, Charity, I am sick to my stomach. Wish I hadn't told ye. Ye'll tell it all over that I'm 'pg'. Well, I'm not 'pg'. I'm hung over. You tell anybody and I'll pull every hair out yer head."

She stepped aside, bent over, and heaved, but nothing came out.

"Was it straight or shine?"

"I don't know—me and C.C.—you know. He felt bad about it." Voice trailed off.

"I'm getting outta here, Charity. I'm going to learn to be a secretary and I'm going to get out of here."

"How old are you?"

"Eighteen. I'm eighteen," she wailed.

"Maybe you could get a job in Harlan, be a secretary."

"I don't want to be in Harlan. I want to go as far away from this hole as I can git. I hate this hell hole." She began to cry.

"Why'n you go to Knoxville?"

"How? How? I've not got a penny—not a red cent." She heaved. "This sun's hot. I got to go."

Charity filled her buckets and struggled back up the hill. Put the work clothes through the ringer. Let the black water run through the hose to water the tomatoes just off the back porch. Cleaned out the inside of the washer. Put in the soapy whites to rinse. She loved washing clothes. Everything worked. The water mixed with the soap in the electric washing machine that James had rigged up on the back porch. Put in something dirty and out it came clean or at least mostly clean.

On she went, enjoying the pleasure of washing dirty clothes and seeing them become clean. The children all on the front porch playing. She had mixed feelings about that setup. The children were good. Not brats. They were sweet. Tilman with his blue eyes and brown hair. Dee Dee kept his hair parted and combed like a movie star and Gypsy in curls, but Spookum's was fuzzy, not exactly curls, just fuzz.

She had worked her way into the kitchen, pushed the cabinet back catty-cornered where the apples stayed. The front room. That old Creton cover was a mess. She stood there looking down. She needed a bigger house. She would move to lower camp. Right that minute she decided to move to lower camp. She walked out on the front porch.

She stood there, not moving. "Oh, laume," she groaned. "Oh, Lois Jean, what have you done?"

"I p'likin I'm the barber."

There sat Tilman in a straight chair, feed-sack towel around his shoulders. She was holding the sharp scissors and had cut his hair off his head in gaps. Charity had never seen anything like it in her life. Spookum started laughing. Charity joined him. She laughed so hard that she had to cross her legs. Spookum and Charity laughing. Mickey started crying. "I got hair, I got hair on my sucker." She had found one of her suckers and had been off behind the swing enjoying it until she laid it on the floor when Charity came out. Gypsy Mae was busy drawing on the little round blackboard. Wetting the chalk in a glass of water. Mayhem! Mayhem!

A scream sailed out across the porch; they turned to see a head then shoulders and body, then legs that belonged to Dee Dee.

"Oh, Jesus, Jesus, my baby, my baby. What's happened to my baby? Spookum, Gypsy Mae, are you'ens. . ." Then she saw them.

Charity was wiping her eyes on her apron. Dee Dee rose to her full height, hands on hips. "Charity, you didn't take care of my children. You let that brat cut Tilman's hair to his scalp. He is butchered. You know better," she wailed.

Charity was well versed in the unfairness of things and went into her role. Not a word did she say. She tucked her chin in. Stood there. It was quiet, not a sound. Dee Dee was losing ground and she knew it.

Charity said, "Lois Jean, Mickey, go into the house." Gypsy Mae had never stopped drawing on the blackboard, dipping the chalk into water. Drawing. Charity opened the screen door, pushed the children in, then stepped inside and latched it. Closed the front door and pulled the shades.

Dee Dee stood, drained, empty. She started down the steps and heard

Charity laughing. James was sitting at the kitchen table with coffee and a cig-arette. He didn't say a thing.

"I'm gonna be a beauty parlor girl when I grow up." Lois Jean sensed that she had done the right thing cutting Tilman's hair.

"No, you ain't," Charity yelled.

"Say ain't, fall in a can of paint," said Lois Jean. Charity had taught her that line from Pine Mountain Settlement School. The women from Illinois had taught their students "the king's way of speaking" and the king didn't say "ain't". Had he slipped, the queen would have said, "Say ain't, fall in a can of paint." Jim laughed.

"No, when you grow up, you are going to college. You are not going to marry some dumb coal miner and raise his kids in some Harlan County coal mine." She began cutting potatoes, frying pork chops, making biscuits, set-ting the table. Four places were set on the table with the Pennsylvania Dutch flowers in the four corners. Pork chops, gravy, eggs, hot biscuits, syrup or jelly, butter and milk from Miz Brannon's.

"Now, Lois Jean, you go sweep the porch, bring in your blackboard and chalk, fold the feed sack. No, it has hair on it. Leave it over the banister."

Later that same day the children passed the house, Tilman wearing a black cap with a strap on one side that went under his chin and snapped on the other side. All boys wore them, but not in hot weather. The children waved when they saw Lois Jean and Mickey on the front porch, but there were no vocal sounds. When Charity told the story at the pump, everybody laughed. "Serves her right. The strumpet."

Several days later Charity reached in the drawer of the tin-topped table to get the scissors. The scissors were gone. The scissors must have been left on the front porch. Dee Dee had taken her scissors. She went out on the porch. She looked around the banisters, the yard, under the floor. Gone. No house could run without scissors nor sharp knives, safety pins, clothes pins, string, and black electric tape. She needed to go to Harlan and get scissors. Truth be known, it was good to need scissors. That gave her a reason to look around. To inquire, to buy, to exchange money for scissors. To feel the bills, to count the quarters, dimes, pennies. She loved the possession and feel of money, not scrip, money.

The next Saturday night had been set aside to get the scissors. However, two Saturdays passed. Jim waiting for money to build up. Ted had asked for a little help at Berea. Books mostly. Jim knew that Charity had chicken money and pocket money from his pocket. He wouldn't deny her. He worked and Ted and Charity spent, but he had a little stash of his own.

Wherein there is a Reverie for Shine

It was a well-kept secret that Shine Smith and James Carter had the best little still in Tways. Since they had begun their operation, it had been small runs, with Nannie checking "the character". Sometimes making a suggestion of maybe peaches thrown in for the more delicate palate. So, in went peaches. Peaches that were gathered at night from Ida Brannon's peach tree. The sweet woman often saying at the pump, "I don't know what's getting my peaches. Whatever it is, it's tall. Do panthers eat peaches?" Nobody knew.

When the shine beaded amber and to perfection, it was bottled in clear jars. An empty bonded whiskey bottle was prized as much as aluminum foil from mining tape and chewing gum. Jim had a funnel that he kept in Nannie's kitchen. He would slip it out when it was time for a "home run". That's what he called it.

Jim and Shine were careful. Very careful. This year showed promise of being a banner one. The peaches were fine. They had named it the "Lady Run," meaning that Nannie would sell the whole run to women in the camp. Men loved it. A tipsy woman was a gift from heaven. They had a little song: "When the moon comes over the mountain, I'll be a'waiting for you." Sometimes the song was, "When will the moon come over the mountain?" The answer, "Just you wait and see." Some laughing, slapping backs.

In the mines somebody always had a bottle or jar hidden nearby. In Tways the miners knew each and everyone. In the dark underworld they were as one, pitting their unity and knowledge against an unforgiving mountain. Some religions go so far as to say God is a mountain. Not God is like a mountain, but God is a mountain. Certainly, God was in the mountain, through the mountain, and off the mountain. Whenever Jim lifted up his eyes unto the mountains, he knew his strength came from the mountain, and the men who stood with him picking the precious black diamonds from the mountains felt it throughout their beings.

That seam of coal that ran for some few miles following the curve of the Cumberland Chain was known to be some of the finest in the United States and brought a very high price. There wasn't a night that Jim did not contemplate that cost when he entered the driftmouth. Tways was his little world.

Moonshine was in the mine. So were punch boards, moon pies, chewing tobacco, and everyone had his very own jokes and stories. You didn't steal another man's stories. You worked; you didn't "slack off". And you did your job so that others were not threatened from carelessness.

Unlike Benham, Lynch and other mines, Tways was small. Not housing a hundred inhabitants, counting babies. Next, it was within good walking distance of Harlan, the town of Harlan, the county seat of Harlan County. The miners in R.C. Tway Mining Camp were unlike any other miners in the Kentucky coal fields. They all were influenced by Harlan's "town" ways, yet they had the closeness of family inside the camp. Many had lived in Tways since it had started with the first boom. They practiced their own ways.

The shine was used for pleasure but also for medicine. This shine was pure. No additives. It took patience and a good watch to bring shine to fruition. Shine was good and good for you. The truth was, all things are good if used properly. "All things in moderation—nothing in excess".

Wherein the "Rain" Ruins Wash Day

The children got up. Charity had built a fire in the cookstove and was making biscuits. Sifting down the flour. Her cabinet, her stove, her kitchen. "Lois Jean, go get eggs. First empty the pee bucket and let it sun."

Lois Jean had on a little feed-sack slip that she slept in. Charity made it and had Nannie sew it up for her. Underneath, she had on little pink panties from J. J. Newberry's.

She slid the pee bucket out from under the day bed and went out to get the eggs.

She raced back into the kitchen, yelling, "It rained paper! It rained paper!"

Charity went out, and there were whole sheets of paper everywhere. Lois Jean began to pick them up.

"Just get them off our yard; don't get the ones in the road."

Lois brought in six sheets of paper. "Can I have them? They's nothin' on the back."

"Let your daddy read them first." She was into biscuits and setting a fine breakfast. Lois waited; stacked the pages evenly edged. She went back to get the eggs. One sheet in the chicken lot. She could make paper cups out of them. Color them. Write on the back. Make show tickets and play movies. She had big plans for the paper. One sheet had writing at the top down a little ways, then a word and a line. Another two or three words and another line and some writing at the bottom of the page. She could make out UMW. It was on the page in several places.

Finally, Daddy came in for breakfast. She had placed them in his chair. He pulled out the chair. She went over and leaned against his knee. Propped her fist under her chin.

"Can I have them?"

He looked down at her. He loved this child, his child. Like Jesus, she had come from a virgin. Except it was Jim and not the Holy Spirit that hovered over the Virgin.

"We'll see."

That was often the answer. "We'll see" meant that there was a wait involved.

He read the invitation to join the United Mine Workers, the UMW. Where did these come from? Who put out this stuff? The answer was so close. He wrinkled his brow. Closed his eyes. Charity set hot biscuits on the table. Fried eggs and hot fresh ham from the Carter's hog. She had soaked it all night in water and buttermilk to remove the salt. And homemade cherry preserves from Nanny's tree.

It was Monday and washday. Weather was beautiful, trees turning first color. What a show. Just beginning with the yellow maples, red coming in on oaks, big black walnut holding out until last, cool, green and aloof. All blending into one magnificent bouquet.

Anybody who was anybody walking into Tways would marvel at the neat row of houses on both sides of the dirt road. Porches painted oak, light tan, or dark green. Flowers in most yards. All to a backdrop of majestic mountains. The branches ran pristine down to the road that went to Harlan under the culvert and joined the Cumberland River on the other side of the airplane/baseball field known as Skidmore Farm.

Birds and frogs abounded. On summer nights under a full moon lightning bugs came out. Huge swallowtail Luna Moths with exotic markings were everywhere on a warm night.

Days, children caught the June bug, tied a string around its leg, and let it fly around. Sometimes that June bug flew hard enough to pull off his leg and escape! Why did a June bug need all his legs when he had wings to fly? The woods were awash in color, and Charity was awash in wash! She accepted the burden of carrying the water from the pump; she actually enjoyed doing the washing, separating the whites from the coloreds and finally work clothes. She let the whites run first in Rinso soap from the A&P until she believed they were clean—sheets, pillowcases, towels, all white. Then she put them through the ringer and set them aside. Into the soapy water went the colored pinafores, aprons, pink panties, dresses, and blouses. Not many blouses. She put them through the ringer. Finally, the work clothes. The water turned black. The overalls were denim and the coal dust worked in so they never ever faded. She washed them when James decided they had to be washed. She was washing them today. She always went through his pockets. Stray kitchen matches, electrical tape, and sometimes a quarter in scrip. That was all. She washed these; then came rinse water. She carried more, and Lois Jean had a little bucket and would parade along. If the clothes were real dirty, that called for second rinsing.

It took all morning to get clothes to the clothesline. And that was if they didn't have much starch or if there were fewer shirts and blouses. Starching took a special understanding of how much and how to starch. Charity was very good. Finally, "bluing" was necessary on white shirts. If the sun was shining, everything hung on the clothesline and dried, smelling fresh and sweet. If the sun was not up and rain was threatening, clothes were hung on the clothesline on the back porch. That was bad. Clothes could hang for days on the porch in wintertime. It was a depressing sight. Coal black overalls hanging beside limp feed-sack towels. Rain threw the whole week off. It threw Tuesday, ironing day, to Wednesday or Thursday. Charity would hang pink panties and socks and sometimes a shirt over a chair and set it next to the cookstove.

This day was a sunny fall day, a perfect day for washing clothes. James was asleep. The children were playing on the front porch. That's when she heard the gun go off—not once, but several times. It was on the other side of the mountain up from the Garden of Eden. She ran to the front porch and grabbed Lois Jean and Mickey. That's when she heard the man screaming, "Don't hit me. Please, God, don't hit me again."

She shoved the children in the bedroom and yelled at James.

"Get up, get up. They're killing a man across the road."

He was out of the bed into pants, no shoes, and ran to the front porch. He heard more gunshots and men cursing and brush being moved and things rolling. It was the moonshine still. It was the revenuers. They had Shine Smith, and they were dragging him down the side of the mountain. They had spotted James and were making straight for the yard. Shine had possibly spoken his name. He didn't know. He did know that every revenuer knew where to look.

"Say ye want a little to drink and the only place is the toilet, where'd you hide your jar so ye could take a nip after dark?" spoke a revenuer to another revenuer in training.

"Why, under the toilet."

"No, yer limited where you can put it with all that shit."

"Well, under yer back porch."

"Exactly. Under the back porch so's when you step down to go to the toilet, ye can almost reach the jar in one swoop."

The two were in the yard running up the steps. They were on the porch.

"We from the Revenuer's office, an arm of the Commonwealth of Kentucky, and we's heah to gather evidence. We have reason to belief you've got evidence! You stay here on the porch while we search the premises." They were in the front room looking in likely places, the bedroom, then the kitchen. Jim stood helpless.

Up the steps came a man. James reasoned he was the leader. He had on a brown felt hat, and Jim couldn't see under the brim. Then he looked up. It was Henry Caddell from up on Buck Creek. They were cousins twice removed. They had played together up on Buck Creek.

"Finally," he said, "I've got ye, ye somabitch. I got ye. I've waited fer this day fer years and years."

James didn't open his mouth.

"I've never forgot what ye done to me."

He sat down on the swing. "I was a little boy a little younger than you. We was playing out in the barn with a bunch and you told them boys that I was a morphodite. You'd heard that story from your ma when my mom told her that I was misformed as a baby. You'ens danced around me, calling me 'morphodite, morphodite.' Then you made me pull down my pants and all of you looked at me. I had one nut--one testicle that hadn't dropped--see. And you shamed me before that bunch of boys. I couldn't face nobody and went into the house and didn't come out for a long time. I sat in the dark, crying 'cause I was different. Then I got the mumps and they fell on me and the other nut dropped. I'm all right. I'm not married. I don't know why. I'm different, and hit's your fault. If I find one drop of evidence that proves you got shine, off you go to the pen for a nice long spell, you somabitch!"

Jim didn't say a word. He knew that Henry would find his quart—half a quart under the post at the back door. He was as good as gone.

They got up went out to the back porch. Charity had sent Lois Jean and Mickey to the chicken lot and they were standing in plain sight looking on. The team was swarming over the yard around the toilet everywhere. Henry walked over to Charity, tipped his hat.

"Good morning, Miz Carter. See you've got washing going. Gather around boys. Have ye checked nunder the post that's near the steps that a man might be able to reach a quart of shine?"

They assured him that there wasn't an inch they hadn't touched.

"Did you'ens look in the flour bin?"

"Yeah."

"Back of the radio?"

"Inside the washing machine?

"No."

He lifted the lid that covered the washing machine and staggered back against the wall. "Gotamitee, hell far. What the—— " he trailed off. By this time others standing on the porch had caught the whiff.

"You'll have to excuse us. My daughter had the bloody flux and I was soaking her things." Here she lifted the lid again. Let them catch another whiff.

They staggered off the porch. "Gotamitee."

"Please," Charity begged, "be careful what you say around the children."

Suddenly a shot rang out and echoed across from one side to the other side of the mountain. Henry fell, his head rolled back. He had grabbed his knee. A voice yelled, "Next time I'll aim at your gonads. Get the hell out of Tways and don't come back." More shots. Boys firing back. Nobody else hit. The boys picked up Henry.

"Harlan hospital fast, fast. He's bleeding bad." They left.

Jim sat down on the edge of the porch. Lois Jean and Mickey came out crying.

Charity began laughing. Bent over. Laughing—tears running down her cheeks.

"What in God's name is funny, Charity?"

"Reach in there and get yer shine."

"Say what?"

"Reach into the washing machine and get yer shine."

He lifted the lid and felt his gorge rising.

"Feel around James. It's there."

"Lord God, woman." There was the quart.

He staggered off the porch, taking deep breaths. "How'd you get that shit into that washing machine?"

"Well, I give Lois Jean and Mickey a dose of Black Draught last night to clean 'em out. I made them go into the bedroom and scuoose in the pee bucket, and I throwed it in on the whites."

He pulled on shirt and shoes. "Charity, I'm going to check on Shine."

He went out the door, followed the well-worn path past the toilet they shared, and onto the back porch. "Shine, you in there?"

Thelma and Geneva ran to the back door.

"Hurry, he's dying. He's bloody and crying."

"They've killed Daddy. Hurry."

Jim went into the bedroom. There Shine lay moaning on the bed. Blood on the pillow.

"Are you shot?"

"No, I'm beat to a pulp— a bloody pulp. They whopped me with their fists. They dragged me out of the tree. I fell. I think ever part of me is broke."

"Could ye all leave us alone, let me work on him? Bring hot water. Tear up a sheet, a pillowcase, and get the alcohol. I'll clean him."

He sat on the edge of the bed.

"Shine, that was you in the sound truck wadn't it?"

No answer.

"Man, they are after you. You got to get out of here. They will kill you yet."

"Jim, the UMW paid me to run that truck. Told me to put the thin rag over the mike and talk slow. They give me five dollars in money. I couldn't turn that down."

"Yeah, I know."

"Jim," he wailed, "the revenuers tore up that still—the best in the world. You know we made pure stuff. No lye, no carbide. We made the real thang. We had a fine little thang going."

Jim took the alcohol from Geneva. She handed him a feed-sack towel and scissors.

"Mommy says cut it up if ye need to."

He cut it and poured the alcohol.

"Shut ye eyes. Take a deep breath."

To Geneva, "Go to the house; tell Charity to send me the salve that Ma made."

"They were at the house, Shine. Went through everything."

"Did they find anything?" Shine knew that Jim had taken his last prize quart from next to his last ever run.

"No."

Then came the alcohol. Shine passed out. Jim worked fast. Finishing with the salve and bandages. Shine came to, screaming, then slowly settled down.

"I'll be back directly." He went to the kitchen. "You need to get out of Harlan. Do you have somewhere to go?"

"I got relatives in Corbin. They could hide us."

There would be those who wanted to string Shine up as an example of what can happen when you do not follow rules. Shine was a liability to everybody.

Jim went to Matt's and Nanny's. Told his story. Asked if they could hide him somewhere. "Yeah, but we're not going to tell you. That way nobody can get it out of you."

After dark, one of Uncle Tom's boys showed up in a car. They took Shine, groaning; put him in the back seat; laid him down; covered him up. Went back up the road. If they were caught on the white side of camp. . . if C.C. found them on that side—whites only—it would be hell to pay.

All the lights were out at the Carter's. The driver saw a red glow of a cigarette coming from the swing. They pulled up as far as they could in the yard. Ora, Ruth, and Alma moved into the front room, and Shine was put in their bed. The whole thing was done and nobody spoke a word.

Wherein Thelma, Geneva,
and the Bible Cards are Gone

Two days later Thelma, Geneva, and their mother were gone. Lock, stock, and barrel. Her church had helped them. Jim found out later that they went to Wallins Creek and finally to Corbin.

Uncle Tom Carter dressed up; let on like he was going to go to Harlan. Persuaded Ella to go with him. Ella dressed. Pretty woman, graying fast, thought Tom. Ella was riding in the front seat with him. Shine in the back on the floor covered with boxes. C.C. was standing on the porch of the shack. He saw Ella in the front seat. Ella pulled up a fan and started fanning like she might faint. C.C. waived them on by.

"C.C. Moore is a moron," Ella said quietly. Ella read all the time. She had an astounding vocabulary. Ella's father had kept a trunk full of books. Her favorite had been *Return of the Native*, by Thomas Hardy. "Hap" is what Hardy had called "luck"—good and bad luck. Hap just happens. Her philosophy went something like: "We have no control over anything and sometimes it happens that God is not watching." Ella read mostly detective magazines now. She had trouble concentrating. She told Lucy that she would be reading and the baby's face would swim across the page. Lucy had told that at the pump. Ida Brannon cried. Nell shook her head. Charity did not respond. Ella felt good helping Shine Farmer. Tom Carter felt good beating an unfair system filled with heathen.

Wherein Jim Receives a Gift

Jim waited a day or so then went over to the still. Nothing left. Their stuff had been as good as any from around Lexington. One of the boys from Anderson Law's funeral home had come back with a bottle from Lexington. Passed it around at one of the funerals. It was smooth alright, but so was his and Shine's. It was fine. Furthermore, there was nothing wrong with having a drink once in a while. Fixing colds with it. It had been in his family for generations. There were some, though, who treated it as a necessary part of their lives—as necessary as the smoke of Duke's Mixture was to him. A smoke and a cup of strong coffee. That did it. But, he reasoned, anything that good, anything that satisfying, was bound to do some harm somewhere. Only God was all good, all knowing, all-powerful.

And recently, God had really dealt them a bad hand. First Arthur, Lurie's baby, Jenny, and now Shine. All in the same year. Then there was work slowing down, added to a wife, added two children. Since April 1930 when James L. Carter had married Charity Angeline Moses, he had really gone on a wild ride. Even the woods looked different. Today it was cloudy, dark, muddy, children inside the house complaining that they had nothing to do. He was, as Ma would say, "given over to the blues." Only a hunting trip could take care of that, and he was too blue to go hunting.

He picked up a stick, stirred on the ground. At first he didn't notice it. Then he pulled back three or four leaves stuck together. A piece of tow sack. Looked like it was melted into the ground. He pulled at it. It didn't come loose. He took his hands and commenced to dig. It didn't give way. Then it dawned on him. Something was in the tow sack. No, it was buried. It was a carefully buried tow sack. He grabbed a piece of pipe from the still and dug on down. He uncovered the sack and slowly pulled it up. He stopped in midair. It had to be Shine's stock that he had hidden from everybody. He dug with his hands, then pulled it open.

"Hell far." There were five quarts of shine. Then he noticed one was different. "What the hell?"

He held it up to the light. "Peaches. I'll be damn." He had made shine and put peaches in it to smooth it out. Miz Brannon's peaches, but for who? Jim knew what he would do with it. Give it to Nanny. She would use most of it for medicine. The rest he would bury in the chicken lot. Suddenly the sun came out. He rose. Took off his felt hat; bowed his head. "Thank you. Amen". He opened a quart; took a drink. "Smooth, smooth."

He picked up the quart with peaches; walked through the Garden of Eden. Pulled some old corn and two green tomatoes. With the quart jar cradled in his arm, laid the ears of old dried corn over it and carried out two green tomatoes. Went to the kitchen door. Charity was fixing dinner. "Charity, give me a poke. I'm taking Ma some of this corn for seeds next year. And could ye fry these tomatoes now?"

Charity was preoccupied.

"Where are you going?"

"This is music day. Lois goes to take a lesson."

"I hope you've got the money."

"I do."

Wherein Sissy Gives Lois a Music Lesson

"James, come here," Charity called from the bedroom. "Look out that window."

He looked past the toilet. There stood Shine's house—empty, doors wide open. You could see all the way through.

"Come here." She led him back to the kitchen.

"Look here."

He looked out the screen door. There was Jenny's door open. He could see straight through.

"This hillside depresses me. It is awful," she wailed. "Let's move to lower camp. Please, James, get me out of this place. It's sad anyway I look."

"I will, Charity. We'll feel better. I promise."

Charity dressed the children, and they began walking to Harlan. Nobody picked them up. They walked all the way. Lois Jean skipped some. Down across from Baby Jones' store was a house on the other side of the road. The place was filled with children. Children all dressed well. Playing.

"What's happening?" she wondered.

They got into Harlan. Went up to Mound Street. Then she had a thought. "Why not leave Lois at Miss Kay Adams' and take Mickey to the Bowers' store and then pick up Lois and go to the A&P?"

"Lois, you go in by yourself. Somebody is in there taking lessons now. Sit in the front room on the settee until Miss Adams calls you. I'll be back. If you finish, sit on the porch 'til I get here. I'll be here when you finish."

Up the porch; open the screen; turn the knob. The big door swung open. Lois Jean went in, stepping on fine wool rugs. She heard music. Lots of notes—way lots of notes. More than she had ever heard in her life. She herself today was ready for "Song of the Volga" from Teaching Little Fingers to Play. She had played ahead in the red book. "Papa Hyden's dead and gone, but his spirit lingers on." She had trouble with that song because it went out of the safe range of the notes C and D and E—"Here we go, up the row, to a birthday party. C-D-E. C-D-E. D-C. D-C-D-E. C-C." It really was a little scary going so far. She loved coming to this big, fine place and playing songs and leaving with a piece of white candy with green in the middle.

She looked around. There was a bowl of goldfish. Two tiny, orange fish. They were alive and swimming around. Two live fish in a bowl of water. Suddenly the music all over the piano stopped and it was all quiet. Miss Kay Adams was waiting for her. She went into the music room. There was Miss Kay Adams and the pretty lady sitting on the bench, just looking at each other.

"Hello, Miss Kay Adams."

They jumped.

"How long have you been here?"

"A long time in the room with fish and on the settee."

"Go back out there and sit until I come for you."

"Why was Miss Kay Adams mad? What had she done to make Miss Kay Adams mad?" Lois wondered.

"It is bad to slip around in another's house. NEVER come here unless you knock first. Do you hear me?"

"Kay, careful, careful. Compose yourself. Come here, honey. Are you ready for your lesson?" The girl by the side of Miss Kay Adams was very pretty.

"Yes."

Lois Jean sat down and smoothed out her dress. She opened the book to the Papa Hyden song. She began "Papa Hyden's Dead and gone, but his spirit"... She stopped. For some reason her fingering was not right, and her thumb refused to go down past the two black notes to "B." She was confused. She stopped. She didn't move.

Miss Kay Adams grabbed her thumb and jammed it against the key. It hurt. They were alone. She held it there.

"That's the key, and you've ruined the song. You've ruined the song. Why did you ruin the song?" Lois Jean started crying.

Sissy Jones was standing there. She said, "Here, I've brought cookies. Kay, take a break.

Kay left the room and Sissy took up the lesson.

"Here, sweetheart, eat a cookie and I'll play your song." She wiped away tears. Pulled curls off of her face. Sissy smiled.

"Don't let the old two black notes scare you. You can go anywhere you want to on a piano and do anything you want to." She said that loud. "Here. Let's play. And sing. Let's sing, pretty thing." She laughed.

"Papa Hyden's Dead and gone, but his spirit lingers on"…

"Now look. Here is Mr. Thumb. Hello, Mr. Thumb, ready to do 'spirit'?" Lois Jean smiled.

"Now let's work on it some more so that Mr. Thumb will be there." Then she glanced at Lois' nails. "Wait." Away she went; came back with a funny sharp-pointed knife. "Let me have your hand."

"No, I need hands to play."

"No, sweetheart, look." And she took the file and the point went under the nail.

"See, it's OK." Sissy smiled. To Sissy, everything was OK. She took the child's hand. Cleaned the nails. "See all the dirt. You can do that with a bobby pin, if you don't have a file."

Kay had returned; sat down; reached for a cookie. When Charity arrived, things were back to normal.

"See you next time," Sissy waved, then rushed back to Kay.

"Kay, oh my, Kay." She went over and put her arms around Kay. "Sweetheart, you've got to control your temper. We are all God's children. God loves us the way we are."

On the way home, Lois Jean told her mother that she played Papa Hyden with the right fingers; that she had used little pinkie to get to the "A" note. It was a good lesson.

Wherein Justice of the Greek Girls
Is Displayed in Court and Explained

They were passing J.J. Newberry Five and Dime. "Mother, get us fish. Get two fish. They'll be Lois Jean's fish and Mickey Fowe's fish."

"Laume, that would cost almost thirty cents." She said that as she opened the door. Charity knew almost everybody there. She had worked stock just before she married James.

Newberry's had luxury items: underwear, nail polish, ribbon, Tangee lipstick, notebooks, candy, socks of all colors and descriptions, hairbrushes, bobby pins, and jewelry. In the back they sold canaries, canary stands, and canary seed, canary covers for nighttime when canaries craved a dark spot. Mostly, miners bought them for their aging mothers. There were few aging fathers. Most had died in the accidents or from "coughing up their lungs," later called Black Lung. The canary and all the extras that a canary needed could run up four to six dollars. Coal miners bought them for wives and mothers. The canary was a showy gift. It announced to everyone that your son or husband loved you enough to pay a price for the canary.

They had goldfish. Just goldfish. Sometimes there might be a black fish. Nobody wanted a black fish. Just gold.

In they went. "Hello, Charity."

"Hello, Phyllis."

"Hello, Charity. How are the girls?"

"Just fine. Lois Jean is taking music lessons."

"Hello, Charity. How's James?"

"Just fine, Arizona." Arizona had dated James a time or two.

"Arizona, we want two goldfish." Charity knew how Arizona hated getting the fish. The floor walker was listening.

"Sure, Charity." She got a little white box with thin wire handles and a little dipper on a handle. She fished around awhile. Arizona was scared of things that darted and moved so fast.

"Here," says Charity. "I'll get them." She believed that Arizona had learned her lesson— not to inquire about James. They got the fish in the box, some candy, two pairs of white socks, paid and left the store.

It was late when they got home. She was setting out leftovers when she heard Matt calling.

"Charity, you home?"

"Yeah, I'm home."

There Matt and Nannie stood in the road. Today was court day and they had gone to court. No business of their own. They had gone for the entertainment. Newspapers from as far away as Knoxville, Tennessee sent reporters to Harlan County on court day. Of course, there was the local Harlan Daily Enterprise. Everybody took the newspaper, not so much for the news as for what you could do with a used newspaper. That paper could fill, wrap, stuff, cover, or wipe—it was as soft as catalog paper. One family had "wallpapered" an entire house with The Enterprise. It was a warm house until one night the flue got red hot and set the house on fire. Nobody killed. Fortunately, they all climbed out windows. It was nice to keep back issues and sit for a spell in the toilet and read. Nobody could chase you out. A good place to contemplate.

Charity told them to come in the back door. The steps at the front porch were too steep. Nannie began the events. She said the courthouse was full. She took a breath and began a long narrative. "This was the case where the taxi driver was killed up across Pine Mountain."

"Oh, Lord God." The groan was from Matt.

Nannie was into the story. The three were in the kitchen, and Charity was setting up supper. She opened a quart of beans that she usually didn't open until around Thanksgiving.

"Well," says Nannie. "The court room was packed. You remember the taxi driver that took them boys out and never returned and they found him up across Pine Mountain with his throat slit? Well they arrested two ol' boys who were proud of their job, it seems. That poor man's Mother and Daddy and relatives sat and listened to one of them brag. Charity, he was under oath. The lawyer asked him if he'd killed the taxi driver. 'Did you kill the deceased, asked the lawyer?' 'No, I deen't.' Here he leaned forward, propped his hand up on the arm of the chair, leaned forward, and said, 'I tuk out the razor and cut till the neck bone popped out. Then Luther tuk over. Luther kilt him. And the sonabitch of a taxi driver deen't have but a dollar and a few cents on 'im!'" Nannie paused. "Then, Charity, there was a single shot from a pistol. It caught him square between the eyes. It was the taxi driver's brother, they think. He just stood there with that gun. Judge raised the gavel and says, 'Case dismissed.'"

"Yeah," repeated Matt, "case dismissed." They sent the other'n. He'll get the chair. You should have heard them folks screamin' when the verdict was handed down. It was a show. Could you pass me a few more them beans? Charity, you are a fine cook. One day ye'll be as fine as this one by my side." Charity loved the compliment.

"How would you two like some of Miz Brannon's peach butter on a toasted biscuit to end on?"

"Mity fine. Mity fine."

They sat long at the table; late sun, nice, not too warm. Late fall sounds, dogs barking, cardinals singing, branch water splashing over rocks. C.C. on the porch at the boarding house, calling to passersby returning from the commissary.

Nannie pushed back her chair. Stood up, leaned out over on the table and swayed, catching hold of the edge of the table for balance.

"Nannie," says Charity, "you all right?"

"No, I've got to make myself go to the doctor. I do dread it."

"Well, you could die waiting like that."

"Honey, it's no matter. God's going to take me when He's ready. Not one thing I can do. The Greeks had it all worked out." She moved slowly toward the back porch.

Nannie's story was that the Greeks had two girls who had a ball of string and they pulled that string along, winding it back and forth into two balls. If somebody passed by that they didn't like or just had a sudden whim, they took a pair of sharp scissors and cut the string. No matter what you were doing—fighting a war or having a baby—you died when that string was cut.

"Ol' woman, we've got to go feed the dogs and chickens. Ruth and Ora and Alma not about to feed anybody except Ruth and Ora and Alma." He laughed.

"Mother, let me go with Grandpa and Grandma. Let me go. Please let me go."

Lois Jean loved Ruth and Alma. Ruth was the baby of the family and beautiful. Alma was her niece, Leige and Irene's daughter. She was her first cousin, but Lois Jean called her Aunt Alma, which pleased Alma.

"Charity, let her go. She'll be all right."

"Nannie, will you bring her back tomorrow, on your way to the doctor?"

added Charity. That part slid out, and Charity felt important saying it. She was directing in such a way as to hold power. All settled.

When they got to the road, Lois Jean was holding hands with Grandpa and Grandma. Sun setting. Off to spend the night.

"Matt, there's Halley in the swing and there's Bonnie. That child does not look like James—not one bit."

"Hello, Halley. How ye doing?"

"I'm doing fine. How are you?" She got up, came out in the yard.

"Oh, we're fine. We're fine."

Out ran Bonnie. Bonnie was a little older than Lois Jean. Lois Jean ran up to her.

"My name's Lois Jean." And she pulled out her skirt and curtsied.

"Who taught her that?" asked Halley.

"Why, she picked it up at the movies. Some little thing called Shirley Temple, I believe."

"Awe, that's sweet." Not very much was going for Halley these days. Her hair was dull; her skin would wrinkle before long; and some rot was showing in her front teeth now. She kept her mouth orange color with the Tangee lipstick and smoked real cigarettes in front of everybody.

"I don't have a blessed thing to lose," she would say at the pump.

Bonnie and Lois Jean had already found common ground. They were squatted down with little sticks, drawing a map in the yard. "Here's where we are."

"Let her come to play with Lois up at our place. They's three to take care of them, Ora, Alma, and Ruth."

"I don't know." Was she thinking about herself and Jim?

"Smooth it over, Halley," says Ma. "Smooth it over. You need friends. You can't sit on the swing all day, everyday. Let us take her and you come get her tomorrow. The only time is now."

"Well, Bonnie, you want to go with Lois?"

"No, I want to stay with you."

"That's it. Thanks, Nannie. You're a good woman and you have a good son."

She left the yard and went back to the swing. They walked home.

Nannie went into the bedroom, pulled off her long-sleeved, high-collar, black flowered dress that she had made and hung it on a coat rack on the back of the door. The girls had hugged Lois Jean and taken her out in the yard to see the latest puppies.

"I want one. I want one."

"Honey, they're all gone," said Aunt Ruth.

They both held little wiggly puppies, giggling when they licked faces and even lips.

Lois Jean held the door stop. First she had to sit in a chair and make a lap. Then Ruth lifted the round silver ball into her lap.

"Oh, hell far—it's big."

Everybody stood still and then whooped, slapping backs, bending over her out of all whooping! Nor did they correct her.

"Hell far, it is heavy!" That set everybody off again.

"Hell."

"That's enough. You ruin it if you overdo it. Besides, Charity will spank you." Ruth put her hand on her hip and mimicked Charity.

"Is this 'portant, Grandma?" Lois wanted to know about the silver door stop.

"It's 'portant to me. That's a load of chewing gum wrappers from every street and every road all over Harlan County. They's wrapping for special tape that the boys in the mines always brings me. They's a lot of thoughtfulness in that ball of silver wrappers you're holding. Rank strangers stop me and hand me silver wrapping."

"How much it costs?"

"It's priceless, child. It some way, somehow brings a rare pleasure without costing a red penny. That's a real treasure. Something that brings pleasure without costing a penny. Let's go feed the dogs."

She was standing in the kitchen in her day slip. She had tied a red chord with fringe around it like a belt and was holding two pones of corn bread. She pushed the screen with her foot and the dogs jumped.

"Yeah, Rex." Rex was the Brannon's dog. Jim had paid money for this border collie, and he had to give it to the Carter's. Rex advanced, showing teeth, tail 'tween his legs.

"Rex. Oh, Rexxie. Come here, sweetie." Rex melted into a smile and waggin' tail. Nannie stooped. "Don't grab; don't grab; easy; easy." She handed him his portion. He sat at her feet and ate it. She waited. Then another bite and another. Other dogs were whimpering.

Then, Nannie raised up straight and began breaking bread, hunks of bread, and throwing it to various places. Princess III, Dusty, Buck, Big Boy, Nig, Lighten' took their places and ate huge pieces of corn bread sopped in grease. Alma came with more pones.

"Ma, these could be a little hot."

"Can you handle 'em, girl?"

"Yeah."

"They'll do."

Everybody stopped and came to the porch to see her feed her dogs. She loved them, and they loved her. After eating, they came up for more. "Don't touch them, Nannie," says Matt. "You'll ruin the hunting instinct if you pet and love on a hunting dog. You'll ruin it. They won't be after nothin' else 'cept pettin'."

"How'd ye know, Matt. How'd ye know?" She grinned at him.

"You're still wild yerself."

"Hell far I am."

Wherein Lois Jean Learns that Love Lives in the Heart, Not in Color or a Banana Fritter

After breakfast, Lois held the silver ball and Grandma had felt her ear. She had helped Grandma feed the dogs. It was play time. Out the door, across the porch, down the steps, across the yard, across the road, and down to the branch she ran.

The clear gurgling branch with tiny fish living in small eddies, large rocks so a person could walk from one side to the other side on dry feet. The water was clean. The place was cool. The branch could be fifteen to forty some feet across, all depending on how much rain there was. In a "washout", the creek could be wider than forty feet and washing out anything that was in its path. The branch began somewhere up on Bird Eye Rock mountain, flowing down the mountain, through upper camp, separating colored and white camps, passing on down past the boarding house around the Garden of Eden, past the pump through the back of the houses in lower camp, through the culvert under the road across Skidmore Farm until it joined the Cumberland River. On either side of the branch grew jack-in-the pulpits, violets, mountain laurel, rhododendron, fragrant heart-shaped leaves, and tall ferns. Above them grew ancient trees.

In the middle of the branch was the car. The old car had been there so long that nothing remained except the chassis, springs where covered seats had been were now covered with a wide plank board, and, most important, a shaft and a steering wheel that still turned. Each child who had played in the car had taken care to see that the steering wheel turned. Actually turned. Grandpa had oiled it for Lois Jean.

The operator—here Lois Jean—sat behind the steering wheel and got the car started. Each driver had his or her own sound indicating that the car had cranked up. Lois Jean used "dar-dar-den (pause) dar-dar-den, dar-dar-den shaunnnn." "Shaunnn" indicated that the engine was running and was ready to fly, actually fly. First came a bounce on the board and sometimes a response from the springs. Turn the wheel and fly away. Above the creek, above the ferns, above the laurels, above the paw-paw bushes, over Harlan to the ends of the earth—as far as the imagination was educated to take the driver.

Lois paused somewhere over Harlan, realizing that she was not alone. She slowed down and landed into reality. On her left stood a colored girl about her size staring at her.

Lois got out of the car and went over to her. They stood in silence. Slowly the girl reached out and touched Lois' silky curly hair. Lois' heart beat faster. The girl touched her arm, sliding her hand down to Lois' fingers. Lois responded, touching heavy braids that felt like wool yarn, then her smooth, brown, satin arm. She had pink fingernails and hazel colored eyes.

She said, "Take off you dress."

Lois did, saying, "Take off your dress."

She took off her dress. Then came the pink J.J. Newberry's panties. She was chocolate brown all over and Lois was white all over. There in the cool ancient spot of trees and fauna in R.C. Tway Mining Camp during the "depression" birds high overhead sang their blessing—a bell on ol' Bossie under the porch rang and water gurgled over smooth rocks.

"Put yer stuff on and let's ride." They jumped into the old car, Lois driving since she had arrived first. They rode into a wonderful journey of a promised friendship.

"Mary Margaret Rose Delight, take me to your house."

"You ain't 'pose to go to my house."

"Take me anyway."

"I can't."

"Take me, plleese."

"Well, start de car."

They bounced twice, and flew away. The car landed sometime later, and both climbed out. They walked up the side of the hill, around the curve to her four-room house with a toilet out back and a well-swept front yard.

"You ain't 'pose to come in," she warned.

"I'm goin' in."

They went through the front room into the kitchen. Inside the kitchen was all that was wonderful in the world of smell. Mary Margaret Rose Delight's mother stood with the baby on her hip, tending a heavy skillet on the coal stove. The skillet was filled halfway with lard so that it had tiny bubbles rising to the top. She was dropping chunks of banana rolled in flour and spices into the hot pan. Then came the bubbling brown sound of frying. Finally the fritter rose to the top of the pan. She lifted the banana fritter out with a fork, rolled it in white sugar and placed it on a piece of a brown paper bag. Lifted the cap off the stove and spit her snuff in on the hot coals.

Saying not a word, she set two cracked saucers on the table and placed one banana fritter on each plate. The girls came up and stood at the table. Lois wiped her hands on her dress and savored the banana fritter. Mary Margaret Rose Delight's mama had just one banana. The girls left, went back to the car and rode away to new delights.

Sometime during the night Lois woke up, sat up in bed, her eyes open in the dark, heart pounding. The whole house was asleep. Outside were the sounds of whippoorwills, hoot owls, frogs and the branch gurgling by. The moon had slid from behind a cloud and filled the room. Lois lay back down and closed her eyes.

Suddenly she sat bolt upright. She knew what was wrong. That banana fritter that she had eaten at Mary Margaret Rose Delight's house had turned her black. That was the reason that she was not supposed to go to her house. Eating at a colored person's house turned you black! She had eaten that banana fritter and she was black. All over.

She got out of bed and went over to the window, closed her eyes. What would be bad about being black? She could go to school with Mary Margaret Rose Delight and could eat banana fritters every day. She opened her eyes. Sure enough, she was black. She pushed her arm closer to the window. It was getting light outside. Her arm was white. She examined her other arm and legs. She was white. She was white all over. With reasoned assurance, she climbed into her bed and went to sleep.

Later that week, Lois went back to Grandma's, down to the car, but Mary Margaret Rose Delight did not come. Lois rode alone. The next time and next time she did not come. Then came the day that she landed the car, got out, climbed the other side of the hill and stood in front of Mary Margaret Rose Delight's house. The door stood open. She went into the front room. Nothing remained. The house was clean and waiting. She went out on the porch. A long chicken snake slithered across the yard and under the floor.

She leaped through the yard, bounded around the curve and down the hill. Stepping carefully on the rocks, she got in the car and flew away. Oh, Mary Margaret Rose Delight, dear banana fritter friend. She looked up at the clouds overhead and there was an elephant cloud, a God face; and lo, there was a smiling Mary Margaret Rose Delight.

Wherein Lois Jean Hears the Dreaded Story

Lois was spending the night with Grandma. The day passed and soon it was time to go to bed. It was time for the story. The story. It was always the same, just on a different "step." There they lay. Alma on one side, Ruth on the other, and Lois Jean in the middle. Ruth and Alma took turns telling the story.

"One time they wuz an ol' no-count man living with his onliest girl, beautiful with yellow hair that lay in curls down to her waist." The house was as still as a mouse. Ora, Matt, and Nannie were all listening. Fact is, they didn't know which "step" it would be.

"Well, her mommy was dead. And her Pa up and married another woman, a Jezebel. She got permanents down at Miz Marcee's in Harlan and painted her fingernails and toenails blood red and ate her meat with the blood running down her chin. And she suckered the ol' man into marrying her and she moved in with him. Ol' woman was mean. She made the little girl go out and fetch in the water from the well, feed the dogs, dig around the strawberries and such, while she just sat around.

One day she was going to the store. Says 'I'm going to the store. Scrub the kitchen so's it's spotless. Don't eat the banana on top the icebox.' Off she set out.

Little girl with yellow hair commenced scrubbing the floor. All at once she spied the banana on the icebox. Oh how she longed for it—just a teensy bite. She got up off her knees, went towards the icebox, reached up and got the banana. It was so tempting, but she put it back anyways. The old devil appeared, took the banana, peeled it, and made the little girl with yellow hair and brown eyes eat it. Directly, in comes the wicked stepmother.

'Ye et the nanner, didchee?'

'I cannot tell a lie. The devil peeled it and forced it down my gullet.'

'Go brang me the ax.' Out the door and down to the kinlin' she ran and came back with the ax. Ol' woman came out.

'Put ye head on the choppin' block.'

She did.

'Pull your beautiful yellow curls over yer head.'

She did.

With one whack she cut off her head and buried the little girl in the garden.

That night her daddy come in from the mines.

'Where's my little girl?'

'She ain't cheer. Eat, ol' man, eat.'

He did. They got up. He was tired. So up the stairs he went to bed.

Ol' woman with the red toes joined him. Pulled some quilts up, and soon they went to sleep.

At exactly midnight, when the dead get up and walk around 'til the cock crows, the kitchen door opened up. In come little girl. She spoke a sayin, 'My mommy, my mommy, she cut off my head and burried me in the garden.'

The old man roused but didn't wake up. Little girl says again, 'My mommy, my mommy, she cut off my head and burrried me in the garden.'

Old man woke up.

'Ol' woman, wake up. Sumpens comin' up the stairs.'

Ol' woman act on like she's sleeping.

'One step closer,' says ol' man.

'My mommy, my mommy, she cut off my head and burrrried me in the garden.'"

Lois Jean was holding her thumb, her index finger and middle fingers wrapped round with the right hand. "Aunt Ruth, Aunt Ruth, how many steps? How many steps?"

On droned the voice. "'My mommy, my mommy, she cut off my head and burrrrried me in the gaarden.' Old man woke up, hair standing up on his head."

Lois Jean remembered that last time there were nine steps.

Then one time just two steps. Her heart was beating. Ruth continued. "'My mommy, my mommy, she cut off my head and burrrrried me in the garden.'

The little dead girl opened the door, went over to the bed. The old woman with blood red toes was shivering."

"Back came one quilt," whispered Alma. "'My mommy, my mommy, she cut off my head and burrrrried me in the garden.'

Back came up another quilt," whispered Alma.

"'My mommy, my mommy. . .'"

"Gotchee," screamed Alma.

Ruth and Lois Jean both jumped! Lois screaming. Then Ruth reached one hand and pulled Alma's hair.

"You scared me." Then they both started laughing.

Alma rolled in the bed. Knees drawn up. She had never interrupted Ruth's telling in all her life. Never. Alma loved it. She loved every bit of it. Nannie came in to put things right.

"You girls will find a new story. That one is worn out. Never again."

Next day after breakfast and feeding the dogs, Ora decided to scrub the porch. Matt led ol' Bossie out from under the floor and Nannie milked her. Ice wagon would be 'long soon. Nannie dried out the icebox. Bossie went to graze. Ora was barefooted; Lois Jean wanted to help. They carried out some warm water in the second bucket. She took the broom, lifted it, tilted it so it would hold the water, and began to scrub across the boards until she was getting a lather from P&G soap. Ora could get good lather. She did it all across the porch. Then she poured out the water and, following the lay of the boards, she put weight on the broom, sending the suds far off the porch into the air.

"Look, honey, look at all them diamonds." Lois stood still.

"Oh! Aunt Ora—they's beautiful. How many, Aunt Ora?"

"A million." They laughed

"Stop, stop," a voice called. "Don't get me wet."

"Laume," says Ora. "Bonnie, little Bonnie—that you?"

"Yes ma'am. It's me."

"Come on up."

There she stood, dressed in a freshly ironed dress, carrying a brown paper bag.

"Mommy sent this. Says to send me back in about an hour or two." She held out the brown poke.

"Come around to the back, Bonnie."

Ma was finishing up with the breakfast and preparing dinner and thinking ahead to supper.

"Well, hello there. How's my girl?" Nannie had helped this baby when she was born. Rubbed her ear to see if she did have the "mark of the beast" that would identify her as Jim's. "Come, gimme a hug." She held Bonnie long enough to check both ears. No, she didn't belong to James. Halley had never said she did. Halley said "could of."

Well she didn't!

Ruth had opened the brown poke. "Oh, Mommy, honey with the comb. Can we have some now?"

"Well, if we can get a hot biscuit and you sit down."

Nannie stuck biscuits back in the hot oven. Sat down. She put white saucers out. "Put the honey in the middle. I'll cut comb."

She took a knife and sawed the comb into six pieces. Tiny pieces. The whole thing didn't fill the tiny pickle jar. It was the thought that counted. "Sweets to the sweet!" She liked that story. Out came the hot biscuits, opened. Buttered, honey spooned in. How good. All six of them sat around the oak table with the smooth oil cloth in the kitchen at an impromptu party.

"Ma, ye want some coffee?" Ora pouring her own.

"I want coffee."

"Me too."

"Me too."

So everybody had coffee.

"Ora, pour some top cream on the children's and put some sugar in."

They sat there in the warm kitchen, chewing honeycomb. Inventing new things to do. Bonnie and Lois Jean shaping their round honeycomb into a square honeycomb. Ruth and Alma pouring Karo syrup over their's and Ora and Ma eating biscuits, buttered with a sprinkling of sugar.

Ol' Bossie in the upper field bawled.

"She wants to come," Lois said, still working with the honey comb.

"Let's let her come in the kitchen." This from Alma.

"No, we'll go see her!" Out Lois Jean and Bonnie ran.

The others cleaned the kitchen. Nannie went to the garden. Last of the tomatoes. Some tomatoes still green would go to frost if they were not picked.

She gathered the green beans, the green having gone to a leather, to be kept for seeds. She pulled them carefully, filling her little seed bags with the drawstrings and keeping them safe in her trunk. Same with corn. She hadn't bought seeds in forever. They did get cabbage starts and pepper from ol' Floridee cross the branch. Floridee took windows for her greenhouse; had her boys take a whole kitchen window from Jenny's house and made what she called a "cold frame" and put in cabbage seeds. Never had Nannie seen a cabbage seed; in fact, she didn't believe it. But, truth be told, Ol' Floridee sold spring cabbage plants and pepper plants and tomato plants all through upper colored and lower white camps. When Nannie went to get hers, she and Floridee drank coffee and shared stories.

The girls were sitting on the freshly scrubbed porch, singing "Jingle Bells, Jingle Bells," swinging their feet out, and Ora embroidering a pair of pillowcases. A day like this was rare, and this wasn't June; it was late fall. Sky cobalt blue. The trees lifting up to heaven, cardinals singing; and, most unusual, an old owl hooted.

Wherein Lois Jean Disappears

"Girls, come here. Help me get the seeds in my sacks." They all sat around the tables separating pepper seeds, corn kernels, beans, and putting them in the fancy sacks and drawing strings, tying tiny bows.

"Where the children?"

"With ol' Bossie."

"They are so sweet. You girls were too. Still are. She smiled fondly."

She stood up to go to the trunk at the foot of the bed. She stopped. Pain crossed her face. She grabbed at her side.

"Ma, you all right?"

"Just a catch, just a catch, girls. I'm all right. Been bending over in the garden. I'm fine." But, she knew she wasn't. That pain had been with her for some good time now. She had wanted to believe it was nothing. It was something. She promised herself that she would see a doctor next time she went to town. None of the company doctors for her.

"Alma, go call the girls in. I'll bet they're trying to milk ol' Bossie."

Alma was gone just a few minutes.

"They not there."

"Not there?"

"Not there."

They all ran different directions. One across the branch to colored camp. One toward the mines. One toward the upper meadow. They called names. "Lois Jean, Lois Jean, Bonnie, Bonnie." Others came out. Frank Jr. came out. He was Joe and Jess' younger brother.

"Ken I hep?"

The Youngs had stayed to themselves after Jess went away to the sanatorium. And Joe had disappeared.

"Have ye seen two little girls, Frank Jr.?"

"No, I been sitting out cheer all daylight. I h'ant saw nobody. I'm a goin' look for them. Nobody goin' get TB if I'm just looking."

Hackles of fear moved up through Nannie, a woman who kept her head. Others had joined in.

"Frank Jr., go up to the shack where Matt is. Tell him we have lost James' girl, Lois Jean, and little Bonnie."

He didn't take time to answer. He was running through ol' Bossie's meadow. Out came others from across the branch.

"Ma, do we tell Charity?"

"No. We won't worry her needlessly." She knew that, regardless of how this came out, Charity had a good excuse for never coming near them again.

There was Miz Becker, Johnny Warren, Floridee, all coming across the branch.

"Has anybody looked at this slate dump close to the driftmouth?" The slate dump was where the gray slate was separated from the coal and pitched over the hill. Slate was often razor sharp on one side. It produced a deep slice just picking it up. Jim was fascinated with the slate, finding ferns, birds, and even a fish embedded in perfect form. He packed them up and had them sent to Washington, D.C. to the Smithsonian. Ted had given him the address.

"Uncle Matt, Uncle Matt, come out." Frank Jr. was out of breath.

Matt came out of the dynamite shack. Inside were kept wooden Atlas boxes filled with dynamite. Other smaller boxes held caps. Matt carried the only keys to the shack. He dispensed the dynamite and kept a complete record of who got it and when. Inside Matt had a cat, a potbellied stove, a gun, a coffee pot, and a quart of Shine's best that he sipped when his back hurt. Truth be told, it was a fine setup. "Lois Jean's gone. She's gone and so's Bonnie, Halley's girl." Aunt Nannie says to tell her daddy.

"Whoa, boy, whoa. Start over."

"I've told all I know. I saw that Bonnie coming up the road early today carryin' a brown poke. That's all I know."

Matt locked the shack; went to the driftmouth. "Frank Jr., tell Nannie I'm getting Jim." He climbed on one of the cars and went to the end of the track. Was this a prank? Was somebody foolin' around? He remembered Frank Jr.'s face. The boy was convinced that something was happening.

He stepped out gingerly. Went to the small hole that led to the new seam. Yelled down.

"Anybody there? Anybody down there hear me?"

"Yeah, it's Ernest McCurg. That you, Matt?"

"Yeah."

"Anything wrong?"

"I need to talk to Jim. He about?"

"Yeah, down a little way. I'll go for him."

Matt sat in the pitch blackness. He closed his eyes. Where would two little girls go? What would they do? He was at a complete loss.

Little girls could cover a lot of ground. He hoped they were alone—just the two. Every now and then meanness got loose. Nothing anybody could do when meanness got loose. People had a way of finding meanness inside their souls and carrying it out. We all come to danger if the meanness of an otherwise perfectly fine human being goes bad just once for a few minutes and changes the world.

"Dad, it's me, Jim. What's wrong?" He was climbing out of the hole.

"Lois Jean's gone. I don't know the details." Jim got into the mining car. They didn't speak. When they got out, Jim ran ahead. Ma was in ol' Bossie's meadow. She reviewed all they had done. He saw a beehive of folks moving about.

"We know that the last place was ol' Bossie's meadow. That's where we saw them going. They were on this side of the branch. Not at the driftmouth. They's too many backyard gardens and fences for them to go around that way."

"Gotamittee, that leaves the slate dump." The slate dump was out to the left of the driftmouth. It was a small mountain of years and years of dumping slate that was separated from coal by "pickers". When a car was full, it ran on a little track out to the pinnacle of the dump. If it got too high to dump, they'd throw a small piece of a stick of dynamite out and settle it down.

Jim ran to the driftmouth. Got in the slate car; ran it out to the end of the rail. He had better sense than to try to walk to the edge. There were loose places that a man could fall through. He always went to the bottom of the mountain when he picked up slate with fish and ferns embedded in it for the Smithsonian.

He was running around the side of the mountain to the bottom of the slate dump. Up above the slate dump was a well-worn path to Bird Eye Rock, where Uncle Milt Farmer's clan lived. He stopped long enough to look as far as he could see across the mountain of slate.

"Whar ye goin'?" Out stepped a man from behind a tree. He was pointing a gun straight at Jim's head.

"It's my little girl, man, she's gone. I have reason to believe she might be here. Help me, oh God, help me." An instant change. The man joined him.

"He'yea, you look he'yea. I'll take the other side."

Jim had reached the bottom and was standing on dirt. He yelled out, "They could be two little girls."

He was walking along, shading his eyes, looking as far up the mountain of slate as he could see. At that moment he saw her. She was lying face down on the mountain of slate. He had stuffed his gloves deep down in the wide back pocket of his overalls. He dug them out and started climbing up the slate mountain. Slate gave way and he slid back down. He started again.

"Slow down, buddy, slow down."

It was the wild man from Bird Eye Rock. He was beside Jim. Skinnying in front, looking back. "This way, buddy, this way. They's a way big hole over yonder." Jim slowed down and stepped where he was told. Jim was winded. The wild man was scarcely breathing.

"Now stop. Let me go. They's a hole that drops that we don't want to commence moving. A single step could do it. Trust me, I'll holpen ye. Stand still."

God sends strange angels. Jim Carter would not wrestle with this one.

The wild man moved up the mountain, Jim behind him. Said back to Jim, "It would of been a bad mistake to go from the top down. A man's weight would have caused the whole dump to move."

He stopped on the dump. "You ok, buddy? I'm right at her. Now you go back down and let me dig in whar I know to plant a foot." Down on his knees. Gently, gently, he turned her over. "She's breathing but purty messed up. Here we come."

He carried the child, planting a foot. Standing. Getting his bearings, planting a foot. Jim glanced up to the top of the mountain. There stood Pa. He had figured out where Jim had to be.

Then he heard slight movement. The wild man had lost footing and sat down. "It's all right. I know this place like the back of my hand. You goin' be all right. I'm a goin' take my time." He stepped, planted his foot, then shifted weight, then took another step. Sometimes he slid but never letting the child come out of his arms. It seemed like an eternity. Finally, they stood face to face.

"I know a shortcut to yer house. Let's go."

"Let me have her," pleaded Jim.

"You sure?"

"Oh God!" Her face was covered with blood, cheeks scraped, forehead, lips bleeding. Her arm dropped. He reached to put it across her chest. "Gotamittee, she looks like she's been crucified. The palms of her hands."

He stopped and just stood there, tears running down his cheeks.

"Come on, buddy. She's alive! Come on. Let's get hep. Yer ma will do just right."

How on earth would he know about Ma? Jim was just following.

Wild man walked up to some dead bushes and commenced pulling them back, lifted a low tree limb and they were on a perfectly smooth path. They walked some little way and he pulled more limbs aside and Jim saw Pa standing on the porch a few yards away.

Jim turned to say, "That's. . ." Wild man was gone.

"He has dealt with me like a thief of mercy." Jim repeated. Ma once said that there were only two things you need to read and that's Shakespeare and the Holy Bible.

He was running toward the house. Nannie ran out.

"Oh, Jim, is she breathing?"

"She was. I can't tell."

"Lay her on the kitchen table. Bring me the scissors."

Ora was there and so were Ruth and Alma standing in the door.

"Ora, put on water. Get the salve, Matt. Jim, get me a teaspoon of that peach shine.

Lois, honey, this is Grandma, honey. Come back to us." Ora handed her scissors and a piece of white sheet. Lois' dress was torn by slate. She cut the dress and slip up the front.

"Ora, pour water in the dish pan."

"You'ens leave Ora and me. Where is Bonnie?"

"Ruth, Alma, go to Halley's. See if she is home."

Pa was standing there with a full quart jar of shine. Jim handed Ma a spoon.

"Let me do a first washing and pick out any slate before we bring her up."

Ora and Ma washed, patting the face—swollen lips, deep scratches on both cheeks, forehead holding a small piece of coal, deeply embedded.

"Get the tweezers. Bring the alcohol and leave us."

Finally they got to Lois' knees, then the hands. The hands were punctured and bloody.

"She looks like she's been crucified."

"Jim, leave."

"No, I'm standing here."

They put the alcohol on the knees and she moaned.

"Give me a teaspoon of shine that has honey on the top. Mix it in a tablespoon. Here, baby, she raised the head. Swallow it. Swallow it. Yer Grandma loves you." Tears were running down Nannie's cheeks.

"Hand me bandages, Ora."

"Jim, go get yer car. Tell Charity just what ye have to. I'm going to nuss her awhile. Get the rocking chair. Here, put her in my lap." They did. The shine soothed. Nannie rocked. It grew late. Ruth and Alma returned.

"Ma," Ruth was telling, "Bonnie was on the front porch in the swing. When we went up on the porch to ask about her, she spread out her skirt. She called Halley. Halley asked us how'd we like the honey. Says that Bonnie had a good time and that she'd got back a long time ago. Ma, she knows more'n she's saying."

"That's for sure," Alma said.

Lois roused and began crying. "Bonnie pushed me. Bonnie pushed me. She told me to look over, and she pushed me."

Soon Jim came back, just as Ora was stuffing Lois' dress in the stove.

"Did you tell Charity?" Ma asked.

"Not everything, not everything."

"Jim, stay and eat a bite."

"Thanks, Ma. Sooner I get her home, better she'll be."

"Is the car up close?"

"Yeah." He reached down, picked up Lois. She was still sleeping in and out.

"Daddy, Bonnie pushed me. Where's Bonnie?"

"She's home, honey." He was carrying her down the hill.

"Daddy, is marked of the beast bad?"

"No, honey, it means you belong to me." Two or three times he looked back in the back seat. She was sleeping. He hoped that she slept through the night.

"God, maker of heaven and earth, I want to thank You for delivering my girl Lois Jean. I am much obliged. They's just one part I don't begin to understand. Why'd You let it happen in the first place? Where were the angels? I believe that You're there, but You need to improve your communication. You can reach me anytime. Was it just "hap" that she didn't fall through that hole? Are You limited some way in what You can do? This is Jim the coal miner. I don't know much about the workings of You. I guess this is just a plain miracle. I don't believe that Yer small enough to get mad at me for voicing doubt and concern. You remember Your Son had that feller Thomas. What ever happened, I'll never be the same man. Don't, if You can help it, let her scar outside or inside. Don't let anything happen to this little girl. If I get all girls, You help me to be good. . . help me to. . . Gotamity, just help me know that Yer out there. Goodbye for now. This is Jim." At that minute a full moon slid out, coming on like the rising sun. Brilliant coating, everything like frosting on a cake.

He dreaded Charity. He dreaded the screaming, the thrashing. She might even try to kill Halley. He had a peace about Lois Jean, but it didn't extend to Charity. He looked down. He was still in work clothes and was hungry. He drove up into Jenny's front yard and as close as he could get to his back door.

Charity was standing on the back porch, light from the kitchen spilling out.

He lifted Lois Jean out in one great swoop. She was sound asleep. Walked up the piece of backyard onto the porch. Charity had slid the spring off the screen door, and it was wide open.

"Bring her in here." Jim had never heard this voice. Low, authoritative, knowing— a voice that knew what the next move should be.

The Creton-flowered cover had been pulled off, and there was an ironed sheet on the bed. A large pillow, again ironed pillowcase. He laid her down. Charity began unlacing the shoes, the white summer shoes, pulling off the socks. They had not turned on the light. Charity put her hand behind a knee and lifted it. Lois Jean moaned.

"Did Nannie put salve on her knees?"

"I really don't know."

"We need to move them so's the scabs won't grow together."

"Yeah."

"Did Nannie nuss her?"

"Yeah."

"You watch her while I lay you out some supper. Yer bucket at the mines?"

"Yeah."

"James, she is going to be just fine. I prayed for her and I prayed for you."

Who the hell was this woman? This was the same woman he saw and fell in love with at the Harlan Hospital when she almost died with a ruptured appendix. The very one.

She opened the stove warmer. Took out a pork chop, little bowl of gravy, sweet potato skin puffed up just right over the potato, fresh-cooked cabbage. Charity insisted on "green leafy vegetables" as an ongoing necessity for the "healthy body." Miss Petit and Miz Aundi had insisted on that at The Pine Mountain Settlement School.

Charity felt and found one of the little bandaged hands. She slid the flashlight from under the day bed. Turned it on. Found the face, swollen, red, forehead, nose, cheeks, and lips. The only other time that she had seen something like this was Pearlie Mae.

Emma and Pearlie Mae had gone out to pick some flowers for the table. Pearlie Mae loved flowers and was good at putting together bouquets. When Gertrude married Andrew Dopel, Pearlie and Emma had made tussie mussies and noseygays. They all wore white and carried Tussie Mussies. Violet leaves, white roses, and a sprig of honeysuckle.

Jim got up before daylight, went out on the porch for a smoke. He had plum forgotten his shine. He went to the edge of the porch, reached under the corner edge of the porch. There it was.

At that second it came to him. It was Wild Man that had shot ol' Henry Caddell, the revenuer. That's what he was trying to connect. That was Wild Man's voice that had yelled down to the revenuer, James' relative. He opened the jar, taking his finger and running it around the edge of the jar and wiped his finger on his pants. Then he had one swig. Communion. He put the jar back, got the kindling, built the fire. About to start breakfast. Out of water. Men did not go to the pumps. Pumps were a woman's work. It was early. Nobody'd be out. He didn't have on a shirt. He grabbed the bucket and walked out. Never let a good action die by thinking too much. "Thus conscience doeth make cowards of us all." That's what Ma said. He was pumping water.

"Jim."

He turned around and there stood Halley. "I know about yesterday. Well, I know one side about yesterday. Bonnie told me that she was searching Lois' ear for the mark of the beast and that Lois slid down the slate dump. I know that's Bonnie's version. I'm so sorry." He hated her. He loved her. He wanted to gather her in his arms. He wanted to shove her away from him forever. All in a second.

"Halley, they's a story about a woman named Eunice who is married to a man named Orfus. She gets away from him and is taken to the world below. He bargains with the devil to get her back on the condition she won't look back. She's climbing out and looks back and is gone forever. Halley, we can't go back. They'll always be a place. But we both are never going to go back."

"I know. I'm sorry, Jim. I'm sorry. Don't bear me a grudge."

"I'll do the best I can."

He came back, set the bucket down. Went to the day bed and looked down. Lois Jean was sleeping that warm sleep just before waking up. Lois Jean's palms would carry scars. A tiny piece of coal would remain in her forehead, and a tiny scar in the corner of her lower lip would linger always.

Wherein the Move to Lower Camp is Bargained

"Charity, we are moving from off this hill. If there's a place in lower camp this morning, we're moving into it." He was pulling on his clothes, lacing up his shoes. Then he changed his mind. He put on a white shirt, suit pants. A pair of Sunday shoes with dark socks.

"I'm going to see Vance Owens, and we are moving. I'm damned if I am going to live on this hill and look out at them open doors another week." He drank a second cup of coffee and left.

"I'll be back d'reckly." He walked down the hill past the Garden of Eden, on down. He planned to walk all the way to the commissary, looking on both sides of the road to see if any door was standing open. He rounded the curve.

There stood Ida Brannon at the pump.

"Jim, how's Lois Jean?" News travels fast to the pumps.

"She's scraped up. We are lucky she didn't fall in one of them holes on the slate dump."

"Aw, Jim, is she going to scar? I can't stand to think of that little face all scarred up."

"Only time will tell. Ma salved her. We'll just have to see."

Ida wanted to know what Jim was doing out. "You going for doctor?"

"No, I'm going for a house."

"Why Jim, I just had Virginia go over and shut the door on the house just across the road. It's been empty since last Sunday."

"Thank you, Ida. I'll be on my way." He walked past the house. Four rooms, two maple trees, and the front yard. Nice front porch. That would be his house. He was sure of that.

He went up the flight of concrete steps to the office. He did not go to the scrip window. He went to the door. Others watched him. He turned the knob and entered. Vance was getting ready to open the scrip window. Vance was surprised to the point of jerking back.

"Jim, what's wrong?"

"More then you've got time to hear. I'm here on business."

How had he stirred up good ol'Jim? That's one you never want to stir up. He was known for packing a pistol and using it.

"How can I help you?"

"Did you hear about my girl Lois Jean? She had a bad accident and is sleeping on a day bed in a three-room house, and I'm moving into that empty house next to Richard's." Vance didn't say a word. He was wondering exactly where that house was.

"I've got two little girls—guess you know about that. I almost lost one on the slate dump. You've gone through the agony of pain with a child, I know." Jim was referring to Vance's little girl, Martha Ruth. Beautiful, beautiful girl child he and Miz Owens had had after a bunch of boys. Martha Ruth was the victim of spinal meningitis. She walked like a baby and was not able to go to school and play like other children.

Jim had touched a nerve. Vance went back, poured a cup of coffee, hesitated, then poured the second cup. "The house is yours, Jim. We were hiring a man from down in Proctor, Tennessee, but he can live in yours. I don't know anything about his family. Can you be out by Friday?"

"I can be out by today, if I don't have to go to work in a few hours."

"The house is yours."

Wherein Charity and James Move to the Society of Lower Camp

Charity had things that had to be done. First was to clean up the house. How to get Lois there? The idea stopped her cold. She could take the Durant out and get Lois in it and take her down to Miz Brannon's. Miners in Tways tried not to be put in a position of teaching a woman to drive a car. Most men drove a woman where she needed to go and told her how to vote on election day. Today, moving day, Charity was taking charge. Jim took off his good clothes, put on work clothes, and left for work.

Charity walked her mind through the sequence. Go get the car. Leave Lois Jean. Take Mickey. Drive the car back. Back it up in the yard. Put Lois Jean in it, and drive her down to lower camp. She took Mickey and left Lois Jean sleeping.

She opened the garage door. There was the old Durant, pointed out. James had turned it around.

She was trying to remember: Turn the car on; feed it gas. No, turn the car on; put it in gear—a gear makes an H. Put it in high. Feed it gas and drive. Unfortunately, Jim had left it in reverse. She turned on the car, stepped on the gas and blew out the back of the garage. For some reason that was funny. She bent over the steering wheel laughing.

The McVeigh's heard the commotion and ran out to see what had happened.

Before they could get to the garage, Charity had put the car in another gear and pushed the gas to the floor. The car came out very slowly and wouldn't go faster regardless of what she did. The back was out of the garage.

Mr. McVeigh came out. He was on crutches, yelling, "Wait! Stop! Wait!"

She turned off the car.

"Yer gonna tear up Jim's car and kill that baby. What ye tryin' to do?"

"I need to move Lois Jean, who fell off the slate dump yesterday. I've got to move her. We are moving into the empty house tomorrow, and I need to move Lois Jean so's I can work on the house."

"Git out. Take the kid and git out. I'll drive the car fer ye. But, yer not gonna be in hit." Frankly, he wondered if he could drive since the mine accident had left nerves in his left leg injured. In he got, and the car worked well. He drove up to the house on the hill, backed the car in, and Charity woke up Lois Jean.

"Walk out to the car. Don't bend your legs." Lois Jean walked, holding her hands up, fingers out.

"You otten move her."

"I'll do what I need to do, thank you." They all got in.

"Wait."

She ran in, grabbed bedding from the day bed. Put it in the car. "Wait." She grabbed rags, P&G soap, newspapers, and lime.

Mr. McVeigh shook his head.

"Woman, I'm thankful that yer none of mine." But he smiled when he said it.

"Ye'd better not leave the Sears catalog." She ran back and grabbed it.

"Why'n you leave the children in the car? They don't need to be around sech as you're usin'."

That was a good idea.

She had worked in the Eagle laundry, stocked goods at J.J. Newberry's, and cleaned rich people's houses in Harlan. She was ready to use the accumulated talents for her four-room house in lower camp.

"I'll come back in the ev–en–ing and place the car in the garage. I'll see if my boys can nail back the part you tuk out."

"I'll thank you, Mr. McVeigh, with all my heart."

She took water from the branch, threw it by the buckets on the rough gray floors of the four-room house. Cut the P&G into small pieces and scrubbed the floor. Cleaned the paned windows with vinegar and the Harlan Daily Enterprise. Threw lime around and down in the outside toilet. Opened the doors and windows.

She needed four linoleum rugs, standard. Four. She stopped. Would Mr. McVeigh drive her to Harlan? Money. She had enough in the sack.

"Charity, let the girls eat with us. Can ye stop long enough for a bite?"

"No, Miz Brannon, but if the girls could have a drink. It sure would help."

"Can Lois Jean walk?" Ida Brannon always got her way.

She went to the car. "Honey, can you walk to Ida's?"

Ida opened the car door. Mickey slid out, sat on the running board.

Then Lois Jean's turn. She surveyed the whole thing, scooted across the seat. Ida was standing close to the running board. Out came straight legs. They hurt. She cried out. Ida grabbed her. Helped her stand. She put her hands up in the air and walked, never bending her knees.

"She looks like Martha Ruth," Nell whispered to Lucy McCurg.

Miz Brannon settled them on the front porch. Out came Ginny, and they all played. Miz Brannon put down a quilt, and Lois Jean slept. Charity went to the pump.

"Nell, could you drive me to Harlan to buy some rugs and stovepipe?"

"Charity, I might could. But that car is so big. I've not had any experience with that, not in the front seat or in the back—if you get my meaning. But Tom Carter can drive that car. He is home. He'll take you. I'll even go ask."

Out came Tom. Charity had raised a window in the front room. Was sitting on the sill with the window pulled down across her thighs, cleaning the outside of the smoked up panes until they shined—no streaks.

"Charity, let's go. I've got to be back in an hour."

"Wait just a minute till I get out."

She didn't have a pocketbook. Nothing. McComb supply was the first stop—for rugs and stovepipe. Brown floral for three rooms, and a green/white pattern for the kitchen. It took her longer to decide on the kitchen.

"That white shows dirt, Charity. Git an avocato green," says Pete Wilson.

"Get what?"

"Avocato, avocato, he repeated, avocato green. Lookee here." He showed her a sample.

"Ain't that the berries? New color, avocato green."

She stopped. She stood perfectly still, not even blinking her eyes. "Avocato," she whispered, "avocato green." It was soothing just to say the word. Furthermore, that lovely sound was not attached to any object. "Avocato green." She came to herself. "Yes, I want the three florals and the avocato green for the kitchen."

"How ye goin' to pay fer hit?"

"Well, it comes well under the going price. You said these was on sale."

"Naw, nothing like that."

"Now you listen to me. When rugs has been rolled up forever, when we unroll 'em, they will crack. You know 'bout that, don't you?"

"Well—"

"They will crack just like a block of ice. These have set here through a whole season. You know that changes them. Look here. Here is ten dollars. That includes this stovepipe and them ol' cheap mining camp rugs. Can you bring 'em up on the truck—that one that stops at Gibson's, the Hall's, the Miller's?"

"You know, lady, I'd do anything to get ye out of here. Yer ruining the business."

"Today. I've got to have them today," she said.

"Will do hit, woman. Just go."

She turned.

"Wait, they's money owed."

"Excuse me. Where's a corner?"

He knew about these women. Carried their funds down in their dress. "Over yonder next to the wall."

She went over to the corner, reached between her breasts, extracted the Duke's Mixture bag, took out ten dollars in bills. Glanced down. Over the table lay an open catalog. The page was smooth and had a picture of twin beds with pink brocade bedspreads on them. Two little beds in one room. Lois Jean and Mickey Fowe in one room. She needed twin beds.

"Charity, we've got to go." It was Tom. He had started coughing again. He coughed up blood most of the time.

"Tom, could ye give me fifteen minutes more? Just fifteen."

"Where?"

"The furniture company."

"Fifteen minutes." He parked near the courthouse. Got out for smoke. Court was in session. He sat down and pulled out a real cigarette.

In she went, determined to have the beds. She could see the children in twin beds. In she swooped.

"Say, do ye have twin beds?"

"Do we have twin beds? We've got twin beds!"

The double bed was still the bed to buy. Three or four children could sleep in a double bed. Two at the head and two at the foot. Children were small. Sometimes it could even be five.

Charity had hit a good day. "You live out in Tways, don't chee? Bill Johnson, the name. I'm Murm's boy." He put his hand out. She was engaged with twin beds. There they stood, made up with pink brocade bedspreads. Mattress and springs, slats to hold.

"How much, everything included?"

"That'ed be seventy-five dollars each. Complete."

"Thirty-five for both? How long have they been here?"

"Woman, we paid mor'n that for 'em."

"You need the floor. I used to stock for J. J. Newberry's. You need space. Besides, the spreads are dirty."

"Well, I'll go fifty dollars for both complete."

"Deliver them tomorrow and I'll give you forty."

"Nothing doing. I want fifty dollars cash for two beds, mattresses and springs.

"I have cash. I've got two twenties and a ten." She jerked her thumb up. "Take it or leave it." She walked toward the door.

"Wait, I'll take it." His face was in pain.

"You'll deliver them this afternoon."

She handed him the thirty dollars. He took it! She left. It had taken fewer than ten minutes. Tom was sitting on the bench outside the courthouse. She waved to him.

When they got back to the garage, they found the McVeigh's boy finishing pounding back the end of the garage. "Lessee the back of the car, Miz Carter." She had really banged up the garage. What had she done to the car? Charity was out of the car. Everybody gathered up close. Not one scratch. The bumper on the back had taken the blow—nothing.

"You a lucky woman. Jim Carter is proud of this automobile." Tom turned it around and backed it into the garage.

"Thank you, Tom. Thank you for everything."

She went to Ida's for the girls. Out came Ida carrying a little dish covered with waxed paper. It was her fine butter. Molded with a four-leaf clover.

"Charity, its going to be nice for you to be across the road."

"Thank you, Miz Brannon. Thank you for everything."

"Charity, I put salve on Lois Jean's legs. Them scabs won't harden and she can bend her legs sooner. Can ye make it okay?"

"Yes, I can."

"She can walk and we'll go slow." Lois walked behind, stiff legged, hands in the air with her fingers spread. They passed the Garden of Eden, went in the back door of the house. Lois could walk in the back door.

Doors still stood open at Jenny's house, and weeds were growing knee high. Same with Shine's place. She went in. On the kitchen table was the Grimm's Fairy Tale book. Johnnie Warren, a niece to Uncle Tom Becker, was a teacher at the Rosewald School where the colored children attended. She had told Charity about the book and then ordered her one.

"Mother, will you read me the 'Wolf and the Seven Little Goats?' Please, please?"

"Tonight, you both can crawl in with me and I'll read it. Now let's have some butter on biscuits with a little honey."

Charity looked around. She needed boxes. How could she get boxes? She needed as many as she could get from the commissary. Of course, Miz Amics would have a few. She could put the knickknacks and pictures in one box, the Lone Wolf and the one of the poor old Indian, head bowed, sitting on his horse. There was the chalk lamp of the family with the fireplace that really glowed. She'd keep the drawers full from the chifforobe and dresser; the drawers could set in the back of the Durant.

"I'm going to go to the boarding house for some boxes. You two sit here till I get back." She was going up the steps across the wide front porch, opening the screen door; glanced in the front room. There stood Helen, awfully close to C.C. Moore.

"Excuse me." Charity loved their discomfort.

"Why'n ye knock?" Helen was mad as a wet hen.

"Well, it's almost supper time, and I thought you might have on an apron helping Miz Amics with supper. Guess I was wrong. I need some boxes. We're moving. Where's Miz Amics?"

"In the kitchen."

Charity never acknowledged the presence of C.C. Moore, except to utter under her breath, ". . .that ol' reprobate."

"Miz Amics, do you have any boxes? We're moving and can bring them back next day."

"Hep yerself. They's there in the pantry. Did you by any chance see Helen?"

"Yeah, she was out there with C.C. Moore."

"Charity, what am I goin' to do about Helen?"

Charity stacked the boxes, fine big ones that held canned tomatoes, boxes of spaghetti, cans of cane syrup, one big double box that fresh fruit came in.

"Believe that these six will do. I'll get them back by day after tomorrow."

Miz Amics was working over the hot stove. About six miners' buckets were on the oil cloth-covered table. She had to have supper and pack buckets at the same time. Tways mines had run round the clock this past week. Good work. James was lucky he could stop at his mother's and eat and Nannie would often pack his bucket.

Charity gathered the boxes, thanked Miz Amics. She went out the front door. There them two were in the swing. They spoke not one word. Neither did Charity.

Charity packed up the picture of the Lone Wolf, the Indian, and the chalk lamp that set on top of the radio. She packed dishes, setting the table for breakfast so they could eat before leaving. She could put them in the dish pan. She stopped. Walls, ceilings, bedbugs, roaches—she would have none of that. How long had the house been empty? Under the floors. Paint every wall with a kerosene paintbrush. When? How? She needed a helper. James would be opposed to this. "Cleanliness was next to godliness". All the walls had to be done. Before the rugs went down.

Wherein They Leave the
Little Shotgun House on the Hill

On she worked. It grew dark. Lois Jean and Mickey just watched. She set the table and packed the rest. She would need to keep out a frying pan and a coffee pot. Mickey was ready to go to bed.

"Lois Jean, play a song for your sister on the piano."

"I can't move my fingers."

"Sure you can. Play something with an index finger. Play birthday party."

Suddenly Lois was interested. She sat down and scooted in on the bench. Opened the music book, Teaching Little Fingers to Play, and played and sang.

"Here we go, up the row to the birthday party."

She leaned over, looked at the dreaded bass clef. The bass clef looked like a bent walking stick. "Song of the Volga." She put her left hand out, turned it over. It was time to let it do something.

De (c) De (A) De (b) De (g)—she liked that and left-hand played it. "Mother, what's a

V-o-l-g-a?"

"I don't know. What does the picture say?"

"There isn't a picture."

"I want to go to bed. Ken I sleep in your bed?" Lois Jean pleaded.

She glanced at the clock. It was eight-thirty. No wonder they were tired.

"Get in bed. You can sleep in my bed. Both of you can. Take off your dress. Put your shoes where you can find them. Put your socks in the shoes. Lois Jean, move the pee bucket in under my bed." She closed the last lid on the last box that she had. Pulled the shades. Took off her dress. On the dresser was the book.

"Oh, read me a story. Please, please, read."

"Oh, Bubber, I sleepy." Mickey.

The three crawled in bed, all in day slips turned night slips. The three shared one pillow. She opened the book.

"The Wolf and the Seven Little Goats. There was once upon a time an old goat who had seven little kids and loved them with all the love of a mother for her children. One day she wanted to go into the forest and fetch some food. So she called and said, 'Dear children, I have to go into the forest.'"

"What's forest?"

"It's woods."

"I have to go into the forest. Be on your guard against the wolf. If he comes in, he will devour." [She looked and sounded it out.]

"What's de ver?"

"That means gobble you up—eat you up. He will devour you all—skin, hair and all. The wretch [she sounded it out] often disguises himself, but you will know him at once by his rough voice and his black feet."

"What the mother goat is telling her seven little goats is that the wolf can play a trick on you. Can change and come in on you and eat you up."

"Like Little Red Riding Hood?"

"Yes. The kids [little goats] said, 'Dear mother, we will take good care of ourselves. You may go without. . . '"

That's when she heard the squeak on the sixth step coming up the front porch. She was familiar with that sound. Her instant reaction was to leap out of bed and see if she had put the thumb lock on the doors. Someone was on the front porch, kneeling down peeping into the bedroom. She glanced down. Mickey was asleep. Charity was completely vulnerable. Nobody could hear her if she screamed her head off. The branch would absorb the noise. She lay there frozen. Lord God, what if it was Joe Young coming to kill her? She willed her arm to move. Cut off the light. Ease out of bed. Go to the bedroom corner. Pick up the loaded rifle and fire it out the window.

Was he at the door? Was he trying the door? Was the thumb lock on the door? She could not move. She was going to be raped and killed—maybe her children too.

She threw back the cover, raced to the corner, grabbed the gun. To the window, pointed out the window, held the trigger. A click—gun not loaded.

He had heard the click. She heard herself saying, "I've got this shotgun right at your head. Run, damn you, down the steps. Run or I'll blow your head off." Not a sound.

There were bullets in the chifforobe next to James' rubbers. She had never loaded the gun. She moved to the chifforobe, opened it. Fumbled around for the bullet. That's when she realized whoever was on the porch was probably gone. He would have been in by now.

She turned on the light. She had locked both doors with the thumb lock and a bent nail.

She picked up the rifle and sat down at the kitchen table. She pulled back on the little metal thing, laid the bullet in its bed, and closed the chamber. Chamber, that's what James called it. She stood the rifle in the corner and went back to bed. She wouldn't sleep. She'd stay awake. . . next thing she knew, Mickey was saying, "Mother, Mother." Lois was still asleep.

James came in before his shift ended. He needed to get the move underway. He told the boys to cover for him. He had set off the dynamite and the boys were shoring up the top. He went down the hill and ate at Ma's. She gave him a stack of brown pokes to put stuff in and told him to return all nine. "I will, Ma." He admired this woman who always had the right thing at the right time. He was home. Charity and the children were up. He walked in. She was finishing breakfast. He reached out to the table and got a biscuit and buttered it.

"That all yer going to eat? I'm going to clean up breakfast and then go to the house." She didn't mention anything about the rugs and twin beds with pink brocade bedspreads. Avocato green! She couldn't wait to lay that on the floor and brag about it at the pump. Avocato green.

"I've got to break down the bed, tie the chifforobe doors, take the mirror off the dresser and take down the flue in the kitchen." He would do that last, after the oven cools.

"James, I can clean out the soot in the bottom of the stove." She spread out some of the precious pages of the Harlan Daily Enterprise. Got the soot raker off the back porch. Unlatched the little box below the oven. Lois Jean and Mickey came in to watch it.

Charity took the rake, about eighteen inches long, with the five-inch rectangular piece of metal on the end and reached into the stove and pulled the rake out. With it came the softest, blackest, dust in the world and poofed down onto the newspaper. Each reach overlapped the last one to draw out the black residue from the burnt coal. If the soot was not raked from the stove, the stove could explode and burn down a house and all its contents. Cleanliness was next to godliness and cleanliness could also save your life.

"Charity, what's the gun doing next to the bed and who loaded it?"

"Lois Jean, take Mickey Fowe—take Mickey to visit Shirley and Miz Piertison. Get the eggs."

She told him the whole story of the creaking step.

"Charity, that's yer imagination."

She stood up. Carefully laid the soot rake down on the edge of the newspaper.

"I meant to look." She went out on the porch. There under her window was a muddy footprint. Right next to the window was a spot that looked like the front of a shoe.

"Now, James, go to the bottom of the steps. Come up to the sixth step; get on the side next to the house. Now come on."

He did. The sixth step squeaked. He spoke not a word. From that day forward the rifle was loaded.

Charity gathered the broom, mop, scissors, newspaper, dishpan, P&G soap, vinegar and precious furniture polish. Tucked in a box were paintbrushes and the kerosene can. Empty. They had used the kerosene on Jenny. Her thoughts trailed off. She had truly loved Jenny.

She had to get kerosene and brush the rooms to kill the bedbugs. Unless she used paint, all cream-colored. She had painted this house first with silt from the branch that came through the Garden of Eden. Then she got calcimine and it worked better. Miz Brannon had told her about calcimine. Calcimine was dry and had to be mixed with water.

All Miz Brannan's rooms were enameled. Paint killed bugs and eggs in the walls. If the new house were enameled, all she had to do was a lye scrub of the floors and the toilet. First clean the toilet, put the Sears and Roebuck catalog out there.

"James, I'm going on. I'm going to let the children play on the front porch or at Miz. Brannon's; I'm going to clean and be ready when you come with the stove and bed."

Not a word about her dealings yesterday. All in good time. Word would travel either to the mines or to the pump. Just a matter of time.

She took the children and began to walk with the dishpan full, and each child was carrying a bag. They did not meet a soul. She opened the front door. Strange that she had not noticed the walls. They were enameled. All in a shiny light tan and unusually good condition. It turned out that Ola and Russ Collins were going to move in, and Ola had painted the walls. Turned out Russ and Ola had a better place across from the Miller's. Russ was up and coming; he needed to be close to the office and the telephone.

Charity could not believe her good fortune. Even the floors were spotless. Just needed sweeping. She had forgotten the broom. Furthermore, she couldn't borrow one; that was bad luck. Brooms were powerful. Witches rode them and lovers stepped over them. Pull straw from one; put it on a wounded place. It would heal it. She needed her broom.

"Look here, I'm leaving you two on the porch. Don't get off the porch. I'm going for a broom."

Just as she was crossing the front yard, the truck drove up. It was the rugs. Bill Johnson was driving the truck, and the first thing that he did was pull out a broom from the back of the truck. "That you, Miz Carter?"

"Yes, it is. We've been waiting for you. Hand me your broom and I'll sweep the rooms." Just like she knew the routine.

In she went. Bill was more interested in telling Charity who he was. "Charity, I'm Merm's boy. I lived across the branch that runs down your backyard." Boys began to come out of Aunt Ella's. Gerald, Tom, attracted by the truck.

In no time the ropes had been hoisted off the truck and placed on the front porch. Then the boys helped. The rugs first.

"Don't crack that linoleum! You be careful." Charity was giving instructions. Nobody even looked up.

Charity stood with her hand on her hip and eyebrows raised to her hairline and continued. "It's not straight. Line it up with the wall, back a little."

Even Miz Gibson wasn't this bad with her wool rugs. Kitchen first. Avocado rug. It was a sight for sore eyes. Nothing like it in Tways. Bedrooms next, then front room.

"They look nice, Miz Carter. Hope you'ens enjoys them."

The boy got in the truck and started off. Charity was standing there with his broom. She stood still, plenty of time to get it to him. He had to go to the pump to turn the truck around, start toward upper camp, swing back toward McVeigh's holler, turn down on the main road. She could walk out and give him his broom or keep it. She went out and swept the back porch. Fine broom.

Lois Jean had been sitting on the front steps. She yelled at the truck, "You forgot yer broom." The boy waved and drove on. Lois Jean went into the house. Mickey followed.

"This is your bedroom right here. Twin beds will go here and here." Charity was excited. She was smiling. Never had she been happier in all her life, not even when she married James. There was something satisfying, soothing about a room, cleaned, with new shiny linoleum rugs, about to get twin beds.

"Come look at this, girls. Come see." Into the kitchen they went.

"Sit down, lie down on your back, spread your arms and legs. Now draw them down." The girls didn't understand so she demonstrated. "Have you ever felt so much smoothness as the avocato rug brings!" All three on the floor giggling. Feeling smooth inside and out. She came to herself. "Oh, Lord." She was tempting fate. All this fine stuff and this fine feeling. Everything good and clean. No threat of flu, or typhoid, or guns blowing heads away, no slate coming down, nor throats being split, nor belts lashing legs and backs, not hands caught in laundry presses, nor snakes biting, nor older or powerful beings lashing out stinging threats if you took bread before your turn, nor losing apples to. . . what a strange, wonderful experience. This was happiness.

"Jim, I got the truck. Some of the boys are goin' to help you." It was Tom Becker. He came into the kitchen, pulled out a chair, and sat down. The truck was outside, two in it. Jim waved them in. Tom sent them to Miz Amic's to get coffee. "Go to the back door." He found a box with cups and saucers. "You know, things will change," Tom explained.

"Yeah, Tom, this little place between camps was comfortable for us," Jim continued. "We never saw a color here."

Tom said, "I felt just as comfortable with your front door as I did with your back door. I felt comfortable in your kitchen or your car, Jim. But all this separation of coloreds and whites is going to change. I know. To tell the truth, this has lasted a lot longer than I thought it would. And it is genuine. The real thing. Things are changing, though. In another hundred years we'll be able to sit beside you at any table anywhere. In a hundred years Johnnie Warren will teach Lois Jean. And in a hundred years my boy can marry your girl. In a hundred years my boy can be president of the United States."

The boys had returned with a whole pot of coffee and some leftover biscuits and some honeycomb. "She owes me one. One of our women did a little favor for Miz Amics. Somebody at the boarding house needed her services." They sat around the table eating biscuits with honey, chewing on the comb. Sun shining through the back door. Not much being said. Jim passed out toothpicks. They finished the pot of coffee.

Tom worked inside while the three loaded the truck. Tom took the broom and swept out each room. Disconnected the swing on the front porch. The stove was the last to be moved. It was as clean as a stove could be cleaned. Jim reached for the stove pipe. He was just a little impatient, gave it a quick twist from the elbow. It came apart and soot descended in a swoosh all over his face. He turned to get water. The boys laughed, hitting each other on the shoulders, bent over in a reel dance.

"That's the way you going, man. You one of us now. They's no water. You's one of us!"

"I've always been one of you. Load that up while I go to the branch." He grabbed a feed-sack towel and was gone. As they started down the hill, Tom told them to wait for him. He went up the hill and closed the doors to the little shotgun house—forever.

Wherein a Dead Man Saved a Life

Gerald Carter, Aunt Ella's son, in the course of the move, had made a fine awareness. Gerald had been made aware of himself in a way that would change his life forever. He would become a success. He had never given thought about life in terms of snot. He had not thought about his snot running down to his lip. But he sure knew when it got to his lip. He knew by wrinkling his nose and jerking the snot back in place that he would not lose the snot. Why had he not given thought to the years that he had jerked snot back? Why had he allowed the snot that much of his thoughts and actions? No wonder nobody wanted him to eat next to them, not even Ma. Snot has its place; it was not lingering in his nose, taking up territory where it has no right to be. Gerald was experiencing an epiphany.

You had to notice. You had to notice your insides as well as your outsides. That day Gerald began to notice his face, his dress, and even those around him. He was changed. He wanted to think that an epiphany had taken hold just as it had taken hold of the Apostle Paul on the road to Damascus. One little girl had changed his life. Lois Jean said, "Gerald, you'd be a purty boy if you'd blow your nose." And he had gone into action. Gerald had lifted the cap off the stove, laid a finger aside of his nose and blew hard against the other side. That was to be remembered. Don't get mad when somebody gives off good advice. Blow your nose!

Gerald went into his house, straight into Ma's and Pa's bedroom, over to the chest of drawers—huge chest, as tall as he was, with little keys sticking out from locks in each drawer. He opened the divided top left drawer where his dad kept a bunch of handkerchiefs for coughing into. He pulled out one and stuck it into his pocket. He went into the kitchen. Ella was cooking supper for her brood. Lethe, Tom, Gerald, Captolia, and Florence, the twin. Florence was a twin. Her twin sister had fallen into the boiling lye water used to whiten shirts, pillowcases, handkerchiefs. Ella had rushed out, tilted the tub. The child was dead. Ella had never been the same since. She was, had been, a beauty; but it was fading now. She still took pride in her dress. And Ella Carter was a fine cook. The children loved Ella and Tom, and Ella and Tom loved them. Gerald sat down at the table.

"I helped Charity put up her stove," he announced.

He sat awhile. "It took some doing. I had to stand on a cheer and push the pipe into the elbow and push it hard. Then it had to be pushed up the wall till it jumped into the flue." The snot had begun down his nose. "Charity was a help. She was a right big help." The snot got to his lip and he snurgled it up. There was a pause. He ran out on the porch, leaned over the rail, blew hard. Took the white Irish linen handkerchief out of his pocket and wiped his nose.

Back in the kitchen, he told his mother what that little girl had said.

"Mom," he continued, "she said, 'Gerald, you'd be a purty boy if you'd blow your nose.' Mom, I'm going to blow my nose."

"Good for you, Gerald. But you take just one of them handkerchiefs. Just one, but keep it clean and folded. You can put it in the wash or you can keep it cleaned yourself."

"Mom, have you ever had something to strike you?"

"Yes, Gerald, all the time. Strike me."

"No, I mean strike you for good. Make things better. Get hold of something that you, that you. . ."

"Were not aware of. The word you want is 'aware'. I've been reading a story in my detective magazine about awareness. It's called, 'How a Dead Man Saved My Life,' and it really happened." She poured herself a cup of coffee and sat down, rubbed the smooth oil cloth, and began. Ella Carter was a storyteller. Never put in an extra word. Voice tone moved smoothly. Never adding unnecessary words or interrupting the flow of events with unnecessary facts.

"There was a salesman from Harlan started out to Barbourville on a dark and stormy-looking day. He was riding along and had expected to get to where his first sample stop was before dark. But he got lost. He was not thinking about anything much and probably had dozed off on his full stomach. When he came to, his horse was off the beaten path and was rambling. He couldn't find his way. He gave his horse rein. It commenced raining." She paused, took a sip of coffee, closed her eyes. Gerald had been joined by some others who waited patiently. "Directly," she continued, "he saw a light off some ways and followed it. He came upon a cabin. Two horses tied out front. Knocked on the door. Heard some shifting, a door closed. Then an old woman opened the door, holding the oil lamp high.

'I'm lost,' says the man. 'I'm cold, hungry. Could you put me up till day-light?'

Ol' woman turned to three sitting at the table. Ol' man rose, and his pistol fell on the floor.

'Why, shore. Come on in, warm by the far. Ol' woman, git him sompin d'eat.' Later they sat around playing setback.

'I'm tired,' said the salesman. 'Think I'll turn in.'

'I ken sees how ye would be tard, but see hey'er. We've got another un up thar.' She jerked her thumb toward the ceiling. 'He's tard and asleep.'

'Yeah, he's tard and asleep,' said the ol' man. 'Jest go up and get on the pallet to the right'.

The man didn't think anything about it. So he climbed up the ladder into the black hole, took off his outer clothes, and laid back on the pallet. Now he was worn out, but he couldn't sleep. That was strange. He couldn't sleep. Then, he felt that he needed to look and see who that other feller on that other pallet was. Pulled himself up on his elbow, then he felt around for his matches. Lit one. It went out. Lit the second, leaned over. What he saw froze him. He didn't move, even when the match burned his finger. He was not aware that the match was burning his finger. He felt his scalp crawl in fear. The match went out. He struck another match. There laid a man with his head bashed in, no forehead, no nose, and his brains were out on the pallet. The man fell back onto the pallet. He was in a den of thieves and mur-derers who had killed this man and robbed him, and in that order. Killed him and robbed him.

What in God's name was he going to do? He was pondering what to do when he heard some movement down below. He rolled over and peeped through the cracks in the ceiling. There stood the biggest colored man that he had ever seen. He was holding a big club. That's how the fellow's brains got out on the pallet. God in heaven, what was he going to do?

'God in heaven, help me'. These words had scarcely come out of his mouth when he heard a voice say, 'Change places with me.' He laid there with his right arm across his forehead. He commenced thinking. All that they wanted was his money. All they wanted was what money he had on him. How could he get it to them and keep his brains in his head? 'Change places with me,' says a voice. If he put his billfold on top of his chest and they came after him, they'd take it and go. But not before they had killed him. 'I'll push this poor feller here onto my pallet and I'll get on his pallet.' He didn't allow himself to think about laying back in that feller's brains. He peeped down. There was movement toward the ladder. He didn't have much time. He heard the voice again. It said, 'Change places with me.' And again, 'Change places with me.' He transferred the dead man to his pallet. Lifted the man's arm, then the elbow so's the arm would rest in the hollow of his head where his brains had been. Pulled the cover up close. Put his billfold on top of the dead man's chest and waited.

Then he heard them coming, putting up the ladder, opening the door. He peeped, not moving a muscle. The big black figure paused, came on up the steps into the attic about waist high so that he could get leverage on the club. He brought that club down and splattered that poor man's head three times. Picked up the billfold, descended the ladder, pulling the trap door closed. When the colored man was down, the salesman looked through the crack in the ceiling.

At the table, the three were dividing the money. Then they got a jar and poured a drink all around. They pulled the table directly over under the trap door, sat back down, began dealing cards.

The salesman didn't know how long he lay there before he was able to move. But, ideas began to form in his head. Why not wrap that bloody sheet around himself. In that bloody sheet, he would lift the trap door, kick out the light, run out the door, find his horse, and ride like hell.

He pulled up the sheet, his gorge rising, and wrapped it around his shoulders. Rubbing brain matter on his forehead and hair, and, last, putting on shoes. He got down on his knees, peeped through the crack. The three were slowing down. The ol' woman was no threat. She might be the brains of the operation, but she was no physical threat. The ol' man had a gun, but the giant was another matter. To his dying day, the man would hear the sound of that club smashing what was left of that that poor man's brains out of his head.

He had to work fast. No easing up the trap door. Success lay in catching them off guard. He threw back the door, screaming his best Indian war cry, the bloody sheet at his neck. Kicked out the lamp and jumped off the table, running through the door.

It had stopped raining. Where were the horses? Where were the horses? He couldn't find his horse. He heard them yelling inside. The oil had caught fire. Then he heard the horses. Without realizing how or the sequence, he got on the horse and rode out of there. There was no road, no path. He gave the horse rein and rode through the moonlight.

Daylight was coming on and he was coming out of the woods. He was just outside Barbourville. He rode into town. It was yet early and not many out.

'Hey, you. . .' he yelled to an early riser. The other man ran screaming. People came out. They would look and run screaming. A sheriff came out with a gun. 'Don't shoot. Don't shoot.' That's when he remembered the sheet. He pulled it off, threw it across the horse, slid down. 'Help me. Help me.' He told his story to the bunch that had gathered. They got up a posse, went back. There had been reports of these murders. They arrested the three of them and hanged them until they were dead. The poor dead man's family buried him, and the salesman turned into a preacher with one sermon. He took it out as far as Cincinnati. 'The night when God answered and a dead man saved my life.'"

She paused, drank her last drop of coffee. "Gerald, be aware when your nose runs ahead of you. Don't ever let the snot command you. You take charge of snot. Now all of you go get me some coal for the fire. And, Gerald, I want you to take Jim my new detective magazine. Tell him I want it back. Put it in Jim's hand or he won't get it. No, better yet, I'll take it."

Wherein James Takes a Bath in the New House

Jim came home from work. Got the #3 tub that had belonged to Jenny and prepared to take his first bath in the new house. Filled it from the reservoir on the stove. It was late. He was a man who loved night. He loved the sounds, the cool, the moon and the dark, the seasons, all giving off different smells, different feels. He loved the camaraderie of the walk down from the mines, wearing a mining hat with carbide lamp that showed the way when he turned his head. He liked all things in their places. He especially liked the three girls in their places: safe, clean, and asleep. Many a night he would peep in on that sight of utter peace. He liked the night shift. Everything and everybody in place.

On this night he had brought down an Atlas box for his dynamite. It was empty. He just set it on the edge of the front porch. A man needed a box. A man needed a wooden box. It was best to keep it empty. But most of the time, given time, a box would just fill itself. A man in a household of females needed a box, his own box, and a drawer, his own drawer, a chair, his own chair. And nobody should violate what was his box or drawer or chair.

He poured the boiling water in the tub, diluted it with the bucket of water that Charity brought home for his bath. He got the P&G soap and a big piece of rough feed sack. Most of the coal dust was on his hands. He often worked without gloves. Gloves got in the way of the feel of the dynamite and caps, the certain feel of the break in the seam of coal, or opening the bucket for a biscuit. He bent over the tub, washed his face, and worked on his hands.

It was good and bad that he had moved. If Henry's boys came looking for him, he'd be gone. If the mud-tracked man came peeping through the window, his girls wouldn't be there.

Tways sure had changed since his family had moved in when the mines opened. A lot of coal had come out of that mountain. He knew that Tways had been a fine little mining camp next to Harlan. In fact, Tways miners and families were an important little part of the financial success of Harlan's commerce. Others came from other camps to do court business or for mending a savagely broken body. But they left without eating chili and meatballs, without going to the Magic Grand Theater or the Green Parrot for a Hickie.

He climbed into the tub of hot water, knees up under his chin. Alone in the kitchen with the tub and The Harlan Daly Enterprise. He surveyed the kitchen. He looked up at the chimney. That was odd. He hadn't noticed the scrape up to the wall. He sat there some good time, squeezing the hot water over his back. No sounds except an old owl here and there.

Another thing that made R.C. Tways were the Carters. First, Matt's family, five boys and Matt, all at one time inside the mines. Then there was Tom, Matt's brother, and Richard, a cousin. At one time, Leige, Bill, James, and Arthur all had families living in Tway Mining Camp. It was a huge family, all for one and one for all. Their chief asset was strong, willing bodies. They had in Tways what they had needed on the huge farms in Whitley County, a lot of strong bodies. Here in Tways they had continued the tradition of community. But here in 1937 things were changing.

After the water cooled, he got out, dried. Reached in the warmer, found a piece of cornbread. Put some jelly on it, poured a glass of milk. The seams of coal were going fast. There was a feeling of loss and of losing control of his universe. The coal in the Cumberland Mountains, covered by a carpet of lush varied trees as old as Jesus, almost gone. Especially that little place known as Tways. Too much to think about. He crawled into bed.

Wherein Lois Jean is Forced to Kiss a Dead Man

A week later Murph and Mary Tweed, Charity's sister, drove up in the middle of the morning. Mary was dressed in a black suit with a white blouse, hose, and matching pumps. Charity had Lois dressed in her Sunday clothes, and Charity was wearing a navy blue crepe dress with J.J. Newberry's pearls and matching earrings. The dress was one of Ide Clotfelter's hand-me-downs. It was purchased; all fine clothes are "purchased" at Millers in Knoxville, Tennessee. Ide had complained that it made her look "washed out." Charity's blond hair set her face off well. She had matching navy pumps and a pair of white kid gloves.

"Charity, don't take them gloves. They're out of place."

"Mary, I'll take them if I want to." Sister to sister behavior. But she put them back in the dresser drawer.

James was asleep and Mickey was with Virginia Brannon until Charity got back. If she was taken to a funeral too soon, Mickey could be "marked," and Charity didn't want her children marked by anything! Not the beast or the funeral. So Mickey was playing on the front porch at Miz Brannon's.

Charity and Lois climbed in the back. Mary and Murph were in the front.

"Hello, Murphy." She lilted the greeting.

"Charity." That was all he said. This was not anything he wanted to do. Except he was curious. He was curious about the dead boy, how he looked without a head. How did they fix him? He was curious about Andrew and Gertie Dopel and how they lived.

Wallins Creek was one of the largest coal and timber operations in Harlan County. It was a town boasting a brick high school, several stores. It was booming, had since it was first built, around 1910. But in the late 30s, the handwriting was on the wall. Not as much coal was coming out. People were facing aging miners and mining equipment. Too many accidents. They urged their children not to go into mining.

The thing was that the Dopel family was now three generations there. Old Cal Dopel married Ester and they had a bunch of children, one being Andrew, and he had married Gertie when she was fourteen or maybe fifteen, and they had a large family. Furthermore, Andrew and Gertie were "steady." They knew the name of the path they were on. They accepted its trials and tribulations. They had known good times and bad. When the bad times came, the whole clan pulled together to salve hurts, bind wounds, and encourage acceptance of the will of God.

Murph drove through the town and out to where Gertie and Andrew lived. Charity could count on one hand the times she had seen Gertie since Gertie had married Andrew. The marriage was against the will of William Moses that Gertie would marry a German. But, Gertie being from the same cloth as her daddy, had married Andrew against her father's will. Andrew Dopel was a fine, solid man.

There was a big crowd on the front porch. The men leaning against the rail on the banisters that wrapped around the long, wide front porch. Men talking quietly, two men in the swing. Men in the two huge overstuffed leather-covered rocking chairs.

Murphy let the ladies out, Charity reaching in to help Lois Jean, today her trophy. Mary and Charity began their parade to the front porch. Smoothing the dress at the hip and down, taking careful steps, heads lowered in a sign of respect. Not saying a word. Now slowly, ever so slowly, ascending the steps.

The men's talk had all but ceased. Mary and Charity, leading Lois Jean, came to the top step. Mary lifted her head, then Charity. Lois Jean knew not to say a word. Lucille came forward. Mary hugged her and let some tears begin. Charity bent over, ever so slightly, and whispered. "God bless you." Others came forward from Wallins. Relatives from Whitley County would not be there for the wake. They would attend the burial.

Murph, Mary, Charity and Lois Jean went into the front room. There lay the corpse. The room darkened, shades pulled. Dim lamps from the funeral home shined soft light at the head and foot of the casket. A dark blue funeral drape was behind the casket, shutting out daylight. Flowers all around the room. One huge wreath from the engineers of the L&N train that had hit the boy. A man from Anderson and Laws in Harlan came up to them.

"Are you ready to view the departed?"

"No," said Mary. "First we must see our sister Gertie."

"She's in her bedroom, and the women are in the bedroom and the kitchen."

"Mary, I don't want Lois Jean to view that corpse."

"Hush, Charity. Don't call him a corpse."

"I don't want. . ."

"Who's going to make her? She can stay in the kitchen and eat anything she wants." Mary patted Lois Jean. "You're the prettiest little girl, honey."

Mary's two handsome little boys, Clyde Edward and Billy Ray, were in school and when they got home, one of the women from her church had taken over the store and boys until they got back.

Lucille was dressed up and had painted her fingernails. She took Lois Jean's hand. "Honey, would you want something to eat?" Lucille was doing well, even knowing that her brother was truly gone forever.

Women were moving around the table covered with plates of fried chicken, green beans, coleslaw, hot roles, potato salad, fresh butter, canned watermelon rind pickles, jellies, and a cabinetful of pound cake, apple stack cake, chocolate cake, and banana pudding with meringue standing in peaks. There was a whole ham soaked in some fine whiskey to remove the wild taste.

"Are we ready?" One of the women queried.

"Yes."

"Lucille, go tell the men to come eat." Lucille grabbed Lois and they went through the front room where the boy lay a corpse. They paid him no mind.

"Please come in. It's time to eat."

The men marched solemnly through the front door.

"Let's ask God's blessing on the food." It was one of the Moses boys from up on Wolf Creek in Whitley County, Kentucky, who was going to do the service. Others were with him to help with the service. He was in charge. Everything grew still. The only sound was the "taking on" in the bedroom. Mary and Charity were with Gertie. Just seeing her little sisters had set off a fresh spell of crying and chanting, "Oh God, oh God, oh God."

The preacher began. "Oh God, our help in good times and bad, we give you praise for this time together. Our hearts are broken because this boy has not and did not live up to your expectations of him. He's gone. Gone in a flash. May God have mercy on his soul. And bless this food to our bodies and restore us to Jesus. Amen."

There was a chorus of "Amens."

Slowly the talk began. Plates filled, men moving out in the backyard, sitting on the back steps. A fine meal it was. Lucille carried out a pitcher of tea, Lois Jean tagging behind with a plate of hot rolls. Not a lot of talk now. Just eating and passing out accolades to the cooks. They ate and ate, then sat drinking coffee and eating apple stack cake and the ever popular banana pudding with a standing meringue. Some slipped behind the house for a little sip from a good bottle.

Murphy had a fine bottle.

"How'd exactly did he get killed?" he asked.

"Well, he got drunk. Real drunk. And for some reason laid his head down on the track and went to sleep."

"No, he didn't. He was drinking and tried to beat that train," said another.

All was silent.

"If 'n his head was on the track, it wouldn't be in there in that casket with him now."

"That ain't his head. That's a made-up head."

"Boys, have a little more." That was Murph.

"What an awful way to go. Not shriven. No, not shriven, but in his sins."

"Now we don't know that. What went through his brain may have been more than what rolled over him. Ain't you boys heerd that saying 'between the stirrup and the ground mercy sought and mercy found?' That means you can be saved in a twinklin' of an eye."

"What if 'n he was too drunk to pray?"

"Lord God, we'll never know."

And so it went.

Back to the kitchen for more dessert.

The women had been mincing all along. Now was the time to get serious. They filled plates. Somebody had showed up with fried cabbage and baked sweet potatoes. The new hot rolls had come in. Some of the boy's friends had arrived with hair all slicked down, chewing gum. They came in and viewed the corpse, went into that form of grief that replaced tears: blowing their noses into handkerchiefs.

They helped a young girl who was dressed in a voile navy blue dress with a string of pearls around her neck. She had on matching pumps. She came up, looked down, and passed out. They lifted her to the chair in the corner. The undertaker took something out of his pocket, put it under her nose, and said, "Take a whiff of this, young lady." She did and began coughing and screaming, shaking her hands. Screaming. All talking stopped. Gertie came into the room, went to the girl. "Honey, honey," then Gertie commenced crying. Then they both "took on." They hugged, moaned, said "Oh, God, why, why, why?" Somebody in the kitchen said, "If'n that boy's looking down from heaven, won't he be pleased to see them 'taken on' so?" Women came in with ice water and towels for them. Men left for the porches. The two women hugged each other, collapsing in grief.

It was getting up toward evening. Millard, Bessie, and their son Keith had arrived late. Millard spoke to several, viewed the corpse, went to the kitchen. The women helped the three of them with their plates. Mary came out, spoke to them. Little Keith was bashful, stood back. Charity was sitting in a corner near Gertie, who had returned to a rocking chair in her bedroom. Andrew was there. He wasn't expected to say much. He just looked out the window.

In came Millard, Bessie, and Keith. "Well, this is just awful, Gertie. We are all sorry and are praying for you." Bessie had spoken well. "Yeah, it's awful, but this banana pudding's good." Millard always did or said the inappropriate saying. He put off everybody. Truth is, he never had the time to play, to grow up, to find himself. Millard had a responsibility thrust upon him that he was incapable of carrying out.

More came. Others came from up on Wolf Creek. Up on Wolf Creek was where the Moses tribe had lived since Joshua Moses (1), 1748 to 1836. They owned farms, practicing the same rituals that fill a lifetime: eating, finding shelter, birthing progeny, and gathering goodness. Their lives were given over to practicing their rituals, using remnants of Chaucerian English, saying to this day, "holpen" for help, just as the Chaucer's Canterbury Tales observed, "The holy blissful martyr for to seeke. That him hath holpen when that they were seeke."

Here came these boys carrying Bibles and guitars, living life to the fullest, enjoying the wealth of the food from the farms, some of which boasted large acreages with land deeds that spoke of "thence to the huge oak tree and back to the stream, etc." Farms perhaps covering rich seams of coal. Nobody bothered this tribe. They lived off to themselves and married. Marrying each other. Charity's grandfather and his wife were first cousins. But, the gene pool was so pure and good that they escaped having them "little sheepy eyes" that a certain clan who lived way up in the hills and off to themselves did have.

What Millard had inherited from his daddy, it was believed, was a streak of anxiety manifesting itself in a fierce, uncontrollable anger. Hot anger that flared into beatings with a belt. Charity had some of this strange anxiety displayed in anger that went into an energetic display—cleaning a whole garden or washing all the windows on the outside and washing and starching the lace curtains or baking a blackberry pie from scratch. And later, an offering of a piece of pie or cake to the sister, the child, or the husband on whom she had vented. That had gone on back as far as anybody up on Wolf Creek could remember. It was spotted in Millard and later on in Charity. Millard and Charity clashed whenever they were together.

The afternoon wore on, people coming and picking from the table. "Laume, I must have a bite of that pudding. Do try this chocolate pound cake."

"I'm slipping me a little teensy piece of that ham in my pocketbook for tomorrow."

"Honey, do you give off your recipe for that chocolate pound cake?"

"Yes, I do, and I give off most all of it." That from a woman who was a neighbor of Gertie's. She laughed, meaning that she didn't tell what it was that made it taste the way it did or hold it together, or about what to do to make the icing set up.

What you did to solve that was to invite all to come eat your first attempt and taste for what it needed. Then add that one-fourth cup bourbon that was missing.

Out on the front porch, the boys were smoking and sipping coffee and also sipping from the bottle.

"I don't believe ye can do that."

"We have seen it. Ain't we, Josh? We've seen it. If'n your minds are so set, you can take one fanger. And four people can take and use one fanger and lift one man on this porch out of his chair. Can't they, Josh?"

Josh nodded laconically.

"See thar, me and Josh and two others here can lift one of you'ens with one fanger."

Nobody spoke; nobody moved. Then somebody said, "Jim Carter is the only man I ever saw who could make a chair walk across the room."

"Oh, gawd."

"Yes, I witnessed it. Up in Tways colored camp, Jim got liquored up at one of them colored boy's houses. He had everybody get out of the room and he set a cheer, a plain old cane cheer, in the corner and commanded it to walk acrost the room. That cheer leaned back on its back two legs and moved acrost the floor, rocking back and forth on them two back legs. May I drop dead if that ain't the whole truth. Ye can conjure up the spirit of levitation. I know, I saw it."

Nobody spoke; nobody moved. Then, Millard got up to get something,

he didn't know what, out of the kitchen. He went to the kitchen, finally settled on the last of a third serving of banana pudding. Women sitting around
waiting to help. He went into the front room where the boy lay a corpse.

Lucille went out on the porch to gather empty dishes and cups, and Lois
Jean followed. Millard called to her, "Come hey're, girl," he called out to Lois
Jean. She obeyed. He was pushing his fork across the plate to get the very last
of the pudding.

"Who's yer mother?"

"Charity."

"Who's yer daddy?"

"James."

"Who am I?"

"You're Runt Nocount."

"I'm who?"

"Runt Nocount."

He sat there for a minute and felt himself getting mad.

"Tell you what we're goin' to do. We're goin' to look at that dead man.
We see him up close and you, little girl, are going to kiss him goodbye. That
ought to do it. Yer going to kiss him goodbye."

He set the dish down. Picked her up. Took her over to the casket.
Leaned her over—she was inches away from the dead face.

"Kiss him, kiss the boy goodbye. Kiss him. Kiss him," he was yelling.

He was squeezing her. The lid was going to come down; she would be
buried in the ground. She closed her eyes and screamed and screamed and
screamed.

Lucille dropped the dishes. Charity was beside them.

"Kiss him."

Charity began beating his arm. Men on the front porch stopped talking
and stood listening. Runt was not himself. Murphy Tweed walked up.

"Here, Runt, let go. Let go. Let her go."

He set Lois Jean down. Charity took Lois Jean back to the kitchen.

Murphy sat down across the room from Millard. Millard was a lost soul.
Circumstances had pushed him into actions incompatible with his true
nature. He had been forced into the wrong time and the wrong place. He had
not had a childhood of growing up being nurtured and given time to mature
fully. With his father's untimely death, he was thrust into the coal mines and
had also become the disciplinarian for the younger childrne. Murphy felt
sorry for Millard's plight.

Then Murph turned attention to himself. He had came from a fine family. His family had experienced tragedy also. His sister Daisy, beautiful, intelligent and promising had died from tuberculosis. So much unfairness of things. Murph took a deep breath and settled further into his chair. He had a fine wife, two fine boys and a fine grocery store. His life was going to Hell.

He pondered the latest event. It had been longer than a year that he had become an active member of the Ku Klux Klan. He had the robe and the hood. He had memorized all of the rituals and carried out all of his assignments. He had been given a new assignment. Something was not right about it. Furthermore, he was losing his fine store. Miners were forced to use the scrip at the commissary. Murph could not accept the scrip.

"Murph, Murphy, are you asleep? It is time for us to go. Charity has got to go home and it is time to pick up the boys." Mary had her pocketbook on her arm. Charity and Lois Jean were behind her.

Wherein Mary Loses the Spirit to Love Murphy

Murphy Tweed had been out all night. He told Mary that he was going to a very important meeting. Murphy was intelligent, innovative, and cunning. He had built a fine grocery store at Brookside. It was a grocery store filled with fine fruits, vegetables, kitchenware and other needs, many of which were not carried at the commissary. He had a lovely wife and two fine boys, Clyde Edward and Billy Ray. His outlook had been exceptionally fine, with one exception. The store was a mistake. He could accept only cash at his store. Miners were forced to use the scrip produced for that particular coal mine. Furthermore, by using the scrip card, a miner could save cash for Harlan. Murphy's business was so bad that he knew something had to change. Tonight was the night to change it.

Of course, there were always the coal mines in Harlan County. He could go into the mines the next day, but Murphy was not a miner. Mining coal had to be done by a man who had no fear of the dark, no fear of smothering in a small, dark place filled with its own movements, drips of black water, and sounds of thousands of tons of black bituminous coal and slate moving and shifting; the sudden deadly silence and then the random pop of timbers supporting the shifting top. A cold, oppressive, clammy menace permeated this underworld, clinging to the walls, the tons of top slate clinging to hands and picks and shovels and clothes and in the eyes and lungs. Coal mining is akin to seafaring or soldiering, heroic, endless, dangerous labor. A brotherhood of an ancient, classic profession was as elemental as labor itself.

Death was a possibility from the time a miner entered the driftmouth until he returned to the sunshine. Miners were earthnauts who loved the camaraderie of a kindred soul. The trust one human put into another human was a trust that declared that lives in the mines were intertwined. One would lay down his life for the other. Miners are a special creation, which few people understand.

Suddenly, Murphy remembered he had to whip Mary. Murphy belonged to the Ku Klux Klan. The Klan was a major civic organization believing that they were making positive societal comments good for positive growth in the mining camps. Murphy was a dedicated member. His white robe and head-piece that covered his entire face hung in the back of his wardrobe.

The topic of the meeting that he had last attended was subjugation of wives to their husbands. Women were not equal to men. Wives must never be allowed to get "out of hand". Even if Mary was a gentle, kind, forgiving woman, even if Mary had given him five boys, two survivors, even if Mary never sassed him, even if Mary kept a clean place and cooked fine meals, cro-cheted and knitted things for others; even if Mary went to church faithfully, even with all these virtues, the Klan had assigned Murphy and the others the task of spanking their wives "to keep them in line".

Up the stairs he went. This was going to be a difficult task. However, he had been assigned this task, and he would complete his assignment. Suddenly, he felt the need of some help. He went back down the stairs into the store, to the safe, struck a match, opened the safe, reached into the back of the safe, got the bottle and poured himself a drink. Sat a few minutes feeling the warmth spread into his arms, his legs. Just a drop more. Warmth and strength. Time passed. Ideas came. A plan unfolded. He got up and went up the stairs. He entered the bedroom. It was dark. Not even a moon. He moved to Mary's side of the bed.

"Wake up, wake up, Mary Jane." He leaned over the bed and shook her shoulder. "Mary, wake up. I've got to whip you."

Mary sat bolt upright.

"Murphy, are you alright? Are you drinking? What's wrong?"

"The matter is I've got to follow orders and whip you. I've got it to do."

"Murphy, it's 4:00 a.m. Get in bed."

"No, Mary." He began to unfasten his belt, sliding it through the belt loops. She heard each little loop release the end of the belt.

"Murphy, don't hit me. If you hit me with that belt, I will never be the same."

"Mary, the Ku Klux Klan is first here. I've been assigned to whip you. I've got it to do." Jerking the handmade quilts back, he drew back and brought the belt across her legs below her knees. He heard her muffled sound of pain. He hit her again and again and again and again. She made no words. Just sounds of pain. Sounds filled with pain. He paused and then one final lash of the belt.

He went out of the room, down the stairs into the kitchen. He pulled out several dish clothes, dipped them in coal oil, rolled them inside the "Harlan Daily Enterprise", lit the torch, and placed them under the brown paper bags stacked neatly near the produce in the store. He went around the room lighting the baskets lined with straw, the thread box, the pulled shades. When he was satisfied that the fires were going to catch, he ran upstairs, got the boys up, went into the bedroom where Mary was in bed.

"Get up. We've got to get out of here. The store's on fire."

Mary began to scream. "The boys, the boys. Murphy get the boys…"

"I've got the boys. We've got to climb out." He looked down the stairs. The store was totally engulfed.

"We can go down these stairs."

"No, the fire will singe the boys' hair. No, we'll burn. No, no, please, dear God, don't try it."

Murphy was one of those men who had not assimilated properly the word "no". "No" became a challenge. It became an action that would be unobserved even if it killed him. He did not say one word but raced down the stairs. Clyde Edward held onto the railing. Murphy jerked him away. In seconds they were outside standing in the early light. "Don't move from here." Back he ran into the store. Mary was almost to the midway point. Screaming and screaming. He raced up toward Mary. For one brief second his eyes were level with her legs. In the light of the fire he saw the whelps left by the belt. He grabbed her arm and pulled her out into the cold morning. Falling to her knees, she stretched out her arms. The boys ran to her.

When she glanced around for Murphy, he had disappeared. "He's in there." It was neighbors out to help, dressed in nightclothes.

"Mary, you alright?"

"I think so. The boys. Look them over."

"The boys are good."

Murphy surely was dead. Burned to a crisp. Nothing left except clean bones. Fire had raced up the stairs, engulfing the second floor. He was dead. Then folks began to think in terms of eulogy.

"Poor Murphy."

"Murphy was a. . . look, look, he's climbing out the window." Murphy got Mary out and something fell, blocking him. He had gone up the stairs and was climbing out the window.

Murphy was sitting on the window ledge, legs inside, reaching for a drainpipe. He reached it, grabbed the drain pipe and swung his full weight on it. He began shimmering down the drain pipe. It slowly pulled from the wall as he slid down the pipe. He felt splinters and nails penetrating both hands. The pipe was gaining on him. He was some feet from the wall, too high to turn loose. The heat, the nails, the splinters were more than he could bear. He turned loose and fell. The fall knocked his breath out of him. Men surrounded him. Pulled him up. He coughed. He was black and held out bloody hands. One of the men handed him a bottle. He tilted his head back.

What a successful night it had been. He had completed his project with Mary. He would collect insurance from the store and build him a fine gasoline station with a little store inside stacked with what miners had forgotten to get at the commissary. Murphy was a happy man, an accomplished man.

Wherein There is a Gathering Up

Charity was standing in the kitchen pondering, thinking about the changes. In upper camp you just went to the pump and got water. Miz Amics, Helen, Halley, and Ginny. They didn't have much to say. They all moved in different worlds.

Lower camp was another thing. In lower camp, it was water in a bucket, news from observers, and advice from the heart. There were several families related by blood in lower camp. John and Ella Carter living across the road. Richard, Maxey, and little Vinnie Carter lived next door.

There was Ola Collins and her sister Nell Farmer. Other relationships evolved. Ola and Nannie Bell, Charity's sister, who had borrowed Charity's voile wedding dress and chased around in Harlan, were best of friends. Nannie with George Leach and Ola with Russ Collins. Nannie married Robert, "Weller", Graham and soon afterward had Jennings on Oct.8, 1928. Her reverie rambled on.

Her reverie rambled on. None of Charity's family lived in Tways. The Carter name, however, dominated Tways. Ide and Homer Clotfelter had told Charity not to marry James. She paid them no heed. Charity stood, looking out the kitchen window. Pondering. Pondering.

Ida Cox had kept her brood together, and Millard "Runt" Moses had been the one who had gone into the mines, moving the family from Proctor to Straight Creek, then to Harlan. Just getting settled in one new place only to move to another. Charity's mind ran on memories of evil, bad things that had been visited on them. Pearlie's head gone, their daddy William dying with typhoid fever, the flu epidemic of 1918. They were living in a little mining camp house in Proctor, Tennessee, all scrounged and cold when the flu struck them, all of them. They were quarantined inside the cold, empty house. Cold and weak and hungry.

Otis was the worst. He was a little pale, skinny, fearful ten-year-old boy, full of misery. He begged to get in bed with his sick mother. "Come here, Otis." He climbed in and she tried to warm him. Next morning he was dead. Ida lay there. She didn't say anything to the children, Mary, Charity, Nanny, Van, Willie, or Millard. Otis was dead; there was nothing in the house to eat. No fire in the grate. Only coughing and groaning sounds.

Ida prayed out loud, "Dear God, I put my trust in you. Send us help," she prayed. "Don't let us all die. You must have created us to do something more than perish in this cold."

She drifted in and out, touching the little cold body grown stiff beside her. The next morning began with Ida calling out, "Who can move?" she called out. "Who can move?"

"I can, Mother." It was Mary Jane.

"Come here."

The child came to the mother's bed. "Get help. We need help with Otis."

Nobody would dare come to this house. Nobody had come in days. Most were taking care of their own. Wrapping rags around their heads so they would not breathe the flu germs. People were dying. They were all dying.

Mary Jane went to the kitchen, nothing to eat. Just the salt shaker on the table. She slid back one of the two windows in the kitchen and yelled for help.

"Help! Oh, please help! Somebody help us. . ."

Nobody answered in that cold winter. She was letting in stinging cold. Suddenly she was overcome with weakness. That's when they all heard somebody pounding on the door.

It was Preacher Douglas' mother. The woman had her hair up in the slicked back bun and a rag covering her mouth and nose.

"Ida Moses," she yelled. "You in there?"

"Yes, I'm in here."

Miz Douglas came in, saw the sheet pulled up.

"Is that one dead?"

"Yes, it's Otis. He's dead."

She went to the door, called out. Soon three men showed up. They took Otis out of the bed. A few minutes later, one of the men returned and built a fire in the stove, and Miz Douglas had potatoes and corn bread on the table.

"Can you take it from here, Ida?"

"Oh, woman, you're an angel sent from God. There are no words, Miz Douglas; there are no words."

"Ida, we'll get your boy buried. They've got a stack of people to bury. In this weather, they'll last. You get better." And she was gone.

Ida crept out of the bed, stood near the stove. She passed out the hot potatoes, making sure they went around, putting bread in the oven to heat and putting bacon grease on it.

Charity came out of her reverie. Something had to be done about Millard. This was not an attack on her. At the funeral Millard had attacked Lois Jean. Why had Millard chosen her? He never went for Mary or Nanny, just Charity and now Lois Jean. Truth be told, she did taunt him. For one thing, she enjoyed getting the best of him. For another, she could literally out run him. Nobody could catch her. She could out run him.

Furthermore, he needed to take into account that she was a married woman with two children. That changed everything about their relationship. He was not supposed to whip her or harm her children. The last time he had tried to whip her was at Mary's. Mary had baked a cake and iced it with white egg foam icing with coconut sprinkled over it. She had slipped the coconut off the store shelf while Murph was away visiting his family. Millard, Nannie, Charity had come to Mary's to celebrate Millard's birthday. It was a good time. Suddenly, Millard asked, "Who'll you vote for?"

Mary said, "Millard, I'm not saying."

"Who's runnin'?" Nannie, giggling.

"I'm voting for Franklin Delano Roosevelt." That was Charity. Sitting straight, left hand in her lap. Taking small bites, chewing with her mouth closed. Everyone grew silent.

Millard stood up, started removing his belt. She was a married woman with two children. He wouldn't touch her. He removed the belt and started toward her. She sat perfectly still until he stepped to the corner of the table. She leaped, turning the chair down between them. He fell over it.

"Run, Charity." It was Mary. "Run."

Nannie loved it all. Charity ran out the back door, screen door banging against the wall, over four steps, landing in a squat. Springing into full run. Millard behind her.

She ran, catching the spirit, feeling a rush, out of the yard, up the side of the hill, lost in the deep trees. She ran, knowing he wasn't behind her. She was free of everything. After a while she stopped, slipped behind a huge chestnut, and peeped around. He was nowhere in sight.

She sat down, drew her knees up. How nice. How clean, how warm, how free. She looked down. There was a patch of heart leaves, dark green, glossy, and each leaf perfectly heart shaped.

She pulled it, crushed it, put it close to her nose. Fresh, sweet, sweet, pungent green. When she got back home that night and got into bed, she could still smell the heart leaf.

Months had gone by. Millard would never touch her again with a belt nor would he ever hurt a child of hers. When James came in for breakfast the next morning, she set the coffee down and said, "James, it's Millard." She told him the whole story about how Millard had acted with Lois Jean and Gertie's boy that lay a corpse.

Wherein Lois, Daddy, and Grandpa Go to the Carnival

The carnival was coming to Harlan. There had been talk about its setting up at Skidmore Farm just across the road from R.C. Tway Mining Camp. Skidmore Farm was a fine place. Baseball, airplane shows. But no carnivals. Miz Hall had said that carnivals were cheap and contaminating. Dr. W.J. Bold had commented on them at Dr. Tye's drugstore. "It does pander to a certain element in our society, and we mustn't dignify that element. That element of our society must be raised to appreciate a 'thing of beauty' and to distinguish between the cheap, tawdry object or event and true art. True art is not found in a carnival, nor is there an artist in this, this carnival idea."

"Dr. Bolt, watch the blood pressure." Dr. Tye.

"You and I both know that the carnival was an element of Greek and Roman society. Let's not forget Nero and his violin. Let us not forget throwing the Christians to the lions. We are put on this earth to enhance and enrich the lives of others. To open their eyes to the beauty of the heavens and the earth."

"Speaking of earth, let me show you something." Dr. Tye reached under the counter and pulled out a piece of slate shaped like the state of Kentucky.

"Look at this."

Across the entire slate was an embedded fern, curving up toward Cincinnati and receding over near Owensville.

"My, oh my. Where did you get this?"

"James Carter from Tways brought it in. His father did the sizing down to the shape of Kentucky from a larger piece. He wants me to pack it off to the Smithsonian in Washington. And I'm going to make sure that it gets to the Smithsonian."

"We don't know the James L. Carters, do we? They are here, but we don't know them."

"I've heard that his mother quotes Shakespeare and Paradise Lost better than you can." Dr. Bolt ran his hands across the piece of slate. Dr. Tye went to a customer.

James knew about the carnival in the fall, and he was a regular. Used to be that the family went. Now it was Jim and Matt. Just the two of them. His mind was made up. He and Pa and Lois Jean were going to the carnival. They'd go in the afternoon. Nobody else. Mickey was too young for the rides and Charity would be too much to handle. She'd find sin in it all. Beauty was in the eye of the beholder and Charity just couldn't get past the avocado linoleum and the pink bedspreads. He was going to take Lois Jean and show her the carnival. He set it up with Pa. Saturday afternoon. Not many there. The boys would come in on Saturday night with good-looking feisty girls posing, giggling and screaming on the rides.

He and Halley had known how to attend the carnival. Charity didn't know. Charity was happiest when she was using her hands—when she was painting, pulling weeds, or washing windows. She had endless energy and endless things to accomplish with that energy.

Now, take Mary, Charity's sister. Mary was a detail person. Crocheting, delicate cake decorating, and arranging flowers. Charity worked from a bigger easel. Her strokes were all performed on the spur of the minute. She'd be happy cleaning, gardening, throwing lime around the toilet, getting water from the pump. Now it was time to indulge himself in the carnival.

"Have ye heard, Jim, they's a morphodite?" Pa, Lois, and Jim were walking to the garage to get the car.

"No, but we'll take turns and check it out. Most of the time that's a setup. A woman can fix it. And there are places in Knoxville and Cincinnati where's you can get things. So get up close. We're not to be tricked."

"No, what they do is tie on something and hide the strings in all those big leaves they wear." They both laughed.

Jim backed the big black Durant out. It was a fine piece of machinery.

Pa opened the door and put Lois Jean in the back seat.

"How'd you bang up the fender?"

"I didn't bang up the fender. What do you mean?"

"Your fender's banged up."

"I'll check it out. Maybe somebody hit her when I parked in Harlan."

"Yeah, that could be."

The day was early fall. The trees just beginning to take on color from the top of the mountains, flaming orange, ruby reds, and yellows working down to the Cumberland River. Not many paid it much attention. It was just there.

A harbinger to the prologue coming on. They stopped at Baby Jones on the left side of the road from Tways, got gas. Jim came back and gave Lois Jean a strawberry BB bat. He and Pa took red hots. After they had moved on out, it was quiet in the car except for an occasional juicy sound. "These hey'er red thangs are to be appreciated. They's truly hot." Matt enjoying it all.

Riding along with Pa and Lois Jean with the red hots. "All's right with the world." A man can't say that often. "All's right with the world." Most of the time there was niggling going on. Something to be thought out. Something to be chewed on. Something that called for your taking a course of action that always would run its course.

The Creator would take care of things. There is a spirit that moves through all things and causes all things to move in a certain direction. That action rippled out in an unending sequence. James had asked Arthur to take his shift. Would that slate have come down on Jim that night? When you had four brothers and a daddy in the mines at the same time, you worked it all out. For years at least three of them were in the mines, many times on the same shift.

Why did that piece of slate decide to fall on Arthur when it did? Why did James decide to ask Arthur to take his place that Fourth of July? Any action changed the whole universe. Any fly in the iced tea at the Parrot could change everything.

"Jim, your chewin' that hot ball!"

"I like it hot!"

"Are ye talking about hot balls?"

They both laughed.

The carnival had been set up in the Georgetown edition in the city of Harlan. A bridge had been built across the Cumberland River that flowed through Harlan. Georgetown was acres of level land. Part of the level ground running up through Harlan, narrowing and widening along its way through Sunshine up through Sizemore Farm, moving past Hall's High School on up and up. Level. Flat as your hand.

The colored folks had moved in there; some in Georgetown had fine homes. They had their barber shops, their stores. On a more evil side, pills were always available for those needing yellow jackets. Yellow jackets were popular. You didn't get on yellow jackets, and if you did get on yellow jackets, you didn't drink bootleg. Some lost souls did both. Beyond redemption. They weren't welcomed anywhere. They slept out under pieces of tin to keep them dry. They would do anything for yellow jackets. Often they would "roust about" with the carnival when it came to Harlan, thinking they would go with the carnival when it left. The carnival always slipped out at night, the reason being that many of the regular "roust abouts" would go into town and steal anything and everything. When the carnival came, everybody packed a pistol and a young boy sat just inside the door of a store. If he didn't know the name or face, he watched the behavior. Sometimes the boy would report a stranger who was suspicious.

"I believe you forgot to pay for that fine brown knife yer a carryin', didn'n ye?" A smile of concern.

"Oh damn, I'm sorry. I's just feeling the weight."

"Just take it all out, please, and turn the pockets outside. How much ye want to pay for? Pins? This watch? Knife? Measuring tape? Electric tape?"

"Look here, just let me go."

"Yeah, we'll let you go to the Harlan jail!"

"Oh, God. Just let me go. Tell ye what I'll do. I'll sees nobody else comes from the carnival."

"Tell ye what I'll do. I'll kill ye if I see ye in town."

"Oh, God. Just let me go. Here. Here's a silver dollar I keep taped to my chest. Take it."

"No, I'm a Christian man. Go, as Jesus said, and sin no more or I'll kill ye. And Jesus didn't say that."

Mrs. Hall wouldn't let the carnival come to Skidmore Farm. It would be in Georgetown as long as she lived.

Suddenly Lois Jean saw the ferris wheel.

"There it is, Daddy. The ferris wheel. There it is. Grandpa, we going to ride?"

"Yes, honey, we gonna ride. That's why we brought ye so's we could ride."

Jim parked the Durant, locked it, and they went toward the ferris wheel.

"There's candy, Daddy, candy!"

"We'll get that cotton candy when we leave. Let's ride all the rides first. Pa, you can take her on the merry-go-round while I look around and then we'll swap. But let's all ride the ferris wheel now so's we can put her between us." Each held her hand. Charity had curled her naturally wavy hair, dressed her in a pink dress and pink socks, and polished her shoes with white shoe polish. She and Jim loved showing her off. He loved his girls. They occupied that warm, proud part of his heart.

The ferris wheel stopped with them on top. "Are we close to heaven, Daddy?"

"Yes, we are," he confirmed, "as close as I'm ever going to get today."

The sun was warm; the air was cool. God's in heaven; all's right with the world. As far as the eye could see was Harlan. Red and gold and yellow of fall, reaching into the purer blue sky, not a cloud to be seen.

Everything was quiet and perfect. The seat moving only the tiniest bit. A minute of sheer ecstasy. "Up above the world so high". And then they began the descent.

When he got off, Pa leaned over and had to turn his head and blow his nose on the ground and take the back of his hand to his nose.

"Jim, I'm not riding them swangs this year. Hit's not safe."

"Pa, take her on the merry-go-round. You stand beside the horse."

What magic on the merry-go-round. Grandpa standing beside her. She sat all by herself on a white steed with gold mane. Grabbed hold of the pole. The music began as the whole world moved very slowly at first. The horse moved up and down, gently as the whole world went around and around. A swirl of color. Jim waved at her on the first round. He was gone the second. By the third pass, her horse seemed ahead of everybody. She looked back. There was Bonnie and her mother standing beside her.

"Hello Bonnie."

Bonnie didn't see her. She turned round slightly and said loudly. "Bonnie, why'd you push me down the slate dump? Why don't you come play? My sores are well. Come see me." Bonnie climbed off her horse and moved away. When the merry-go-round slowed enough, she jumped off. Halley was waiting for her. She was talking to Jim.

Lois and Pa rode the merry-go-round the third time, then went to the shooting gallery. There were the teddy bears, chalk dogs, salt and pepper shakers in the shape of a woman from the breasts up. Three shots that took down three ducks and a bear was the reward.

"We'll do that later. We don't want to lug that around. Let's go ride. . ."

"Grandpa, let me ride the swings. Do, please do. I will hold tight. . ."

He looked at her. "Look at me. Are you ready to hold on no matter if you get sick to your stomach?"

"I sure am. I'm a big girl. I can hold on."

"You can get killed on that thang."

"I didn't get killed on the slate dump. Let me."

"Here, squeeze my hand," he said, holding out his hand.

"Again, harder." She did. "I believe you. I believe you can," Pa said. Pa and Lois moved toward the swings.

The swings slowed down. Big people stumbled away. Lost their early morning hot dogs and RC colas. Lois Jean got on one of the swings. And the man pushed her legs through the holes and fastened her with a little strap of duck webbing. She waved to Pa. The swings started slowly. She could see Grandpa. Then a little faster and she could not see anything except a swirl of gray black. Then a complete blur. She looked up at the cobalt blue sky and it was heaven. The swings were straight out, flying around. Jim was standing by Pa. Neither man spoke. Pa had not realized the extent of the velocity of the swings. After an eternity, they slowed down. She was on the other side. Both ran. The man was unbuckling her.

"Thank you," she piped. She was a little dizzy.

"Stand still and count to ten. Ye'll be fine."

"One—two—three."

Jim swooped her up.

"Daddy, Daddy. Can I do it again?"

"She's your girl, Jim. She proved it today."

"Jim, how was the morphodite show?"

"We'll discuss it after you come back. I want to get your take on it."

Lois and Jim rode the bumping cars, first together then two cars. Jim hunted her in the big circle and bumped her. She giggled, then she bumped him. The floor was crowded. Everybody was bumping someone else and laughing. Why couldn't people do this all the time? Not get mad, just play the game?

The day went too fast. They ate hot dogs, and it was time to shoot targets for loot. Jim stepped up just as Pa did. Took the rifles. Pa examined his. So did Jim. Aimed, shot, nothing went down. Again, nothing went down. Third time.

Jim put his rifle down. Motioned to the man to come over, grabbed him by the shirt, and said, "You come stand beside me, and hand me that rifle over there, and if I don't shoot that little moving duck, you're goin' to die." He pointed to a rifle near the money register. Everyone knew about the miners in Harlan. They all carried pistols, got drunk and killed anybody in sight. The man got the rifle from the corner and handed it to Jim. It was loaded, no blanks in this gun.

The ducks moved. He did have presence of mind to push the button to make them move as fast as they would go. Jim began. Down went the moving ducks. He took a stuffed bear, then a second stuffed bear, then the salt and pepper set. Folks began to gather around. The boys swapped out the rifle that worked. Folks gathered round. Lois Jean was holding both bears. A boy was ready to swap a bear for the salt and pepper set.

The head man had come on the scene.

"They's a limit to how many ye can win," says.

"Do tell," mocked Jim.

"We'll call the police."

"While you're talking to him, tell him about the fake rifles that you tried to put on these dumb coal miners."

"Now, wait a minute. We didn't mean no harm, buddy." My daddy's a miner up at Closesplint."

"Name him."

He whispered "Hensley, buddy. His name is Hensley. I was jes' carryin' out orders, buddy."

Jim turned to the crowd. "Line up, boys. Don't use no rifles from the wrong corner."

The line stretched back some seven or eight deep. Soon the bears and salt shakers were gone.

The day was as high as it would get; soon be evening. The time of day to slow down. Pa and Jim and Lois Jean were eating hot dogs and drinking RC Colas. That's when she saw the bearded lady. "Oh, lookee, lookee. Can I see the bearded lady?"

"Pa, you seen her?"

"No."

"Any reason she couldn't see the bearded lady?"

"None."

They paid. She got in free.

There was the big woman dressed in green. She had long black curly hair down to her shoulders and a veil across her face-—across her nose and going around over her ears and tied behind.

The spill began. "This hey're is a beautiful, educated opera singer who has to shave like a man during the opera season in New York, London, and Paris. But she travels the rest of the year to show how she's been marked by a cruel curse perpetrated on her by an ancient relative. Come see. Come see."

In they walked. Stood around the platform. Out from a curtain stepped the woman. She was tall. She was hairy. She stood until everybody got quiet She sat down in a cane-bottom chair.

"I was marked by a curse put on me by my grandma. I grew up in Cincinnati, Ohio, and started growing this here beard when I was thirteen years old. They's a word fer hit. 'Hairsuit'. I'm hairsuit. She commenced crying. I'm hairsuit all over my back, my chest, my arms, my legs. When I'm on the opera stage, I shave all over, all over my body. Then I rub it all over with lotion and sing. "It hurts, she moaned, hit really hurts. . ."

Everything had grown still. You could hear the smallest belch of hot dog.

"I didn't shave until I sang opera." Here she dropped the veil. A gasp went up from the crowd. She looked like one of the boys on the cough drop box. Poor woman.

"Now, I know ye think this ain't real. It is. Would somebody like to look close?" Her voice was high.

"Yeah, I would. I'd like to see if'n yez got titties!"

Everybody laughed.

A boy came forward. Went up on the platform. "Be gentle, don't pull hard and don't touch my privates." She had a woman's voice.

He bent over, pulled the stiff black whiskers. He bent closer, took a finger and parted the beard and went back to the skin on her face.

"Hits real. Hits real."

Most everybody became very quiet. They forgot the cotton candy. Then she rolled up the sleeve on her arm. Black hair, so thick the skin was not visible. Poor woman. Nobody would want to sleep with that.

One of the miners from Mary Helen said, "Let me look. I believe that you are a boy."

"Yeah." A whole chorus.

"Well, come ahead. Just don't pull."

Then the Mary Helen miner pulled. Her whole jaw pulled out and she slapped him.

"Hit's real, boys. I'm from here. Some of you know me. Hit's real." Slowly the crowd filed out as the next wave came through.

There was a man swallowing fire and a "snake woman" letting a snake run over her almost naked body.

"Hit's about time for us to go, ain't it, Jim?"

"Yeah, let's head back."

That's when she saw the pink birds flying. Pink birds tied by a string to a slender stick. The man made a little "S" movement in the air and the birds opened their wings, flew, and made a little singing noise.

"I want a bird. I want a bird. Oh, Daddy, I want a bird."

Grandpa reached into his pocket. "Here, Jim, get two—one for her and one for the towhead." Finally, they went out of the circus with cotton candy and pink birds.

They went toward the Durant. "I moved it over to the Baptist Church when I put them bears in the car. We would've been blocked in." They walked across the bridge and down the sidewalk, just behind the Harlan Baptist Church. Lois Jean with cotton candy and the singing birds. Skipping ahead. Fine day. Mighty fine day.

There was Millard Moses walking toward them. There was Millard without Bessie. Millard's head was down, but Jim's first blow lifted it to the stars. There was not a sound. The second blow hit him square on the nose. Blood splattered around his head, and Lois Jean began screaming. The birds flapped their wings and she dropped her cotton candy. The blows continued. Millard Moses fell to his knees. He had threatened Charity and then tried to force this child to kiss a dead man. The blows continued.

Matt reached for Lois' hand and held it firmly. She, dancing in fear, screaming.

"Jim, that's enough. That's enough. Stop. Stop it, Jim!"

Jim stopped.

Millard lay limp. Then a groan. Jim knelt beside him. "Now don't you ever touch anything that belongs to me, or I'll kill you. Come on, Dad, let's go home."

He wiped his face with his shirt sleeves. Took Lois Jean's hand. She was crying. The little birds had stopped flying. The three got in the Durant. Lois Jean shaking. She sat between the two of them.

"Pa, I looked at that back fender. Something did happen to it."

"I told you so."

"Well, it looks like maybe something ran into it or it ran into something."

Jim knew exactly what had happened to that fender. Miz McVeigh told it at the pump and Lucy told Smoky and Smoky told it at the mines, ending with, "Well, you got to keep a woman barefoot and pregnant, or else. . ."

Jim knew all about that. He had gone out and examined the back of the garage. It had been poked out and then nailed back. Who drove it? When? He needed more information before he made any comments. He'd keep still; it was best to keep information like that until he needed it. It all came together. Charity had put the dent in the back fender of the Durant.

"How was the circus?" Charity was glad they were home. Safely home.

"Mother, Mother, I rode the ferris wheel, merry-go-round, swings, cars, saw the bearded woman wearing a hairsuit."

"James, what happened to you?"

" Why nothing, Charity."

"Yer face, you've got some blood on yer face."

He went to the bedroom. Returned.

"Just a little dried ketchup. See?"

He pushed his face close. It had been Runt's dried blood.

"Mother, I brang Mickey. . ."

"Don't say 'brang'. You brought, you brought Mickey what?"

"A bird that when you swing it, swing it. . . it titters. "

"What?"

"Titters, titters." James laughing.

"I brought Mickey a pink bird with twitters." She never ceased to amaze them.

"Charity, I'm driving Pa home. He's tard."

"Tired, James, tired."

"I'm tard and he's goin' to look at my tars! See, somehow the fender might be rubbing my tars. Fenders been messed with."

"You take your pa home, James. I'll have us a good supper when you get back."

Yes, indeed, much good can come from that banged up fender.

Wherein Charity Remembers Beginnings

It seems that soon after the circus left town, Millard, Bessie and Keith moved to Whitley County, Kentucky. Close to where Emma lived with Lonse Shone. They lived on Lonse's place. No electricity, no radio, no newspaper. Emma and Lonse had several children. Charity never bothered to learn their names. She hadn't seen Emma in years. She seldom saw any of her relatives except Mary, Nannie, Van, and Willie.

Van Jasper Moses had asked his shy sister to come share an apartment when she began working at J.J. Newberry's. Newberry's Five and Dime Store adjoined other fine brick stores on Main Street in Harlan. Charity worked in the stockroom, carrying boxes of pink panties, fish food and Tangee lipstick upstairs and arranging them in a display. She was neat, organized, and good help for the stockroom. She dressed well and presented herself well.

One day her appendix had swelled and ruptured. They rushed her to Harlan Hospital. Put her on the table and gave her ether. Anybody could watch an operation so long as no one fainted. Some doctors liked entertaining with a knife and scalpel and forceps. There was a young man from Lexington. He was practicing in Harlan. Charity was brought in.

"Well, look at this."

Charity, blond, fair skinned, fine bone structure. Actually, a beautiful young woman. He pulled back the sheet. "Bow legs." He laughed. "China blue eyes! But, she could hug you to death! Well, let's go."

Charity woke up, nauseated.

James, coming down the hall, heard her. Went in, put a pan under her chin. Got a towel, wiped her face, and was promptly put out of the room by Carrie Forsyth.

Carrie ruled the hospital, and every man, beginning with Captain T.M. Gibson, was taken with her power. They loved being ordered around and dosed on the side. Any attention from Carrie was a pleasure. The hospital was filled with high drama, from babies arriving to miners leaving forever.

James and Charity had fallen in love at the hospital, and he had vowed to others that he was going to marry her. Some tried to warn him. Others tried to warn her. The warnings fell on deaf ears because they had fallen in love. Two people could not have been more ill suited. They rode on love for awhile, then dependence on the other to cook, clean, raise children, and work in the mines, provide a good scrip card, a Durant, and keep them all safe with carefully locked doors, windows and a loaded gun.

When he got back from driving Pa home, he came in. She put out pinto beans cooked in streak of lean, coleslaw dressed in mayonnaise, with lemon juice, fresh-baked cornbread, fine dark crust top and bottom, fried bologna, curled and crisp on one side, topped off with apple cobbler and whipped cream. Jim loved Saturday night. It had everything good.

All four sat down at the table. Mickey taking as many beans as she could count and placing them around the edge of the plate. Just a tiny piece of bread and a teaspoon of coleslaw.

Wherein Doc Settles the Argument

Monday came. For Charity, it was wash day. Connect the washing machine, separate the clothes: whites first, coloreds next, and overalls and shirts last. All in the same water, using Rinso. The bright sun with just a hint of a breeze promised a worthy wash day with everything blowing dry. In weekly retrospect, it had been a more than satisfactory weekend. The circus had come and gone without anybody being killed. Lois Jean and Micki Fowe had been dressed and sent to the Miller's to go to the Harlan Baptist Church.

For Jim, this Monday would be unusual. The carnival would be discussed from equipment to performance. Perhaps every man in that hole today would have taken in the circus.

This was a new hole, well timbered. Russ Collins had ordered timber, no secondhand timber. Russ was dedicated to having a good, safe mine. No shortcuts anywhere. However, the R.C. Tway Mines had depleted the original seams of coal. In less than another decade these seams of coal would be worked out.

The miners had loaded several cars and had sent them out to the tipple, a device that tilted a loaded mining car into a Louisville and Nashville railroad freight car. When the freight cars were all filled, the L&N moved from Tways tipple through Harlan, Pineville, ending in Louisville, Kentucky, or Nashville, Tennessee. It was time to open the buckets. Some had white bread samwiches with peanut butter and ho'made blackberry jam or jelly. Some newly married miner found a love note stuck in his bucket. Some had fresh fruit. Almost all carried Moon Pies. Jim had the finest biscuits with pork chop and gravy sprinkled with black pepper neatly packed. His bucket carried ho'made pickles and apple pie. Tways women packed fine buckets. Only a sorry nocount woman would send a man off to the mines without a fine bucket. Some men picked up buckets from Miz Amics' boarding house. The talk about the circus began.

"Well, you'ens have a fine weekend?"

"Yeah, can't complain."

"Yeah, I took Lois Jean and Pa to the carnival. She rode just about everything."

"Yeah, I saw you and your Pa comin' out and her a wavin' them pink birds."

After this prologue, the discussion took its proper turn.

"Jim, I heard what ye did to that damn duck man. They's stuffed bears and chalk dogs and them salt shakers everywhere. Even little Dwayne Farmer took home a bear. He shot one of them movin' ducks his own self."

Jim sat silently, cutting into his apple pie. Never brag about any accomplishment. He sat quietly, letting others enhance the story. The discussion took a turn.

"What chee thank about the morphodite?" Who said that? It was a little soon to go to the discussion on the reality of the morphodite. Not a word spoken.

"Did anybody brang a toothpick?"

"I've got one. Hit's ivory from Chinee. Just wipe it off and hand it back when yer finished."

"Much obliged."

The querulous voice continued: "Well, let me say, I saw that thang, and hit was a hoax."

Long silence. This whippersnapper needed to learn his place. The discussion of the carnival should begin with an older, entitled man. Obviously, he did not know his place inside the mines. A man earned his place. Furthermore, this man had been in the mines not more than a year or two. He had awhile to go. Finally, a voice, an older voice, an experienced voice, a respected voice, said,

"It wasn't no 'he'; it was a 'she'."

"Hell, no, that wuz a man." Another experienced voice.

"Warn't." The ritual of the circus discussion was back in its groove.

"Now let me tell you. Hit was a man. Let me tell ye how hit wuz done. You find a man that's a little enlarged in that area. Git ye a piece of strang. Common ordinary strang, go up to the groin in about two or so anches, pull up tight, wrap hit around yer waist, twist and tie a hard knot. Press in some dried corn silk around and thar's a morphodite." That was Fat Sheehan.

"Fat, sounds like ye worked in the carnival."

That was going far. Careful. Quiet.

"No, I says hits a woman with something strapped on." It's easy to get a sausage casing and fill it with any kind of ground up pig lites and. . . ." Suddenly Fat was interrupted.

"You are both plausible. However, both are incorrect. There are such errors concocted by Mother Nature wherein such a monstrosity is the result. It occurs from some rather delicate assault to the fertilized egg, perhaps within the first trimester, the first three months of gestation." Not a sound. "And, if there happens to have been any kind of inbreeding by that woman, that is, cousins marrying cousins, resulting in both parents carrying some genes, it can be displayed in their progeny." Silence.

"Boys, this is Matt. I brought the Doc up here. He's preparing to leave Tways and desired to see the inside of a coal mine." There was a pause.

"Hell, Doc, that's why we left Whitley County and Procter, Tennessee. Too much 'same stuff' messing up the progu. . . what you call hit, Doc?"

"Progeny, P-r-o-g-e-n-y, progeny. In my part of the country, this may be observed when a colored woman has a baby by a white man, as a far removed relative of mine did. His name, gentlemen, was Jefferson, President Thomas Jefferson." Silence!

"Now, to return to a more serious subject. Did anybody examine, with your eyes, this morphodite?"

Silence.

"I did. I've visited this side show since I was a boy. This here wuz the best. I'm here to tell ye that it all was real. I swear to God. That thang, that person, was real."

Doc continued. "Yes, and it was accepted. It could not accustom itself in a regular neighborhood to the gossip and segregation that accompanies stigma. So it joined a carnival where it could stand out as something, as any-thing with a story that gendered compassion." Here he paused. "The worse hell is to be cut off, cut out and become a 'Man Without a Country'."

"Doc, how'd it happen that you got cut off? Ye are one of us, but you ain't. How come?" This from a dark corner.

"Ho, boys, boooys," there was a low wail. Does anybody have anything to drink?"

"I'll be back." Jim left to find his bottle.

They all waited. Not a word. Some chewing could be heard.

"Here."

He handed Doc a pint.

"It's the best. Ma uses it for children with flu and colds, Doc."

Doc sat and sipped. No miners' lights shining on him.

"Boys, I'm a real doctor. From Chicago, Illinois. I have a fine education. Went on to medical college. I especially like baby care. Pediatrics, that's baby medicine. I was one of the hot shots. I could straighten out little backs. I even drained water off of a water-head boy. I began to believe that I was better than most. Hubris. The same kind that killed the Greek boys. My best friend, we were in school together, and I was his best man at the wedding." Some didn't understand that. "Well, he had twins. Twin boys, six years old. He was a Jew." His voice trailed off.

"So is Jesus." This from back in the hole.

"He asked me to take out their tonsils. Both at the same time. . ."

"Boys, I went out to a party the night before and woke up in 'bad shape,' as you say. But I thought I'd be fine. I did the first one. It was hot under the lights. . ."

There was a long silence. Not a sound. "Then, then I passed out. On the way down, the instrument jabbed that little boy in the throat. He was under anesthetic, ether. When I came to, he was still out. They got me to a chair. The child was bleeding; nobody knew it. He was hemorrhaging. He died. He died." I got in my car and drove away. I didn't go to the funeral. I didn't go back. I've never been back. I don't use my name. I am soooo. . . lost." He began to sob.

Slowly the men got up to stretch, to think about going to work. Then a voice spoke.

"Bow yer heads."

"Our Father, which art in heaven, look at us here. We are your sons. You placed us here to do what we have been placed to do. The sin is that we have not done it; others have messed up. Oh, God of ages past, present and to come, have mercy on us. Don't let us fall into everlasting perdition. Straighten up this brother of ours. Let some light shine on him. On all of us. Have mercy, Father in heaven. . . Amen." It was the miner who had begun the discussion out of turn.

They went back to work.

Three days later, Jim felt in his secret place for his bottle, knowing it was almost gone. In its place was a pint of Early Times. Matt, upon Doc's orders, had one of the boys put it there. Doc was gone.

A coal mine is a strange place. So many men come to a coal mine because anybody could become a coal miner. Their fathers, their uncles, their brothers were there. Then there were those who needed sanctuary. They came because there was no other place to run. Everyone who came during the booming of coal fields in Harlan and surrounding counties was hired. A coal mine could set a body free. Only time would tell if a body had more running to do. Sometimes it was the mines and religion, or the mines and a good woman, or the mines and sheer determination that changed a man for the better. Sometimes a stint in the coal mines worked to straighten out a life; for others, it did not. Jim went home and hugged all three of his girls.

Wherein Mickey Dips Her Sucker in the Branch

When Charity went back through her mind, she knew the minute that Mickey got the trench mouth. It was on a Monday that James came in with suckers for Lois Jean and Mickey. Charity was washing clothes.

Tuesday was for ironing. Starched dress shirts in first starch. Starched Sunday summer clothes, and finally starched aprons in weak starch water. Charity's starched clothes were better ironed than anybody else's for the simple reason that she had worked at the Eagle Laundry doing small work; then she was promoted to the big pressing machines, she learning the feel of cotton and linen and knowing when there was too much starch or not enough starch. Her boss was a fine upstanding Christian man. He didn't chew tobacco or gum. He didn't drink. He didn't use strong or vulgar language. It was a shame that he shot himself to death. She remembered scrubbing the floor. His brains splattered some freshly laundered shirts. What would make a grown man take a gun and kill himself? She never heard why.

Charity starched the clothes, wrapped them in a towel, and had the children come in on a cold or wet day and listened to them play. The girls had a new play they carried on. Unfortunately, Miz Piertison and Shirley had not made the move. They were never mentioned. Now it was Delia and Julie. Whoever said it first got to be Delia. Most of the time they fought over who was Delia. Julie and Delia had never been heard of until Miz Brannon talked about them at the pump. They lived down around London, Kentucky and were actually relatives.

The names were magic. Delia was in charge, calling the shots, and most of the time Julie acquiesced. Sometimes Julie became demanding; that called for "quiet time." Quiet time was the worst punishment of all. The punishment was to be put in the bed during the daytime. Shades pulled and one was forced to be alone for at least thirty minutes or an hour.

Lois and Mickey were playing in their bedroom. Low voices, Julie and Delia. Charity had begun the shirts. She pinched the shoulder, doing detail work around the buttons. When she finished and hung it on a rack, it stood out almost as if an invisible man were inside. She hung it in the chifforobe with other Sunday clothes.

"I've got to go pee. Go with me, Lois Jean?"

Passing through the kitchen, Lois opened the drawer of the tin-top table where the water buckets were and took out two grape and cherry suckers. Mickey got the cherry. Lois liked to see her happy. Besides, you could really taste grape. Out to the toilet. Mickey went in. Didn't close the door all the way.

"You right there, Lois Jean?"

"Yes, Mickey Fowe."

"Don't call me that name!"

"OK, Mickey Mouse."

She came out, pulling up her pink panties. Lois Jean had wandered down toward the branch at the back of the house, Mickey beside her. The branch was running clear. The tiny eddies were teeming with darting minnows. It was a fine place to play "graveyard." The wet clay was smooth. A mound would harden and stay until it rained and the branch rose. You could bury a flower, a rock, a sucker stick.

A sucker stick.

"Let's play graveyard."

"OK."

"What's dead?"

"Let's eat our suckers and bury the sticks, Julie."

"OK, Delia."

"Let's plike it's Gertie's boy layin a corpse."

"OK, Julie."

"Let's plike we fix him a teensy head, Julie. I'm Delia."

"No, I'm Delia." Unwrapping the cherry sucker made her forget. Lois Jean unwrapped her grape, had it in her mouth not quite a minute, and she bit hard and chewed. A big piece fell out of her mouth and dropped in the clay sand.

"Oh, hellfar."

"I'm goin' tell, Delia! I'm going to tell mother you said the bad word."

"OK, you can be Delia if you don't tell.

Mickey had watched Lois get the clay sand off the sucker piece. She squatted down and dipped her sucker in the cool branch water and put it in her mouth. Again and again. It was cherry juice! Again and again.

All Lois Jean could do was watch. Her grape sucker was gone, and she was fashioning a marble sized "head" so's it could lay a corpse beneath the sandy mound.

"What are you doing?" It was Charity. She saw Mickey dip the sucker in the branch water and put it in her mouth.

She jerked her by the arm into the air, just as she would have done had she seen a cottonmouth snake.

"Oh, Lord, have mercy!"

Neither child could attach a sin to the action. What had Mickey done?

"Oh, Lord!"

She was dragging Mickey up through the yard. Mickey was whimpering, knowing worse was to come. "Oh, Lord, have mercy!" Then she began her lesson. "Toilets empty in that branch where you just dipped your sucker. Toilets set over the branch in some places in upper camp and the branch gits up and washes all that sh—-scuoose into the branch. You dipped that sucker in the branch and you are going to get typhoid or flu and die! You are going to die."

Mickey didn't take all that in, but she was about to. Charity reached up in the shelf, grabbed the "Black Draught." Dreaded Black Draught. A compost of herbs guaranteed to move the bowels. Charity didn't sweeten it in any way. She put it in Mickey's mouth and had her drink water, water, water.

Lois Jean waited for something to happen. Nothing did. "Come on, Mickey. You can be Delia." Mickey "exploded" sometime during the night, didn't even make it to the pee bucket. Charity worked getting the mess cleaned up. Mickey crying, this time in shame.

How long did Mickey have before she died?

"Mickey, come sleep with me," Lois Jean begged.

Next day Charity carried water from the pump. Nell had news. Bessie told Mary and Murph about James beating up Millard. Murphy got the news to Nannie through a miner who worked in the mines and stopped to get gas at Murphy's store. He told Nannie and Weller. Weller said that James had no business beating up Millard.

Charity was silent. She pumped her water and did not say a word. How bad was Millard? She had always been afraid of him. He got relief when he beat her. He would never do it again. But, for a reason she didn't understand, she took sides with her sisters and brother. Millard against James. James had not mentioned it to her. She thought about the last time they were all together at the funeral. One thing that she was clear on, nobody would tell her how to vote. Behind that curtain, she could vote any way she wanted to and she would vote for Franklin Delano Roosevelt for the four terms that he would run.

A week and a half went by. Mickey was well. The Black Draught had removed all germs from her body. The girls brushed their teeth with baking soda. Soda tastes like soda.

But when you rinse your mouth and spit, it is sweet. It tastes sweet. Charity had them brush, after the "sucker in the branch" episode, three times a day. Then came the bloody mouth. Mickey brushed and spit.

"Mother, it's blood. Mickey spit blood." Mickey was spitting in the enameled wash pan and, sure enough, there was blood.

"Let me look. Oh, lau, Oh, laume." Mickey's mouth was blistered from front to back, even in her throat.

James had to go to work. She had to take Mickey down to the drugstore to Dr. Tye's to get help. Dressing the girls, she combed Mickey's white hair. She woke James, told him about Mickey's mouth.

"Trench mouth," he said sleepily. "It will run its course. Put some Vick's salve on it. Don't let her swallow it."

Charity was a modern woman, not given to mining camp medicine. She wanted professional help. When he got up, she was gone. She caught a ride with Uncle John Carter. She called him John to his face. He did have an almost grown child; he and Ella married young.

"Charity, she has trench mouth. It will run its course. Put some Vick's salve on it and she'll be fine."

Charity turned a deaf ear. John let them out at the drugstore there on Main Street. The place was spotless. Little marble-top tables, wire chairs, and rows and rows of jars, boxes, and bottles. The girls sat down at one of the little tables and Charity began. She poured out her story. Anybody could see she was scared.

"Let me look, honey." Dr. Tye pulled down Mickey's chin.

"That's a bad case of trench mouth, Miz Carter. You need peroxide and," he hesitated, "some sodium purabrate. That's going to burn. Take the peroxide and rinse it around. Don't swallow it. Then take your finger, make sure it's clean, and rub the blisters with the sodium purabrate." She paid him and he left. No drinks; they were too young for Coca-Colas. They walked home past Baby Jones' store. No penny candy today.

Charity read the directions. "Once at bedtime. Dip the swab in and dot the affected area." That wouldn't do any good. She began to swab her mouth, rubbing out that filthy disease. It was vital to rub out a disease; this vile thing had set up in her child's little mouth and she would rub, rub, rub it out. Nobody had rubbed out her daddy's typhoid from the drinking water at the mines; nobody had rubbed out the flu, and Otis had died. Frail little Otis had died. Now it was Mickey's mouth.

James heard Mickey screaming. He got to Mickey, picked her up. "What is it? What's happening?"

"It's the trench mouth in her mouth. I'm putting sodium purabrate in and rubbing it in."

"Here, Mickey, put this water in yer mouth. Now spit it out." Her gums were bleeding.

"Again, honey." She was sobbing, and he felt her little heart beating.

"Here." He got butter out of the icebox. Ran his finger across the top and again and again.

Slowly the screams subsided.

Charity came to herself.

"Here, I'll take her."

"No." He went out of the front porch. Sat in the swing. Lois Jean followed.

Charity began the noon meal, breakfast/dinner, for James.

"One time," James began, "there was a billy goat. That goat's name was Ricum. And he was out in the woods eatin' hickory nuts and wouldn't come home."

"A goat can't eat hickory nuts." This from Lois.

"This goat ate hickory nuts," said Jim. "Boy went and said, 'Ricum, come home!'

Ricum just went on eatin' hickory nuts and wouldn't come home.

'Dog, dog, go get Ricum. Ricum is outen the woods eatin' hickory nuts and won't come home.'

'No', sez the dog.

Boy went to a stick, sez 'stick, stick, beat Ricum; he's out in the woods eatin' hickory nuts and will not come home.'

'No', sez stick.

Boy went to the fire, sez, 'Fire, fire, burn the stick; stick won't beat dog; dog won't go after Ricum, who's outen the woods eatin' hickory nuts and won't come home tonight.'

'No', sez the fire.

Boy went to the water, sez, 'Water, water, put out the fire; fire won't burn the stick; stick won't beat the dog; the dog won't go after Ricum; Ricum's outen the woods eatin' hickory nuts and won't come home tonight.'

'No', sez the water.

Boy went to the ox, sez, 'Ox, ox, drink the water; water won't put out the fire; fire won't burn the stick; stick won't beat the dog; Ricum's outen the woods eatin' hickory nuts and won't come home tonight.'

Ox sez, 'No.'

Boy went to the rope, sez, 'Rope, rope, choke the ox; ox won't drink the water; water won't put out the fire; fire won't burn the stick; stick won't beat the dog; the dog won't go after Ricum; Ricum's outen the woods eatin' hickory nuts and won't come home tonight.'

'No,' sez the rope.

Boy goes to the mouse, sez, 'Mouse, mouse, chew on the rope; rope won't hang the ox; ox won't drink the water; water won't burn the stick; stick won't beat the dog; dog won't go after Ricum.

Now, girls, say it with me.

'Ricum's outen the woods eatin' hickory nuts and won't come home tonight.'

There was a new voice. Florence, little Florence, the twin, had slipped up on the top step.

'No,' sez the mouse.

Boy went to the cat, sez, 'Cat, cat, chase that mouse.'

Mouse won't gnaw the rope.

Rope won't hang the ox.

Ox won't drink the water.

Water won't put out the fire.

Fire won't burn the stick.

Stick won't beat the dog.

Dog won't go after Ricum. Now, say it with me:

'Ricum's out in the woods eatin' hickory nuts and won't come home tonight.'

Cat sez. Now, Cat sez, 'If'n you'll get me a bowl of cream, I'll do hit'.

Boy went to girl milking the cow. 'If'n ye'll give me a kiss, I'll do hit!'

Boy kissed the girl, and she gave him a bowl of cream. Pussycat drank the cream. Sat and cleaned his whiskers in the warm sunshine. Directly he was ready. He commenced chasing the mouse. Mouse commenced to gnaw the rope.

Rope commenced to hang the ox. Ox commenced to drink the water.

Water commenced to put out the fire. Fire commenced to burn the stick.

Stick commenced to beat the dog. Dog jumped up, ran outen the woods, found Ricum. Ricum stopped eatin' them hickory nuts and went home.

The end!"

"Tell it again; tell it again."

"No, you'ens play here. I gotta get ready to go to the mines."

"Thank you, Uncle Jim." That was Florence.

"Much obliged, honey. Much obliged!"

For a few minutes, Mickey had forgotten her painful mouth.

"James, your breakfast is ready." He left the girls on the porch playing Julie and Delia. Florence was Florence. Mickey and Lois were both Delia.

James didn't speak. Neither did she. She went off to make up the bed and go through his pockets. Life settled in; rhythms changing ever so slightly. Winter coming on; before long it would be Christmas.

Wherein Lois and Mickey
Visit Chief and Miz Miller

Charity got up early. By late afternoon all the dirty clothes had been run through the washer. Bright sunshine for drying clothes. Clotheslines could announce to the world what was happening inside a house. Some would lay around in bed, not washing until Tuesday or Wednesday. A clothesline full of Birdseye Diapers announced a new baby. Some newlyweds hung out pastel slips and new underwear. But if nothing hung on lines, it stated that something was amiss. Except for Miz Hall, Miz Gibson and Miz Owens. They all had help from upper camp. Some of the mothers who had daughters and sisters teaching at the Rosewald School washed and ironed and cleaned for the Hall's, the Gibson's and the Owens'. Their fine clothes flapped in the breeze in colored camp.

Charity went to the pump for rinse water, while others were just beginning wash water. Hers were the first hanging; that included the starched clothes.

The girls slept until a little after eight. She tiptoed in and looked at them in their twin beds, spreads folded and hanging over the bed rail. Both were healed. Lois Jean had a white scar at the corner of her lower lip and a pink place above her left eye at the hairline, but the ugly scabs were gone. Scars in the palms of both hands. Scars on her knees. Mickey showed no signs of her trench mouth.

While others were just beginning to rise, Charity had her store list and was on her way to the commissary. Only Chief Miller's wife was out. She was cutting canes from her famous climbing roses.

Chief and Miz Miller had been in Tways since it began. They had no children and they were hermits. She slipped out after dark to get water. Nobody had ever been inside their house. They were quiet and kept to themselves. Chief's routine was unique. The big gates that swept across the road out of Tways were closed at nine p.m. during the week. After nine p.m., Chief had to be contacted personally. He shined the brightest light up and down a body, and if he knew that person, unlocked the padlock to let them drive through.

Ever since the sound truck and hoodlums had started trying to unionize Tway Mining Camp, rules regarding the gates were rigidly enforced. Chief did not hesitate to shoot. He would fire a warning shot. If no identifying name was made, then came the real thing. He went to work at dark and stayed until daylight. He sat on the front porch of the shack across from the commissary. His habits were nocturnal, and he slept all day long.

This caused a slight inconvenience to neighbors. Nobody blew the car horn. Chief's sleeping. Nobody called out "ice wagon" in front of his house, Chief's sleeping. Children did not play red rover or hopscotch in front of Chief's house, Chief's sleeping. Lois Jean and Mickey were about to break those rules.

James had bought the girls a toy car. It had not been used. It had set out on the porch in upper camp and was a little rusted. In lower camp the road was better. Children all played in the road. It was smooth and hard and sloped slightly. It had been black topped during the last election and got a new coat every presidential election. So boys rolled hoops and car tires; girls played hopscotch. Ginny Brannon rode a new girls blue bicycle she got for delivering The Harlan Daily Enterprise to folks in lower camp. Girls jumped rope to "Cinderella, dressed in yellow, went upstairs to see her fella. How many kisses did she give him? I don' know. Let us count them." Then the counting of the jumps began.

In summer time, when it was hot, there was a rite of passage, pumping your own drink from the pump. Pump, pump, bring up the water and run to the spigot before it stopped and drink. The real enviable event was watching some pump and drink at the same time. Future basketball players could do it.

Finally, there were marbles and jacks. Girls played jacks and boys shot marbles. Draw a big ring and use a prized steel ball your daddy brought you from the mines. No girls. If a girl tried to play marbles, they would sing out, "A whistling girl and a crowing hen always comes to a bad end! No girls allowed!"

In warm weather children played in the road following the ice wagon, stepping in cold water that had run out of the back of the wagon pulled by a horse. Butchell drove the horse pulling the ice wagon and he'd stop and chip off a piece of ice for children who got to the wagon. Lower camp was lively every minute of the day.

Lois Jean and Mickey took the little car out in the front yard. Lois pushed Mickey around in it. "Peddle, Mickey, peddle, peddle, peddle. . ." The car, a green job with a metal seat, was rusted and squeaked. "Let me ride, now." Lois Jean, three years older, was able to move around in the front yard. Around the maple tree. Up close to the porch where the yard was swept smooth and clean, as all good yards attested to the kind of housekeeper living there.

"Mickey, it's better in the road." Out they went. They first rode in small circles, then Lois Jean got in and went down the road peddling. It worked! The car set up a horrendous, teeth-gritting noise. Then it was Mickey's turn. She climbed into the little car. She sat, began peddling, and away she went down the road. Lois ran. They squealed and hollered with joy. Back down the road, loud, wonderful whooping all the way. Again and again.

Ella pulled back the shade and saw the girls. Smokey McCurg just got up went out on the porch for a smoke. Then out came Chief Miller, dark shirt, baggy pants, black suspenders, lace-up shoes, gray hair, not combed. He spoke not a word. Stood in the road as Mickey came swooping by and caught the car. Mickey looked up. There stood the boogie man. She froze in fear. Lois was beside her. Chief lifted Mickey out of the car and placed her beside Lois.

"Stand right there, and don't move." He pulled the car inside his fenced front yard. Closed the gate. At the end of his front porch was a closet. He opened it, took out a shiny copper oil can. Turned the car up and oiled the front wheels.

There appeared a woman in the front door. She came across the porch and down the front steps. "Come in. Come in." They did not hesitate. They went through the front door into a world the likes of which they had never seen. Soft Belgian wool rugs, a wall lined with books, a leather chair, a drop chandelier. In the kitchen was a cherry drop-leaf table, with cane ladder-back chairs and a silver bowl on top of the table. Shelves holding canned peaches, red tomatoes, jellies. A copper kettle on the stove. Needlepoint on the wall. Cross-stitched place mats. She set two little plates on the table. Opened a pie safe. "These are special. You each take one. You won't remember this. This is a date bar. A special, special date bar."

The girls sat up straight, took small bites, and chewed with their mouths closed. Tiny pieces of chewy dates, tiny pieces of pecan, sugar, butter. Wonderful, wonderful date bars.

"Mickey, where did you get that white hair?"

"It came with her," piped up Lois.

"I had a little girl once. Come see." She led the girls back into the front room.

"Up there she is." There was a little girl. Laying a corpse, in a casket. All in white. Miz Miller started crying. "You must go now. And don't tell anybody," she paused. "Don't tell." Out the front door they ran.

"Come on, get on it. See how it runs now." Chief was pleased with his work.

Mickey climbed into her car. Lois Jean pushed her out the gate, turned it toward the commissary, and gave one push. The car flew down the road. Lois running behind. "Stop. Stop. Put on the brakes. You'll die. You'll lay a corpse." Mickey rode on. James eased out of the swing and went back into the house.

Some weeks later, when they were in Harlan, Lois Jean saw some blue dishes. "Mother, that's what Miz Miller has. She had them plates. We ate the cookies off them plates."

"Blue Willow—from China. They are expensive dishes," Charity whispered in awe.

Wherein Thanksgiving Dinner is Interrupted

At Easter when Charity bought baby chickens for the chicken yard, she bought two little ducks. Something happened to Lois' duck. Mickey's thrived. Just a bundle of fluff on toothpick legs waddling across the floor. She cuddled the duckie up to her cheek. Cuddling the baby duck, she would croon: "Duckie. . . Duckie, I love you." One day she said, "Duckie, Duckie Luckie, Duckie Luckie, oh Duckie Luckie." Duckie Luckie responded to her love and grew. Mickey took her down the steps and out into the wide world. Duckie Luckie found worms, June bugs, and Mickey fed Duckie Luckie corn-bread and even pinto beans.

"Come on, Duckie Luckie, let's go to bed." Duckie Luckie slept in a shoe box filled with Easter grass beside Mickey's twin bed with the pink brocade bedspread. At night Charity came to hear prayers. First both would pray:

> *"Now I lay me down to sleep.*
> *I pray, thee Lord, my soul to keep.*
> *Fi-shou-die before I wake,*
> *I pray, thee Lord, my soul to take."*

Then added to this prayer came the blessings. First Lois: "God bless Mother, Daddy, Mickey and take care of Daddy in the coal mines. Amen." Then Mickey. "Help Daddy bemember BB bats and chum gum. Send me some pennies, and take care of Duckie Luckie and send her worms and June bugs that go..."

"Mickey." Finally Charity said the second time, "Mickey."

"Bless the June bugs. Ah men!"

Duckie Luckie was already in her shoe box. Mickey felt that downy duck. Yes. There was the gold cross. Mickey had found a chain with a gold cross out in the road. James had put it around her neck and she kept it there until one day the chain broke. James could not fix it. Charity ran a fine piece of embroidery thread through the cross and put it on Duckie Luckie's neck. "Good night, Duckie Luckie."

Next morning Mickey was awakened by a faint splashing sound. Worst fears confirmed. Duckie Luckie in a moment of primal roosting had lost her footing on the rim of the pee bucket and fallen in. Little feathers all wet and pasted to her scrawny body. Mickey jumped out of bed into the middle of a screaming dance involving all of her. "Save her, oh, save her. Somebody save Duckie Luckie!"

Lois Jean pulled the cover over her head and waited. Neither one could bring herself to reach into the pee bucket to save Duckie Luckie. Duckie Luckie was trying to climb out of the pee bucket. Charity ran into the room, thinking that Mickey was having some kind of fit. "Save her, Mother. Please, Mother!"

Charity bent over as Lois and Mickey watched her put her hand into the pee bucket and draw Duckie Luckie out. "Here, Mickey. Dry her off with the dish rag and take her out into the sunshine. The sun will take the smell away."

It did. Duckie Luckie grew in wisdom and stature (she put on a lot of weight) and was loved by Mickey.

Here it was November and Duckie Luckie was full grown. Fat, sleek, and still wearing the gold cross. She followed Mickey everywhere. Mickey took her to the branch and let her play in the water.

Then came Thanksgiving. Usually they had baked hen. Last year Jim had won the turkey raffle and he could have a turkey or a fresh ham. He had chosen the ham. The table was set with the best dishes. Then the Sunday glasses. Forks, knives, spoons. Next came the shuck beans, creamed potatoes, home-canned corn, tomato slices, onions, pickles, jars of apple jelly, cherry preserves, blackberry jam, hot yeast rolls; for dessert there was the famous Ida Cox Moses' seven-layer apple stack cake with hot coffee and iced tea.

Lois and Mickey could also have sweet tea. Then the dishes were washed and a tablecloth would cover the leftovers. Potatoes and beans were put in the stove warming shelf. The meat in the oven.Everyone ate all day long, coming back for a pickle sandwich or another slice of the layer cake smothered in brown sugar frosting. Took naps, children played, neighbors visited. At night sang songs and pondered the wonder of it all.

This Thanksgiving the day began as usual. Charity had begun earlier this week. Making the cakes, soaking beans, setting blue Ball canning jars filled with corn on the cabinet. Early in the day, Lois and Mickey had helped set the table.

Finally, it was time to eat. "Call your Daddy." That was the signal for all good things to come together into one fine time. James came, took his place, and all three girls sat down. Charity asked the blessing since James did not "pray in public."

Charity began to fill the plates. The "turkey" was in the middle of the table near James. He picked up the sharp butcher knife and cut a slice from the side breast for Mickey and placed the dish in front of her. Mickey looked at the "turkey" when James turned it around. He sliced another piece from the "turkey". It oozed pure juice. "Charity, you've done a fine job…" Mickey was standing, beginning her dance of death. She looked again, ran out of the door screaming, "Duckie Luckie, Duckie Luckie, Duckie Luckie."

Then Lois realized that she had a piece of Duckie Luckie in her mouth. She spit it onto her plate. Lois looked at the platter. There lay Duckie Luckie dead. Duckie Luckie was lying dead on the platter with her legs cut off and the stumps up in the air. James had calmly detached a leg with a thigh. He was eating Duckie Luckie. She watched in horror. Slowly she put her fork down and ran out after Mickey. Mickey had opened the chicken lot gate and was sitting among curious hens, sobbing. Charity sat at the table. Neither did she eat Duckie Luckie. Lois Jean and Mickey closed the chicken gate, walked around the house to the front porch swing. They got in the swing. It did not swing. They sat in silence.

After awhile Charity found the girls in the swing. Without saying a word, she handed Mickey the gold cross, still on the embroidery thread. Mickey went back into the kitchen. Lois and Charity followed her. Mickey stood a minute. Then she went up to the carcass and laid the little cross on top of the remains. James stopped eating, got up, went out on the front porch. "Damn duck."

After dinner was cleaned away, what was left of Duckie Luckie was covered with waxed paper and James took the platter to his folks. That night Mickey prayed and blessed the "choo-choo train" and Duckie Luckie in heaven, but she didn't bless Daddy for five whole days!

Wherein Charity Begins Christmas

Charity had begun early, before Thanksgiving. Just thinking about Christmas. Her most immediate memory was the big red apple rolling out of her lap into the toilet and hearing it plunk in the scuuse. Loss. Now she could fix that. She would celebrate the season by buying every toy she ever wanted but never had.

Early fall. The commissary was getting in toys. Toys went well in mining camps. Tways did a good business. Tways did a wild business. Women and men lined up to buy bicycles, train sets, games, puzzles, dolls, doll carriages, small electric stoves, tables and chairs, marbles, candy, jig-saw puzzles, carom boards, musical instruments, tea sets from China, sets of miniature silverware, knives, forks and spoons, miniature skillets, with lids. Added to this supply would be Christmas decorations beginning in early December.

Right after Thanksgiving women would make fruitcakes and begin soaking them in bourbon that came from Bourbon County, Kentucky. It was necessary to begin preparing early for Christmas. In this process, children were the excuse for the celebrating. Most women and men bought the toys, the dolls, stoves, table and chairs, the bicycles, roller skates, and guns that they had never had.

Lois Jean and Mickey were not really toy oriented. They would rather play "Julie and Delia." They loved building playhouses, covering boxes with towels, playing riding to Harlan in the swing, playing dress up. Dolls were not all that important. Only one doll, Betta Lou. Betta Lou was a real rubber baby doll with blue glass eyes and once brown hair like Lois' hair. Betta Lou was her first doll. Now she stayed under the bed in a corner or in a box or in the yard, sometimes for days. But she was there. She never just disappeared. She was steady, a constant. When shoestrings broke or hair got tangled, or there was a fall down the slate dump, or there was a looking at Gertie's boy laying a corpse, or Daddy was beating up Runt, or Charity was spanking with the egg turner, Betta Lou was there.

That day, Charity dressed Lois Jean and Mickey and left James sleeping. They would be back in time to see him off, and down to the commissary the three went. It was after nine o'clock. The commissary was almost empty. She had made a good move. Some colored people were in line. They let Charity and the girls in front of them. Yes, the toys were out. Over on the right front side of the commissary in or near the large front window were the bolts of material, threads, rick-rack, jars of Jergens lotion, face powder, sharp scissors, quilting frames, Black Draught, aspirin, olive oil, and canning jars. Laume, there were the Horseman dolls. Several women were gathered around the dolls. Beautiful, big dolls looking like movie stars, eyes that closed, blond hair or brown hair and dolls dressed in fine Sunday clothes, woolen coats with silk dresses with underclothes.

"They're Horseman dolls," someone whispered. Horseman dolls. The words flowed in awe from lips. There were about six of each. Charity stood silent.

Lois and Mickey gazed up, speechless. How they would love Horseman dolls.

"Excuse me," she spoke to a woman from colored camp.

"Would you mind taking them out on the porch for just a minute? I'll save your place."

"Mr. Haynes? Oh, Mr. Haynes?"

Mr. Haynes was a good man. He had hit Charity's mother with a car as she was returning from Wednesday night prayer meeting, and Charity's mother had died in Harlan hospital. They poured peroxide on her wounds, and that could be heard boiling out in the hall .

"Mr. Haynes, could you help me?"

"Excuse me," he said to the colored man who was buying pork chops.

"How can I help you, Charity?" Lee Haynes and Charity Carter had never talked about that tragedy. Not a word.

How could he help her? He could help her by not hitting her mother.

"I'd like two of the Horseman dolls, the blond and brown haired ones."

Mr. Haynes reached up to pull out boxes. Her eyes followed his reach. That's when she saw the avocado green steel-top table and two chairs to match and the little electric toy stove.

"And," she continued, "I'll take the table and chairs, the stove, the pots and pans, and the little blue china dish set. Set it back with my name on it. She handed Mr. Haynes the scrip card.

"You know, you've got to get these items taken from the scrip card from Vance Owens out on the porch."

The line was long. "Well, write my name on each box and I'll be back."

She turned to the line. "Would you hold my place in this line? All I have to do is hand Mr. Haynes the scrip." Nobody said a word.

There was only one table and four chairs; she had them.

She went outside. The girls were sitting on the steps talking to someone in line. She got in the scrip card line. Nell Farmer was in line.

"Charity, you want in front of me? What are you buying?"

"Yes, Nell, I do want in front. I've just bought Christmas for the girls."

Nell told Charity that they were going to buy Dwayne his first bicycle ". . . and his feet don't reach the peddles. His daddy is going to put blocks on the peddles." She threw back her head and laughed. Lois Jean and Mickey were going down the steps. That's when Lois Jean saw Mr. C.C. Moore on his front porch—the front porch of the shack. It was time for a shift change. Chief Miller goes; Mr. C.C. Moore comes. Lois Jean remembered the story how Mr. Moore had run over and clamped his hands around Joe Young's ankles when he took the electric lights up to Schoolhouse Hill.

"Hello, Mr. Moore," she piped up.

"Hello yourselves," he yelled back. "Come and see me."

Lois Jean took Mickey's hand and they ran across the road. Up the three steps to the porch.

"Where's your mama?"

"She's at the store."

He glanced at the porch, full of folks now. "Would you two little girls like some candy?"

"Do you have a red sucker?"

"Why, I believe I do."

He ran his hand across his head to make sure his hair was in place and took both their hands. "Let's go in here. I keep red suckers in a drawer."

An old desk was up against a wall with an office chair pushed up against it. C.C. lifted Mickey first and then Lois Jean up on the desk. Then he stood just looking. Something was wrong. Lois Jean was suddenly scared. His hand was on her leg. Her heart was beating fast.

"Well, what we got here?" It was Chief Miller.

C.C. jumped like he'd been shot.

"Nothing, nothing at all. I's just getting candy for. . ."

Chief was holding a gun. "All I have to do is go outside on that porch and call out to them boys over yonder and you're a dead man."

"I swear, I swear, I's just given them suckers."

"I think I'll go get Jim Carter. I think he might want a sucker."

"Oh God, don't do that."

"You son-of-a-bitch. You've hurt more women and girls and now, you bastard, you've started on children.

Lois Jean and Mickey were standing on the desk.

"No, I'm not going to tell so long as you leave Tways by Friday. If I see that ugly bald head, that greasy hair, one more day, I'll blow it off your head.

Set them children down—no, don't touch them little girls. Go ahead, get them a sucker."

C.C. opened the drawer. It was filled with penny candy. He rummaged around until he found two red suckers.

"Now go find yer ma and don't say a word about this or C.C. won't give you another sucker." Mr. Miller escorted them out the door and down three steps.

"Mr. Miller?" It was Mickey Fowe. "My car don't squeak no more. Thank you for fixing my car."

They ran down the steps, across the road, up the steps, and into the store. There was Charity, buying pinto beans, cabbage, apples, and a bag of candy.

"How did you get the suckers?"

"Mr. Moore gave them to us."

As the three marched out toward the door, Charity heard Nell say, "I'll take that little round blackboard up there." A blackboard would be nice. It would be a fine thing for her to buy on her next trip. There was a pile of blackboards, but the Horseman dolls were all gone.

Wherein the Heart-Reading Birds
Read Lois Jean's Heart

It was close to Christmas, and it was time for the heart-reading birds. Charity first introduced Lois Jean and Mickey Fowe to the heart-reading birds. They came about two or three weeks before Christmas. They had a specific mission. Flocks of heart-reading birds flew in and sat in trees, on the chicken fence, and on the electric wires that carried the juice to the house. They heard every word Lois Jean and Mickey Fowe said and flew straight to the North Pole and repeated it to Santa Claus. This year Lois Jean was in school and in Miss Milsap's room. The heart-reading birds were outside the window! Up in the tree! On the telephone pole! They were lined up listening to Lois Jean! And what was she doing? Truth be told, Lois knew she was in trouble with Santa Claus and Jesus. For example, she was supposed to be practicing "Country Gardens," from Teaching Little Fingers to Play. Instead, she was playing one of her own compositions. It was kind of a religious Indian tune which faintly resembled "Song of the Volga". She was also taking Mickey's clean socks and trying to stretch them to fit her feet. Lois had learned to complain about a pain in her leg when it came her time to go get a bucket of coal. She had also skipped the stories in the front of the Basic Reader. All the pictures were orange and black. First page: "This is Ben." Second page: "This is Alice." Third page: "This is Ben and Alice." Only after Christmas did such wonderful things appear as "The Three Billy Goats Gruff." Miss Milsap told her students not to go "past the assigned reading; boys and girls, that is the wrong thing to do." She shook her blonde curls vigorously as she spoke.

It was sometime around Halloween that Lois became a cheater. Cheaters turned over and read the stories, spellbound by the orange and black pictures of the talking goats. Lois Jean was a cheater. Nobody, she thought, knew it. She began slowly to give in to a sinful life. She had taken up some heavy talk.

When she was with Mickey and they were playing playhouse, she would tell Mickey "the witche's gonna getchee" and Mickey would run off crying. When Lois was alone, she said "darn". Darn good; darn, darn good! She led a rich, wanton life.

Then, at Christmastime, things changed. Things changed. Lois would never forget the day Charity told her. She bent over, squinted her eyes, scrooched up her mouth so it made a perfect "O", and looked right into Lois' face. She began, "The heart-reading birds read every thought you have, everything you do, and they fly up to the North Pole and tell Santa Claus. They tell Santa Claus what you think and what you do. He makes a list and checks it. You can't be naughty! Charity had picked up that word from the picture show. Lois Jean knew in an instant what it meant. She knew that she was in deep trouble and needed to change things in a twinkling of an eye.

Lois began to look out the window. Sure enough, there sat the heart-reading birds, looking, listening. When she opened the door, they flew off. She heard them all day, breakfast, dinner and suppertime. Any time she looked out the window or opened the door, they were there. It was hard to miss them. It was sometime around then that Lois Jean became a quintessential hypocrite. She would ease the backdoor open and say so that the birds could hear, "Mother, I'm gonna get a bucket of coal," and "Mickey, here are your clean socks. I didn't wear them, honey." She even began to think nice thoughts that would pay off. For instance, she would say in a whisper, "I will go now (adding 'now' made it sound like the Bible) and practice the piano; I will play 'Country Gardens.'"

Lois was so good that Charity began to worry. She told Miz Brannon that she was worried about Lois Jean, that maybe she was sick. What an idea! That night Lois prayed:

> "*Now I lay me down to sleep.*
> *I pray Thee, Lord, my soul to keep.*
> *Fi-shou-die before I wake (soft whisper),*
> *I pray Thee, Lord, my soul to take.*"

Then she climbed into the twin bed, with the pink brocade spread, pulled the little Dutch Girl quilt up, and said, "Good night, Dear Mother." Charity felt her head to try to determine how sick Lois was.

It was getting closer and closer to Christmas. The heart-reading birds continued to come in bunches. Everyday when Charity went out to feed the chickens, here came the birds. They lit on the top of the chicken fence, flew down into the chicken yard and even had the nerve to eat the chicken feed. Lois could tell they were listening to her thoughts by the way they would cock their heads. Sometimes when she couldn't help herself and had thought a dirty word, she would stomp her foot. They heard it. They were quick. They would all fly up at once and go straight to the North Pole. The North Pole was off the front porch, down the hollow, and over the mountain. They always went the same way. It was getting harder and harder to play up to the heart-reading birds.

Then came the day when Charity took Lois and Mickey to the commissary. Up the concrete steps into the big store they went. First Charity stopped on the porch, took out the scrip card and got the scrip that she needed to buy the groceries. Mr. Owens wrote pretty writing on the card and gave Charity the scrip.

Lois and Mickey pranced through the doors ahead of Charity. Lo and behold, Christmas was out everywhere. Candy canes, red apples, oranges, nuts, filberts, chocolate drops, pecans, and chestnuts, red wagons, tricycles, skates, tables and chairs, tea sets and. . . Lois stopped moving. She stopped, batting her eyes, her mouth dropped open. A doll. A doll like she had never seen on this earth before. Mr. Miller came up and said, "Charity, that is a Horseman doll." That became the first brand name that Lois ever heard. Horseman, a Horseman doll. That's what Mr. Miller told Charity. "Charity, that is a Horseman doll." That doll had real hair, brown eyes with long eyelashes. She was wearing a green velvet dress with teensy buttons up the back and she had on underclothes and shoes and socks. From her wrist dangled a little tag; it had $8.00 written on it. There were three Horseman dolls. The one that Mickey liked had on red velvet, and she had blonde hair and blue eyes. Lois and Mickey neither moved nor spoke the entire time Charity was paying the store bill. She came over to where the girls stood and said, "Come on, girls. Let's go." No one spoke a word all the way home.

That night when Lois went to bed and besides the "nowilaymedowntosleep" and God bless and saying every relatives' names, even praying for Gramma's dog and for Miz Piertison and Shirley, her rooster and her big Rhode Island Red hen, she put the Horseman doll at the top of the list. She sweetened the request by saying that she would not hate Miss Kay Adams when she moved her finger to the right note in "Country Gardens" and she would put all the nickels in the offering plate and not save any for Baby Jones' candy store; and she would never say the "d" word that fit so many occasions. More than anything, Jesus, she wanted that doll.

Lois began her mission the next day. She rose early, put on her school clothes and her dirty socks and went to the window. Charity was feeding the chickens and the heart-reading birds were sitting on the top of the chicken fence, swooping down to hear what the chickens were saying and to eat a little morsel off the ground while they were there. Chickens must have stuff they wanted for Christmas too.

Every day Lois wore dirty socks, and every night she prayed. She would run to the windows and think lovely thoughts about Miss Kay Adams. She even added Lottie Moon and the starving Chinese to her list. She learned that in Sunday School. She became so craven that she volunteered to carry the water from the pump and even to help wash and dry the dishes.

As Christmas came on, nothing mattered anymore. Lois was changed. She did everything in kind of a trance. She even admitted to Miss Milsap that she had cheated and read the whole book. Miss Milsap said not to worry, that she could read it again. Tonight, Lois was ready to go to bed and lie awake to see Santa Claus. Lois and Mickey took a bath in the tin tub by the big kitchen stove. Charity dried them on a clean feed-sack towel, put their petticoats on them and tucked them into bed, to wait for Santa Claus.

Lois had totally given up. If she got those two darn goldfish and a darn Betta Grable cut-out doll book from darn J.J. Newberry's, that would be darned ok. She didn't even pray. She and Mickey went sound to sleep. Very early the next morning Lois awakened to the feeling that something was different. What was it? It was just breaking daylight. She was the only one awake. What was different? Suddenly she knew what it was. Besides her mother and daddy not being up, there were no heart-reading birds! It was as quiet as a grave outside. It was almost as quiet as a grave inside!

Why not slip out of bed and get the darned goldfish and cut-out book and get the candy and orange out of her dirty sock. She slipped out onto the icy floor and into the front room, now gray in the early light. And there a sight for sore eyes! What was that—could it be? Then she began to scream and scream and suddenly her daddy was standing beside her with a piece of big kindling in his hand. Then Charity and Mickey. There was the Horseman doll, in a bottle-green velvet dress with teensy little buttons. She sat in a little chair by a little table and on that table was a little electric stove and a round blackboard with chalk. They all hugged and danced. Later, Lois and Mickey ate half-raw potatoes fried in lard on the little electric stove for Christmas dinner. Lois Jean knew then that that moment would seldom be surpassed in her whole darned life. "Thank you, heart-reading birds—dear, dear heart-reading birds!!"

Wherein Lois is Caught in Exodus 20:15

Sometime after Christmas Lois Jean ran out of chalk for the round blackboard with little wooden ABC's that moved around a track. The track not only went around the blackboard, but also across the middle of the board so little letters could be moved in and arranged to spell words. Lois had learned to keep a-e-i-o-u together. For some reason, they were used more than the other letters. Santa Claus had left these boards all over Tways. The problem was the blackboard was tin painted black and chalk had to be dipped in water to make a mark on the blackboard. Very soon she ran out of chalk. She needed chalk.

This morning she walked out of her house up past the pump and started up the mountain known as School House Hill. The mountainside was steep and worn paths ran across the side of School House Hill for those who needed to move at a more leisurely pace. It was cold, mountain cold. The hoarfrost stood in sharp frozen spikes, not lying in a soft silver blanket, as regular frost lay. Myrtle Mitchell, Ruth Carter, and Doug Ramey pulled coats tightly against the cold and walked straight up the hillside, abandoning the path to get to the warm school. They were in the other room, Miz Anderson's room. They were all in the sixth grade.

They all followed the path that the first one had made, skipping over ruts, going around frozen patches of water, stepping on rocks and, finally, like Christian on his way to the Celestial City, coming to the smooth, level, grassless yard. The basketball court was at one end and the two toilets were just behind the school. Gerald was ringing the bell. Lois Jean and Dwayne Farmer went to the first grade row. The others went into the other room that began with the fifth grade and went through the eighth grade. Miz Anderson taught penmanship and arithmetic—no counting on fingers.

Lois Jean warmed at the huge stove, burning coal and with a medal jacket around it so students did not get burned. Then she sat down at her desk. She lifted her desktop. There was the little brown drawing book with tulips in the back. She loved drawing tulips and coloring tulips. Miss Millsap called the roll. Lois Jean had perfect attendance. If she had perfect attendance for one month and was not tardy, she received a tiny piece of Dentyne Chewing Gum and a movie in Harlan. Oh happy thought! Oh! *Steamboat Around the Bend!* Oh! Chili and malt balls! Oh! Wonderful life!

Suddenly she noticed a new piece of chalk laying in the chalk tray. The side blackboard went all the length of the room, and above it was the alphabet in print and script. There it lay, a whole piece of chalk, flat at both ends. Never, ever used. Round, smooth, flat at both ends! One piece of chalk.

"Take out your writing books, and let's begin with tulips."

Lois Jean reached for the book in her book sachel next to her biscuit with bacon and jelly sandwich. Then entered her mind a stunning idea. Like Lucifer from Paradise Lost, it split her mind open. If nobody saw her, she could put that chalk into her book sachel. At that time the word "stealing" was not a part of her vocabulary. The chalk was all that she could think about. The tulip was not important. She drew it carelessly, the point in the center pedal lopped to one side. The red spilled over into the green grass. Her heart began beating faster. Then she gave up the idea.

She did not move the chalk. But a strange thing happened. It moved. It rolled slowly out of the chalk tray, up through thin air, and into her book sachel. Then came recess. She got a drink from the communion bucket, dipped with a tin dipper. Today Ruth was in charge of the dipper. Everyone who wanted a drink first had to fold a piece of paper from a Blue Horse tablet into a cup that would hold a dipper of water for about three seconds. Then a hole would form in the bottom of the cup and water would run down clothes, wetting everything. Lois Jean drank without mishap. She went to the toilet, ate the biscuit and jelly. At the end of the school day, she put on her coat, went down the path, around the mud, over the big rock, down the hill and into her house.

Then came the time for the chalk. Would it write on the round blackboard? It did! Oh, happy day! It wrote without being dipped in water. Oh! Joy unbounded! There stood Charity, hands on hips.

"Lois Jean, where did you get that chalk?"

"I don't know," she offered lamely.

"It's from school, isn't it?"

"I don't know. I don't know how it got here."

"Don't lie to me. Get the Bible." She sat down, opened the Bible and read: "Thou shalt not steal. Exodus 20:15." Charity had learned these skills at the foot of her mother, Ida Cox Moses.

Lois Jean had her first epiphany. What she had done had a name. A cold, ugly name. "Steal." The word was "steal". Lois Jean was the "thou," and the chalk was the thing that she had "stealed". It was a bad time. Was it worth it?

Charity continued, "You stole that chalk. God keeps a record which will be opened on the Day of Judgment and the record will be read and Jesus will say, "Depart from me. I never knew you."

"Oh, Mother, what can I do?"

"You're getting down on your knees by this chair and asking the Lord to forgive you."

She did. "Dear Jesus, Lord, forgive me. Amen."

Instantly the burden rolled away. She was free and she had the chalk! She got into her twin bed beside Mickey's bed and snuggled up under the Little Dutch Girl quilt. Drifting off into a feathery sleep, she felt loving and loved.

Wherein Lois Jean Eats a Golden Pear
in the Middle of Winter

Next morning Lois Jean got ready for school and sat down at the table. That was when she noticed that Charity had on her good Sunday dress. Why was she dressed in her good Sunday dress? She did not say a word. She followed Lois out the front door, leaving Mickey with James. Out the door, up the road, up the hill, over the rocks, across the path as it wound around the side of the mountain, across the barren schoolhouse yard and into the school. Nobody spoke above a whisper. Nobody stayed around the stove warming before beginning drawing tulips.

"Miss Millsap," Charity spoke so everyone could hear her, "could I speak to Lois Jean's class?"

"Mrs. Carter. . ." Charity interrupted her.

"Class, last night Lois Jean came home with a piece of chalk in her book sachel. She stole that piece of chalk. It was wrong to steal that piece of chalk. She prayed for forgiveness. Now she would like to ask your forgiveness. Come up here, Lois Jean."

Lois Jean stood up and walked down the long aisle from the third desk in the row to the front of the room. She stood in front of the first grade row. There she stood, facing her class and, most of all, Dwayne Farmer. Dwayne was smart. He could add without counting on his fingers. He already could say his 2's, his 5's, and 10's. He was sitting in seat five, looking at her. Joying in his own good fortune. Lois stood beside Charity. She could smell the banana oil that cleaned the hardwood floor. The room was silent. Row one, first grade; row two, second grade; row three, third grade; row four, fourth grade. She looked at the floor. Then, she began.

"I'm sorry. . . I'm sorry. . . I'm. . ." She ran back to her desk and put her head down, crying in great choking sobs. Charity left. Miz Millsap and row one went back to the tulips. Lois didn't like tulips today. She could not stop snubbing.

When recess time came, Miz Millsap came over, leaned down, and said, "You don't need to go out today. Just go to the toilet and come back in." She did. She wished that Miz Millsap was her mother. She came and sat down at her desk. The room was warm and quiet. Putting her head down on crossed arms, she thought about this bad day. Knowing that Jesus was busy writing down her sins in his Blue Horse Tablet with her name on the back. She awakened when she heard everyone racing in, scrambling around the stove to warm, then shuffling to their desks.

"First grade, take seats and take out your reading books. And you may look ahead at the pictures."

The rule was, don't look ahead. Stay on the assigned page. Lois Jean had gone through the whole book of orange and black pictures. She recognized Ben, Alice, Blackie the dog, and Whitey the cat. Father and Mother. Another sin. She glanced over to the tray below the blackboard. There was the chalk. She lifted her desktop. At first she didn't see it. Then her mouth flew open. In her desk lay a golden pear. A ripe pear. A perfect pear. How did it get there? Her first thought was to take it home. Then she could hear her mother saying, "Where did you get that pear? You stole that pear." She looked back at Dwayne. His head was holding up the top of the desk. Good ol' Dwayne. He had given her the pear. No, a boy would not bring a pear to school. Then she looked at Miz Millsap. Miz Millsap smiled. Suddenly, Lois liked tulips again.

Wherein Lois Jean Learns to Ride a Bicycle

Life had settled in—almost. Charity missed her old chicken lot. James was going to move it. Miz Brannon was busy with making butter, buttermilk, but no chickens to sell. Charity had that trade. She touched the little Duke's Mixture bag. Never empty.

Then came the surprise: Jimmy Brannon. Jim and Ida Brannon had Frankie, Jewel, and Virginia, and now Jimmy. He was a change-of-life baby. He was begun, according to Ida, when Jim Brannon's horse won the horse race at Churchill Downs. He didn't expect to win. It won. And Jim celebrated, and the result was a fine boy.

Ida Brannon had kept it a secret that she was expecting. Nobody knew until about a week before he was born. She continued making butter, lifting, swinging, climbing, squatting. All this was believed to be dangerous. The naval cord could get wrapped around the baby's neck, and it would die. The baby could be "marked;" a big red spot on its face, or deformed some way. Not many were deformed or sickly, or died. Rumor had it that Miz Chief Miller had had a little sickly baby. Just rumor.

Jimmy came round in all the right places. A baby doll, loved by three big sisters. Jim Brannon put a gate across the steps, and the front porch was filled with toys. Jimmy was spoiled. Miz Brannon took pride in that. She would come out and sit in the swing and watch the girls play. Time passed. Jimmy learned to walk, to climb, to play, to trust the girls who told him what to do. His favorite time was to sit between the girls and play "going to Harlan".

"Going to Harlan" was created by sitting backward in the porch swing, Jimmy between them. Lois Jean's feet reached the porch. They pushed the swing, starting the car: "Dar-Dar-Dunn, Dar, Dar, Dardunn, Dar, Dar-Dunn-Shaaun! The car had started. Higher and higher they went in the swing. Down to the store. Get out, go buy candy, get back on the swing and drive home again. The bad thing was, it wasn't sustaining. After a few Dar-Dar-Dunns, the whole thing could be boring, allowing other activities to bloom.

Another wonderful real thing was Virginia's new girls bicycle with the basket on the front that held "The Harlan Daily Enterprise". Newspapers that she delivered. She rode up and down the road, leaving papers on porches. Almost everybody wanted a newspaper; first, for the news, next for utilitarian purposes. Put newspapers down on a clean, mopped floor. Wad them up and lay them neatly under the kindling and make a fire in the cook stove. Stuff them around jars kept through winter, waiting to be filled with half runner white beans or red tomatoes or moonshine. Put the newspaper anywhere where water had to be soaked up, especially under the big tub for Saturday baths. Ginny could ride the bicycle and stop it on a dime, deliver the newspaper and hop on again. Newspapers were important.

Lois Jean wandered down the steps, out to the yard next to the McCurg's. There was the bicycle. Ginny was folding the papers and getting ready for delivery.

"You want a ride?" Lois Jean looked at the bicycle. Big blue bicycle. It was a girl's bike. Her feet fit! Ginny held the back of the seat and around the yard she went.

"Get the feel of the handle bars."

Then the most wonderful thing happened. Something inside Lois' whole body came together and she could ride that thing.

"Let's go around again."

Ginny didn't tell her that on the third "around" she, Ginny, had not touched the seat. Lois Jean was riding by herself.

"Lookee, lookee, y'all, lookee, I'm riding!"

Mickey and Jimmy peeped over the front porch banisters. She was riding, pumping the pedals and riding around the smooth front yard.

"Virginia," sang Miz Brannon. "Come here, Ginny."

Ginny helped Lois Jean off the bicycle. Lois looked at it, leaned against the maple tree.

She went up to it, put one leg on one side and leaned her body against the tree. She sat there a minute. The thought came. If she took it out in the road, she could ride better.

She opened the gate. Mickey and Jimmy were playing car, the swing flying high. Out she pushed the bicycle. Along came Vesti McCurg on her way to the pump.

"Here, let me help you, honey." She held it while Lois climbed on.

"You ready?"

"Yes, I'm ready."

Vesti gave the bike a little shove, and Lois Jean began pumping the pedals. She was riding. She was riding a bicycle. She was in front of the Miller's. "I'm riding, I'm riding!"

Miz Miller, who was working in her rose bush, turned to see her pass. Lois Jean was going too fast. She was pumping the bicycle.

Past the Farmer's, the Collins', faster and faster. Past the Miller's.

"Oh, lau, she don't know how to stop it," said a woman.

The road curved around the commissary. She went straight. The bicycle flew across the branch, missing big rocks that water ran on. It stayed in the air; everything in the world stopped; the blue sky. Then all was silent. Men and women ran from the commissary.

"Is she dead?"

"How bad hurt?""

"Oh, it's James and Charity's little girl."

She was tangled up in the bicycle, the basket off to the side. She lay still. Only one thing went through Lois' mind. "How do you make a bicycle stop?"

Someone was lifting the bicycle.

Someone was feeling of her legs.

No blood. That was a good sign.

Her eyes were opened.

"Oh, her eyes are open. Are you all right? Are you. . ."

"How do you stop a bicycle?"

"Wha'd ye say?"

"How do ye stop a bicycle?"

Some sat down. They laughed. Someone hugged her.

"Honey, ye got to know when to put on the brakes."

"Her knees are really skinned up."

"Lois Jean, Lois Jean, are you hurt?" It was Virginia Brannon.

Lois felt guilty. She looked at the crowd.

"It was her first lesson." She took it out on the road. Ginny was crying.

"Honey, your bicycle don't seem to be hurt."

"Here, let me put the basket back on." One of Murm Johnson's boys was ready to take it away, had it been junk. He took out a screw driver from his pocket. Down on his knees, to work on the blue bicycle.

"It ain't even scratched," he said.

Uncle Tom Becker said, "Set her back on it. If she doesn't sit on it now, she'll encounter fear. Put her back on it. This lesson will show how to pedal backward to put on the brakes. And tell Jim Brannon he has a fine girl."

Wherein Charity and Miz Brannon
Lay Out James A. Hatfield

Charity reached behind the cabinet to gather a little puny apple from the almost empty box. Since the move, a square box fit the corner better than a round bushel basket. She sat down at the tin-top table, yanked her dress above her knees, pulled open the drawer, took out the sharp kitchen knife, and began to peel the apple. The apple was old. Charity peeled it, leaving one continuous ribbon of red-to-yellow satin peel, finally falling into a little mound.

She took a big bite and halfway through stopped. Nothing moved in her entire body except her heart. There was the sharpest pain in the gum of her lower front tooth on the left side. Slowly she pulled the apple out of her mouth and gingerly touched the spot just below her lower lip. Carefully she pushed in just a little. Yes, there was a lump there and it was sore. She got the hand mirror off the dresser, took it to the back door, pulled down her lower lip. There was a lump below the tooth, but it wasn't red. Just a lump.

She picked up the apple, sliced slices and ate them carefully around the spot. What was a lump? It was something that wasn't supposed to be there. It was a disease. It would spread throughout her body. When she swallowed, the infection would travel to her stomach. It could spread to all parts of her body. It could kill her. Her children would be orphans. She raked the peelings into her hand, opened the door on the hot stove and laid them in. She stood rubbing the spot just below the lip.

Ideas swam around, but nothing settled into action. She started to cook bacon and eggs for James. It was almost time for him to get up. Charity had never been to a dentist in her life. Her teeth were white and she had no decay in her mouth. She had beautiful full lips framing white teeth and a smile that went all the way. Blue eyes, flawless complexion, and blond hair framing her face. And Jim could attest to the truth that she was the original in bed who often chanted, "Í was a virgin when you married me." The accented syllables emphasized in a passionate display that he had never before experienced.

Here was a thought. Dr. Mayhall, Dr. C. P. Mayhall. She had seen his sign in Harlan. Others had talked about Dr. Mayhall's being a fine dentist. Charity had never been to a doctor until she had had her appendix removed. The second doctor was that one who delivered Lois Jean at the hospital. Then the one who delivered Mickey. No one ever went to a doctor unless he or she was sick. Furthermore, Black Draught and a Vicks salve took care of much of what ailed the body and the teeth.

There was a thought. She reached up on the high shelf of the cabinet and took down Vicks, put a small, small bit of silvery Vicks salve on her gum. She stood in the warm kitchen, lifting the cap off the stove and spitting into the greedy flames sizzling the spit. James left for the mines. They saw little of each other. He was a night man. That suited her fine. Charity loved having a house, two girls, and reputation of being a good, clean Christian woman. She had reached her goal. She didn't need much and certainly not anymore children. She wanted a sofa for the living room. They were just about over the expenses of the twin beds, the linoleum rugs, and other stuff. Charity, truth be told, was playing playhouse and hers was better, more modern, more like those that she had cleaned in Harlan. She made up the beds, occasionally returning to the kitchen to spit the Vicks salve into the fire.

"Chari tee!" It was Miz Brannon at the front door. What did she want? She never visited anybody. "Chari tee!" When Miz Brannon called "Chari tee!" she went from a "G" note to the next "G" note. "Chari tee!"

Charity opened the front door.

"Honey, somebody has died up on Bird Eye Rock. They need help laying him out. Honey, could you go with me and hep me?"

"When? What do we do?"

"We lay him out."

"Well, yes. What about children?"

"James could help out. This is death. He could go in at three o'clock or later."

"I'll send Ginny to tell Basil Colins what's happening, and we'll be back around that time." Plans were loose. Charity liked being needed and James was pleased that she had been chosen for such responsibility. Off they went. Miz Brannon insisted on carrying a knife, a sharp kitchen knife, in a folded brown bag. "You never can tell." is what she said. "You never can tell."

Turning the curve, a feeling came over Charity. There was the Garden of Eden, all grown up. The doors to Shine's house were wide open. Her house, both doors opened. Jenny's house had been ransacked for wood. Even the chimney bricks were gone. The remainder of the porch banister and rails gone. A big fat pig was rooting in the backyard.

"Laume, Miz Brannon! I can't believe what's happening here." They crossed the branch on the little footbridge. The boarding house. No C.C. Moore. He was gone. Good riddance.

"What become of Helen, Charity?"

"James says she went to Middlesboro and then on up to Louisville. I really don't know."

Passed the Mitchell's, the Cloud's, the Young's, and some new people that neither knew. Up to the Carter's. Both doors were shut. Dogs roused. Lay back down when they scented Charity. Cow out in the pasture.

"Look at her tomatoes. Charity, she has tomatoes big as a saucer."

"Yeah, and she grows them from her seed."

"She's right smart, Charity. Now Ella is another case. Trouble with Ella Carter is that she reads too much. I have seen Ella Carter read a book or a magazine at one sitting. Them old detective stories all day long. She didn't used to be that way. It hurts us to be held and swayed by reading. Reading a newspaper is necessary; reading a catalog is necessary; reading a scrip card, a bill is necessary; reading a Bible once a week is a must. Beyond that, reading is almost the work of the devil. The house goes unsettled. The garden goes unplowed; the children goes without care." She paused, "It's not good to read too much, to dance too much, to you know what too much. Oh, laume, I didn't mean to go so far. My mother had a saying, 'all things in moderation'."

"Nothing to excess!" Charity.

"Who said that?"

"Ide Clotfelter said it to me. Ide said it was all right to do everything a little bit. But not all the time."

They had reached the upper field, curved into the mountain, a green pasture for the cow, well fenced. Charity pulled the barbed wire top and lower strands. Miz Brannon crawled through, then she held the wire for Charity. The hill grew steeper. If you craned your neck straight up, you could see the dynamite shack that Matt Carter kept. There were two people up there.

"Who's that?"

"It's Mr. and Miz Carter."

"What she doing up there?"

"I don't know."

"Let's walk up there and make sure we're on the right path."

It was a real climb. No path.

"You need the path. Go back down and follow the path." It was Nannie Carter.

"Come have some coffee." It was Nannie. She was outside the dynamite shack. They went in. Boxes of Atlas dynamite from floor to ceiling. Backed up to it was a single bed, and in another corner, a potbellied stove and across from that was an oblong wooden table with a drawer and cane chairs. By the stove was a rocking chair. The windows were covered with brown paper and signed. Anybody who had put a foot inside had signed his name on the brown poke paper that covered the two windows.

"Come in. Matt's riding dynamite back through the driftmouth to the day shift. Where you going?"

"Laume, we're going to bury one up on Bird Eye Rock."

"Would you like a little coffee?"

"Yes, Nannie, I would. It smells good."

Charity was observing every detail. By the door was a doorstop made out of chewing gum wrappers and she noticed that there were bigger pieces of "silver."

"Where'd you get the big pieces of that silver foil?"

"Why, from electrical tape they use here in the mines. It keeps the tape dry and it won't lose its power to stick. Everything has to stay dry." Nannie laughed.

"Ida, would you like some cream?"

"No, I drink it black. Do you grind your own roast?"

"Yeah, I do. It's fresher that way."

"Well, this is fine. Do you come here often?"

"Yeah, especially now that the children are all gone."

Leige and Irene drove in from Knoxville and took Ora and Ruth back with them. Then they bring Ruth, Alma and Junior. I come up and keep Matt company. But, I go down and milk the cow, feed the chickens and dogs."

Charity was looking around.

The single bed had one of Nannie's homemade quilts. Wedding ring pattern.

"Do you two sleep on the same bed?"

"Yes, we do. We spoon!" She threw back her head and laughed.

Charity looked at her in disgust. "Yeah, and you have a bunch of kids from it too." She sneered up her upper lip.

"Well, we've got to be going. Thank you, Nannie, for the coffee. I wish I had a little getaway like this. We'd all be better for it."

"Thank you, Ida Brannon, for all you do for James and the girls," she paused, "and Charity. They's a path that will take you right to the house, the place where yer goin'."

"Thank you, Nannie."

Charity was well on up the path.

"She's an independent little thang, isn't she?" Ida nodded. "Charitee," she sang out. "Wait for me."

Charity was fast. She could move fast. But she stopped and waited.

They walked, following the path. The path was not much. They had walked a good half hour, when a boy stepped out in front of them. He did not speak. They followed him. He would hold back the growth so it didn't hinder the ladies. On they went. He pulled one final rhododendron branch, and there was the cabin, smoke curling up from the chimney and flattening out against the cold upper air, forming a little cloud just above the cabin. Charity and Ida walked up to the porch, a huge, wide affair with the banister that would support weight. There was a rocking chair with leather upholstery. Empty. The boys were on the porch and in the yard. Not a woman anywhere. They went inside. A fireplace held a big pot of boiling water. There sat Wild Man beside the corpse, still lying in its bed.

"We ain't been able to move him since the old man died," one said.

"Well, now." Ida responded. "Well, now." She was organizing her mind.

"Get me a pan of water. I brought some soft rags and some soap."

Wild Man got up and returned with a wide enameled pan. Dipped the water from the black pot, scooted the table over, and stood back.

Ida walked over to the old man. His mouth had been tied shut with a single strip of cloth that went under his chin and was tied in a knot on the top of his head to assure that his mouth was closed. Two gold pieces lay on his eyelids.

Ida looked at the Wild Man. "You've done well, boy, you've done well."

"Ok, Charity, lets shape him. It's too late to put a smile on his face. Charity, make up lather. Put the soap in the pan and lather it up."

"Just as soon, Miz Brannon, as I can get my hands into it." She began with the surface and lathered her hand, then both her hands, rubbing the softened soap, and lather began to form.

"Honey, it needs to be thick. Lather it more."

Ida untied the strip that went under the chin and up to the top of his head. It was a hard knot. She reached in her apron pocket, took out a pair of scissors and cut the string. The mouth did not move.

"He's set. And he's set well."

"There now, the lather's ready, Miz Brannon."

"Put it on both sides." She looked cheery.

Pearl's faceless head with some brains exposed, swam up in her mind's eye. She hesitated just a minute then took both hands, filled them with lather, and patted out on both sides of the face.

"Now rub it in."

Charity did. She rubbed and rubbed.

"Some more lather."

Charity rubbed the lather.

"That's right, Charity. That's right."

Ida picked up a brown paper poke that had been folded and was lying at her feet. Unfolded it and pulled out the finest kitchen knife. Sharp as a razor. Suddenly wild man was beside her with the straight razor. She took it. Wiped some of the mound of lather off and made the first slide. Not a hair cut loose. The hair was like pig's bristle. On the second swipe, this one with more pressure, she felt the hair snapping. A clean strip was left. She made three more swipes before she called for more lather.

Charity stirred the water, asked for more water from the boiling pot. Wild Man obliged. They were into the rhythm of the delicate operation. Three swipes, rub and lather onto the face. Hot water, lather up the face with quick movements. Lather on the face, three more swipes.

Ida moved to turn his head. Of course, it didn't move. She moved everything to go to the other side of the bed. It was against the wall. Wild Man moved it out so she could wedge in. Suddenly, a flash of sunlight glinted against the handle of the straight razor. That was when she saw the initials TMG. That would be T.M. Gibson. She was shaving the dead man with T.M. Gibson's silver straight razor.

"Do you have a little lard, honey?"

Wild man went to a corner where some shelves stood and returned with a small bowl and handed it to her. Ida put her finger lightly across the lard and smeared it into the thick black hair.

"A comb or brush? Do you have a comb or brush?"

He shook his head, no.

"Do you have a toothpick?"

He did. He came back with three. Ida began to smooth the black hair back.

"Here, Miz Brannon, let me do that."

Charity made a "comb" with her fingers and moved it down through the thick hair.

"Here, Charity, make him a part. Make him a straight part, here?"

Charity angled the toothpick and parted the hair, glued down with lard, ran her fingers through the front. That's when she noticed that the coins on his eyelids were $20 pieces.

"Miz Brannon?"

"Charity, I think he's ready."

They stood back. Ida went to the door. "Boys, he's ready."

Several people came in the room. No sound except for a few shuffles and sniffles. Finally Ida said, "Boys, let's sing Amazing Grace."

"Amazing Grace how sweet the sound" . . .her sweet voice followed by Charity's. . . "that saved a wretch like me. I once was lost, but now I'm found. 'Twas blind but now I see."

Someone commenced crying softly.

"Do you'ens have a Bible?" Miz Brannon asked.

Nobody spoke, but one went off and came back carrying a fine leather Bible.

"Charity, read Psalms 23," handing her the Bible.

Charity opened the book in the middle and, sure enough, there stood the book of Psalms. That you can count on. A minute later she had turned to the 23rd Psalm:

> "The Lord is my shepherd, I shall not want.
> He maketh me to lie down in green pastures."

Others joined in.

> "He leadeth me beside the still waters.
> . . .Yeah, though I walk through the valley of the shadow of death,
> I will fear no evil."

One boy moved up toward the place where the old man lay now on the door that was placed on two cane-bottom chairs. He had a pair of scissors. Pulling down a piece of his hair from the back of his neck, he cut a small piece and laid it over the old man's heart side. The others followed. When they all had finished, Wild Man stepped forward.

He closed his eyes, tilted his head back, opened his mouth. Out floated a sound, a high tenor voice in perfect pitch. "Going Home, Going Home; I'm just going home. Work all done, life all gone, I'm just going home." The sound floated out and soared into the hollows and crevices of Bird Eye Rock.

Charity opened the Bible in the middle:

> *James A. Hatfield*
> *Married*
> *Lucinda McCoy*
> *By stepping over the broom*
> *December 25, 1898*

"Here, I'll take that." It was one of the boys. "And don't ever talk about what you just read. See I'd know where it came from. You've got two purty little girls, haven't she?" He smiled, setting the Bible back on the mantle.

"Yes, I do have two little girls and I'm married to James L. Carter and I don't plan to talk to anybody, thank you."

The boys were carrying their daddy out the door up to the graveyard.

Up came Wild Man.

"Thank you for all you've done. We lost our old lady sometime ago. She was from Virginia. She could read, write, cook. Most of all, she could sing. She took lessons and could have been a singer. Then she met my old man and they run off here. We've always stayed just here. James Carter knows about us. Now you do. Don't ever let it go anywhere else. He turned and ran up the hill.

"Laume." Ida shook her head slowly. "Charity, haven't we seen something?"

"Yes, Miz Brannon, we have." Charity had a gift for never saying it all. For keeping the best part, the incisive part to herself.

"The Hatfields and the McCoy's."

"Charity, we don't tell nobody any of this, not anybody." Her voice trailed off. "Do you hear me, Charity? Nobody."

"Miz Brannon, are James and Jim 'somebodies'? Tell me that."

Ida paused. "Well, now, my guess is they are. In the bed with the lights out I think we could tell them what we did today. Jim knows. I have sold butter and eggs to them for years."

"How?"

"Jest set it on the back porch and next day money was there. Come on. Let's get out of this place. I want to get some greens for supper." They walked down the slope, around a curve, down a steep embankment, and then they stood in an upper meadow. The cows came this far sometimes. Dandelion, blackberry, and poke. Poke was digestible at three or four inches high. Beyond that, it could kill a body. This was high poke.

They stuck the brown paper bag under their arms and clamped down, leaving both hands free to cut greens. Not much here now.

"Have ye ever eat violets, Miz Brannon?"

"No, and I don't know why. If you've never done it, it's hard to start."

"I've got potatoes and beans out, cooked apples, cornbread. That's a nourishing meal."

"Where'd you learn to say that?"

"One of the cooks at Pine Mountain Settlement School told us that. Good nutrition is necessary for a healthy body and good hair. Her hair was awful and her breath would knock down a horse. She dipped soda. She knew nobody would want to kiss a mouth like that!"

They bent over laughing, releasing fear, horror, and accepting the truth that we would all be cold and stiff some day. What about the resurrection of the body? Was there the presence that could infuse life into that rotting old body? Was there? Jim didn't much believe so. Charity said she did, especially when she went to church. Miz Brannon kept her own thoughts to herself.

This meadow was filled with songbirds, creeping things, hopping things, and occasionally a panther and even a bear. Thoughts swam, diffused by laughter. They were glad to be in the meadow on the way home.

Wherein James is Identified as a 'Versal Man

James was waiting for Charity and Miz Brannon to get back. The girls had out the "encyclo-pledias." They were standing open, forming a ring, and they were inside the ring playing. Jim sat in a chair, drinking hot coffee out of the saucer and smoking a cigarette.

"Daddy, look!" screamed Lois.

He jumped up. The girls had not been allowed outside. He wanted them safe.

Mickey tuned up to cry. "I was Julie all day. It's my time to be Delia and your time to be Julie. Daddy, hit's— it is—my time to be Delia. Make her let me be Delia," Mickey whined.

"Lois Jean, you be Julie and you can have this cherry sucker. He pulled one out of his jacket pocket on the back of the chair. "Here."

"OK, Mick, you can be Delia." He handed Mickey a sucker. That all worked out just fine.

Lois pulled an encyclopedia over and something caught her eye. It was a naked person. She looked closer. The person didn't have on a stitch of clothes with his arms outstretched above his head and his legs apart.

"Shit–house–mouse, Daddy. What's this?"

"Don't you ever say that again! You're not going to grow up that kind of a woman. Do you hear me? You're going to college. You're going to speak the King's English. Let me see what you got."

He threw back his head and laughed.

"What is it, Daddy?"

"It's a man. It's him. It is universal man. It is universal mankind."

"What's that between his legs?"

"That is a man."

"Are you a versal man, Daddy?"

"I reckon so. Well now, here's your ma!"

He closed the book, stood up, and put the book on the top of the kitchen cabinet.

"James, get the children out and let me fix you something to eat and get you off to work."

"How was it, Charity?"

"Everything went well." She unfolded the whole story.

"James. . ." she trailed off.

"I know. I know."

"James. . ."

"I know."

Suddenly, she was sweet, appealing and there was the woman he had loved so long ago. He moved toward her. She met him. He held her, tilted her face up, and kissed her long, long and sweetly.

They spoke not a word.

"Boy," he thought. "I'm all for funerals." It was the best of times. It was about to be the worst of times.

He walked out to the back porch. Charity reached for the iron skillet. For some reason she ran her tongue along the inside of her upper teeth. Her tongue was resting. It turned firm, commenced against the eyetooth on the right hand and swooped across the big molars and then came sweeping back. This in rhythm of sliding the skillet out of the cabinet. She stopped. The kitchen was silent. She did it again. Yes, there was a sore lump on the left side. . . just between the eyetooth and the one to the left of it. "Oh," she moaned. The hair rising on the back of her neck. She moaned. Was it pyor-rhea? She would have to have all her teeth pulled and get false teeth.

Jim stepped into the discussion Charity was having with herself and found his universal rising. He went towards her again. She was whispering, "Oh God. . . Oh God." What a response. He reached for her. She did not protest. He pulled her to him. A funeral can affect you that way. She needed comforting. "Oh, God—"

Ecstacy. He pulled up her dress. Started up with the slip.

"Oh, God. . . Don't you touch me. Get out of here." She screamed.

He felt the deflation of his "universe" and assumed that of a befuddled coal miner. In the twinkling of an eye she had. . . he trailed off.

She stood, gently moving her tongue across the sore place. It was raw, swollen, waiting to break forth and let the poisons ooze out and she would swallow it and she would die. The biscuits burned. She opened the oven. Black soot rolled out, bitter and threatening in some undefined way. At this minute, Mickey ran into the kitchen. Charity grabbed the child, lifted her by the arm. Then grabbed the egg turner and began hitting the little legs. Again, again, again, again.

James grabbed the egg turner and Mickey at the same time. Took her out on the back porch. Hugged tight. "Hush, little baby. She's OK, just reacting to funeral. A funeral, little baby, a funeral, little baby."

Lois was there.

"Mickey, you can be Delia. You can be Delia." Mickey was scared. All three stood in a tight knot on the porch.

"Come on. Let's eat. You don't want it to get cold. Come on," Charity called.

Eggs, pork chops, gravy, just the bottoms of the biscuits, blackberry jam, and butter, jelly glasses filled with milk. They sat.

"Let us ask the blessing." Charity prayed; the others mumbled:

> *"Be our shepherd, Oh Lord,*
> *We entreat thee.*
> *And may we receive all good things*
> *From thy sweetness.*
> *Amen."*

They heard Butchell coming with the ice wagon. They heard dogs barking, birds singing, and Charity was chewing everything on one side of her mouth.

Wherein Charity Sees a Fine Dentist

Dr. Mayhall was upstairs in one of the imposing brick buildings in Harlan. Only two people were in the waiting room. The man had been there before her. She waited for him to come out. Then she was escorted in to see Dr. C.P. Mayhall.

He had a little mirror—round and on a handle. Stuck it in her mouth. He'd look at all her teeth, her gums. Dr. Mayhall was a fine dentist and a fine man. Outstanding. He looked and looked.

"Miz Carter, this is a common gum boil. It's nothing."

Silence.

He put a little salve on the spot. "Put this on it and it will go away. A gum boil is often started by a stray food particle. Often a bit of vegetable husk, perhaps corn, or apple peel that begins the irritation. You have a fine set of teeth."

"I want them out."

"Pardon me?"

"I want them out."

"Miz Carter, your teeth are fine."

"I want this twisted out of my mouth."

He looked at her in disbelief. "You want me to pull the tooth?"

"I want you to extract all of them."

"I can't do that."

"Yes you can. I have pyorrhea of the gum. I want all of these teeth out. How much will it be?"

"Two dollars a visit plus three dollars a tooth plus replacement dentures.

"How many can you pull a visit?"

"Miz Carter, your teeth are fine."

"How many can you pull a visit?"

"Once they're numbed, as many as you can stand."

"You numb my mouth?"

"Yes, I give you some gas."

"It will be painless?"

"You won't care with the gas and a little novocaine."

"Can you do it now?"

"I can, but I won't. You go home, settle down, come back and if you insist, I'll extract your teeth. I will not extract any teeth today. None. Not one."

"Thank you, doctor." She looked up and smiled sweetly. "You have been a savior."

She slid out of the big dental chair. He took her arm. Suddenly her demeanor was that of the well-bred lady. It was as if there were two women there. One rational, appealing, the other very angry. "Miz Carter, who is your doctor?"

"Dr. Clark Bailey. Dr. Clark Bailey." She repeated.

She didn't tell him about Tways doctors, the mining camp just outside Harlan. About two miles away.

Charity could be a compilation of Miz Petit, Miz Aundi, Miz Whitefield, Miz Gibson, and Miz Miller.

"Well, if you don't change your mind, I'll see you next week some time. Your teeth are good teeth, Miz Carter. They don't need pulling; that's plain crazy."

She walked all the way to Tways. Nobody whom she knew came by in a car. She ran her tongue across the place. She would go home and put some of the salve on it. How would she know if a streak of red did begin in her mouth? She could die and leave the children. James would marry Halley or some other woman and. . . . Suddenly, she paused to take in the place where Lee Haynes' car had hit her mother. When they got her to the hospital, the nurse poured peroxide on her. The peroxide boiled so hard it could be heard out in the hall of Harlan Hospital.

She ran across the road, ran through the gates, then quickly up the road to Nell's house.

She thanked Nell for letting Lois Jean and Mickey play.

"Charity, you've got smart girls. Lois was telling me about the 'versal man."

"The what?"

"The 'versal man!" Nell laughed. "Charity, she saw a pitcher of a man in the books you have. The ones the girls line up to play paper dolls with. This book had a naked man and James told them that it was a universal man. Me and Ola are going to get us a set of them books."

Charity couldn't decide if Nell was making fun of her or enjoying the moment.

"Well, thank you anyway. I'm going to bring you some slices of the cake when I bake it, Nell."

"Charity, you don't have to do that. Neighbors are neighbors. See you at the pump."

Charity went in and began to bake an applesauce cake. She put on her apron. She peeled the apples, sifted the flour, added sugar, heated the cookstove, laying extra kindling. She pinched salt, mashed apples, stirred in eggs, beat the batter, beat the batter, beat the batter—it felt good to beat the batter—greased the pans, added the apples, found the peach brandy that Miz Carter had given, added the secret ingredient that set her cake apart from anybody's. The kitchen glowed in afternoon sun. The children were playing. James was working. All things were proper. Simple as that. Everything was doing what it was supposed to do! Simple as that. She ran her tongue across the gum. It was smooth and there was no salty feeling.

A week rolled around. She had an appointment to have seven teeth pulled. She had decided on seven. Would she go? She owed it to Dr. Mayhall to go. She had promised him that she would be there. She had given her word. She hated to disappoint a doctor. She was on the horns of a dilemma. Anyway that she went was a bad decision. Charity hated decisions. It's a far, far better thing just to do something; don't think about it. Just surprise yourself by doing it. But what did she need to do today? Were her teeth poisoned? Was the pyorrhea spreading? Oh God! What if it went throughout her body and poisoned her and she would die?

She took off her dress and put her work clothes on and went to the pump. There stood Murm Johnson. Murm Johnson. Murm and her brood lived just outback of Charity across the branch. And at the back edge of the largest field in Tways. It was not clear who owned that field. Did it go with the Gibson house or did it go with the camp? Didn't matter. R.C. Tway Coal Company owned it all. Murm was pumping water frantically as if it would save somebody's life by pumping hard and fast.

"What are you doing out over here at this hour?" Charity felt empowered. Here was a woman beneath her.

"I can go any damn place any damn time I want to and pump all the damned water I want to pump." This said in a staccato beat that kept time with the chewing gum. "And how about chew, Charity Carter? How about chew? What chew doing here? Ye 'spect milk and honey to flow in your bucket?"

Charity was stopped completely. She stood there; then she spoke.

"I'm trying to decide to have seven teeth pulled today."

"Gotamitty, seven teeth—pulled out yer head, seven teeth today?" The gum never stopping, Murm never missing a beat. "Why yer having 'em pulled?"

"I could get pyorrhea of the gums and the poison go through my body. I would die. My children would be orphans."

"Well, say," Murm's voice trailed off. "Well, say." She repeated. "Do ye want to die and leave it all? Do ye now?"

"No, I want to be here and. . ."

"Then go woman, go now, go this minute and get the pisen looked adder. I got to take this wader home." And she was gone.

Charity began pumping water. "The Lord works in mysterious ways, his wonders to perform." That's the old saying. He had sent Murm Johnson to tell her to get rid of teeth that might cause pyorrhea of the gums. She picked up the bucket and strolled thoughtfully back to the house.

James was sitting at the table smoking a cigarette. He had made coffee. For some reason, his actions verified Murm's voice from God that she, Charity, needed to have seven teeth pulled that day. She began the breakfast of eggs, bacon, biscuits, pork chops, milk and coffee. First the biscuits. She opened the cabinet door and sifted the flour in the bowl. Added the salt, baking powder, lard, worked it well, poured in milk. All from the memory of the feel of the ingredients through her hands, and the look of the fullness of the bowl, and the length of time it took for the milk to run out of the bottle. She had stopped measuring anything and never missed. The biscuits were the best. Never a failure. She had made biscuits since she was ten or eleven years old and the nice thing was, they were always the same. A constant in her life. Today she was quiet. Jim could only guess what she was up to.

"You're doing something today?"

"I'm going to town this morning. I have a doctor's appointment."

He wanted to hear no more. No more came. He went to bed.

She dressed in her best. Asked Nell to keep watch on the girls, and she set out for Harlan. She had no more than rounded the commissary, when Smokey McCurg came along. He picked her up. They spoke a greeting, nothing more until Harlan.

"Where you want out?"

"Right here will do, thank you." She went up the stairs; she would be the third patient.

C. P. Mayhall could pull a tooth in a flash. He would numb the gum with novocaine and add the gas pump, which the patient controlled. Nothing was different if you had one or one dozen teeth pulled out at one time. Recovery, now that was something else.

She climbed into the chair. He numbed the teeth with the sharp sting of the needle. She went back to the waiting room and waited for the numbing to take effect. Medicine worked well with Charity. She believed in good medicine, and it worked for her.

She got back into the chair.

"Now, Miz Carter, when you want to, pump on the gas; it will do the work." He put the little black bulb into her hand, adjusted it up her nose, and they began the project.

He had thought about which to pull. She needed one side that she could eat on. "I'll extract the seven left upper." He proceeded with the front teeth and moved to the back.

"Spit and pump." He spoke often to her. She cooperated. She pumped until they were both laughing.

"It's going to be better, isn't it?

"If it's what you want." He packed sterilized cotton in the bloody holes in back and moved forward. He worked alone. Forty-five minutes later, he grasped the last tooth with the silver instrument and pulled hard.

She moved.

"Spit and pump. Did that hurt?"

"No," she giggled.

"Spit."

He removed the teeth from the plate where they rested and swabbed the mouth. "Don't take the cotton out for at least two days. Don't rinse your mouth. It will start bleeding. Don't sip liquids through a straw. Don't chew anything on that side. Take some aspirin if it hurts. See you next week, same time. Oh, sit down fifteen minutes in the waiting room before you leave."

"Thank you, doctor." She spoke reverently. She went by the desk where the receptionist sat.

"How much do I owe you?"

"$20."

"For what?"

"For pulling your teeth."

"It's two dollars a tooth."

"Well, the gas was six dollars."

"He didn't use six dollars worth."

"Yes, he did."

"You wasn't there. You don't know."

Dr. Mayhall came out. "Laura, its three dollars."

"That will be $17."

"Sixteen is all I have." She reached into her pocketbook and pulled out two fives and six ones. "That's it. See you next week." She walked out, downstairs and out into the bright sunshine.

She went down the street, past the stores, to the outskirts of Harlan. Two-mile walk. Someone would pick her up soon. She felt a little light headed. She walked past the hotel, past the new Harlan Theater. Across the bridge. Up the sidewalk past the two-story houses with big yards, big trees on each side of the concrete sidewalks leading up to big front porches with swings on both ends. If maybe she could go up on the cool porch and sit down. She could open the door, go into the cool kitchen refrigerator for a cool drink of water. She knew the kitchens of many of the houses in Harlan.

Her mouth felt full and she leaned forward and spit in the dirt. A big bloody spit. She stooped over, looked down. The bloody spit was heavier than the soft, fine dirt where it landed. It had soaked down into a tiny bloody pool with dots of blood around it. She stayed bent over, utterly fascinated by the shiny bright red tiny creation.

Mrs. Whitcomb, Lois Jean's Sunday school teacher, called out from her porch, "Charity, are you all right?"

"Yeah, I'm all right."

"If you need to cool off, come up here."

"No, I'm all right." She glanced down and the tiny spot had sunk into a dark red hole.

She walked on. "Wish I'd brought me an umbrella," she whispered aloud.

On she walked. She passed Baby Jones' store. He marked up prices on what you needed just because he stayed open on Sundays. He was a heathen. Dried up old man.

She bent over and watched the shiny blood sink into the soft, brown silt. It reminded her of the mercury the children rubbed on pennies. The pennies were bright, but with use, turned old again. Nothing bright could stay.

She passed where her mother was hit by the full force of the car and taken to Harlan Hospital. The peroxide bubbled up 'til you could hear it outside the door in the hall. Not one car passed going in her direction. Not one.

She crossed the road into Tways, looking both ways. She didn't stop at the commissary. Went straight home. James was asleep. The girls had not gone to Nell's. They were in the living room, playing inside the circle of encyclopedias, opened to form walls. They scarcely noticed her.

She went to the kitchen, lifted the cap on the stove. Her mouth was full from the time she'd been just inside the gates of the commissary to this minute. Her mouth was full. She spit, and bloody spit sizzled like a streak of lean hitting the hot skillet.

It was time for James to get up.

"James." She heard herself saying it.

"James, get up. It's time to get ready for work."

She was pulling her tongue back, making it thick. She relaxed her tongue, put it up against the ridge and said, "James, do you hear me?"

He rolled over. "I'll be up directly." And he was. Came into the kitchen, pulling overall straps across his shoulders. She spoke not a word. Set pinto beans, fresh coleslaw, hot fried cornbread, bologna, cold milk, jelly, water and hot coffee before him. She stepped out on the porch and spit in the yard. She stood there a minute, then gently, gently put her tongue against the warm wet cotton where her teeth had been.

"$16. Seven teeth."

She pretended to be sorting clothes out of the washing machine that was on the back porch. He picked up his dinner bucket, went to the back door.

"You all right?"

"Yesh."

"What?"

"Yes," tongue against the ridge.

"Are you pregnant?"

"No."

Not a "goodbye". Not "be safe". Nothing. He walked past her, down the steps, and around the house.

Suddenly her knees went weak and things went black. She grabbed the edge of the washing machine, breathed deeply and went into the kitchen. The kitchen was hot. She went into the living room and stretched out on the divan. The front room, the guest room, the room with the divan and piano. She stretched out on the divan, took a soft, clean dish rag, and wiped her mouth. It came out clear.

The pain, the pulsing pain. She had never felt pain like this pain. Furthermore, she didn't believe in medicine. She lay in the pain. She moved.

"Lois Jean, get me an aspirin off the dresser. No, out of the chifforobe."

Lois Jean had never done anything like that.

She went into the bedroom, opened the drawer on the chifforobe. Everything in that drawer was nothing that she had ever seen. A strange feeling swept over her. She picked up a little square package about the size of a pocket watch. It felt bad. It felt ugly. She threw it down. Then she saw paper letters folded. There was a watch that Daddy never wore. Neatly ironed and folded funeral handkerchiefs.

"Bring the aspirin, Lois Jean."

She saw a small tin box with writing. It was aspirin. It rattled when she picked it up.

"I've got it, Mother."

"Get me water."

She went to the kitchen, got the jelly glass, poured it full of water, and took it to her mother.

"Get me two out. Don't you two go out of this room." She relaxed, believing in the goodness of the aspirin. She was soon asleep. The girls played paper dolls, and Mickey Fowe stretched out on the cool floor and went to sleep.

Charity slept hours. The girls slipped into the kitchen and fixed biscuits and jelly, drank water, and went back to the living room.

Finally, Charity got up. For some seconds she totally forgot about the teeth. Then the pain flooded back into her mouth. She got up. Built up the fire and fixed scrambled eggs, apple butter. She went out on the back porch and spit. All clear. No more blood.

"What a strange day," she thought. "I didn't get much done in the house." She did notice that the floor needed washing and waxing with Johnson's Glow Coat. Pain is a curious thing. It dams up all pleasure. It takes all energy. It scares you. Exactly what does pain feel like? How is pain different from pleasure? Sometimes pain and pleasure were close together. That didn't include a headache, or a. . . it was not easy to. . . She lifted the cap on the stove and spit.

She washed the dishes, wiped off the oil-cloth table. That was a pleasure. The oil cloth was smooth, like satin. It responded well to wiping with a clean rag. She wiped the eternal flowers on a white background, and breathed deeply. Pure pleasure to clean the table. It got clean. Easily.

"Whata you doing home?" It was James standing behind her in the kitchen.

"The mines flooded."

"It didn't rain here."

"It didn't rain there. It rained on the other side of the mountain and honeycombed through. We had a helluva time gettin' out. One of these days," his voice trailed off. He often reminded himself that he was lucky. Not one part of him had been taken by the coal mines, and he had been in longer than any of the rest. Then there was his baby brother Arthur.

"Where the girls?"

"In the living room."

She fixed him two bacon, lettuce and fresh tomato sandwiches. Duke's mayonnaise, iced tea with lemon, and a large slice of applesauce cake.

He went off into the bedroom and stretched out on the bed. She heard him snoring. She stayed up late battling the pain. Finally, she broke over and took another aspirin and slipped into bed.

Sometime later James woke up. Got out of bed, went on the back porch in the pitch black and peed. He heard a rushing noise, some varmint rudely interrupted. He stood in the darkness, everything still, most everybody sleeping. His girls all sleeping. Everything silent. "God's in His heaven. All's right with the world." He slipped back into the bedroom, eased into his side of the bed. He was stretching out long when he heard her. Why was she moaning? He had not identified the sound. Maybe she needed turning. He reached across, found her shoulder, turned her. When he did, she turned toward him, moved closer, found the part of his body that fit hers and moved quickly.

Was she awake? She seemed to be moaning. Her chin was in the hollow of his collar bone and pumping hard. His body bloomed in response. Suddenly the ecstasy—that single ecstatic moment. Release. And sweet play-back. She rolled off of him. And said, "More, more, more gas!" He chuckled, rolled over and went to sleep.

He awoke. The sun was bright. He leaned back on the soft feather pillow, remembering every sweet drop of last night. He got up, pulled on his pants, was walking past the dresser and glanced in the mirror. "Gotamitty, what was that? Blood. Gotamitty, it was blood all over the undershirt, bright blood. That meant just one thing. It was active bleeding. Gotamitty, Gotamitty, Gotamitty." He went into the kitchen. "Charity. . .

"James, you raped me last night."

"You're mumbling."

"Yes, you did. You raped me last night. I woke up, all slimy. And it was yer slime!"

"Charity, who'd the blood come from?"

She stopped stirring the sweet milk gravy, turned to face him. Eyes widened when she saw the blood on that shirt. "Where'd this blood come from? Where'd this blood come from? It's not mine!" Slowly, she began a grin on the left side and grew across her lips then, tilting her head back slowly and opening her mouth wide, exposing him to the bloody holes in her gum.

This coal miner had seen everything in the coal mines, including brains oozing down from the place between the rocks where Arthur's lifeless head had been. He reeled back into the table, catching the edge. Not a word. She turned and commenced stirring the gravy. "I had seven teeth pulled yesterday, and you raped me."

He took five steps to the kitchen door and ran to the toilet. He pulled off the bloody shirt and stuck it down the hole. He came out, went back into the bedroom, pulled out a shirt from the chifforobe. Pulled out a fresh shirt. Froze. "Oh, my God, no rubber." He went out the front door and up the road for the mines.

Mining coal had to be done by a man who had no fear of the dark, no fear of smothering in a small, dark place filled with its own movements, drips of black water, and sounds of thousands of tons of black bituminous coal and slate moving and shifting; the sudden deadly silence and then the random pop of timbers supporting the shifting top. A cold, oppressive, clammy menace permeated this underworld, clinging to the walls, the tons of top slate clinging to hands and picks and shovels and clothes and in the eyes and llungs. Coal mining is akin to seafaring or soldiering, heroic, endless, dangerous labor. A brotherhood of an ancient, classic profession was as elemental as labor itself.

Death was a possibility from the time a miner entered the driftmouth until he returned to the sunshine. Miners were "earthnauts" who loved the camaraderie of a kindred soul. The trust one human put into another human was a trust that declared that lives in the mines were intertwined. One would lay down his life for the other. Miners are a special creation, which few people understand.

Wherein James Goes to the Mines
for Communion

Smokey was taking a smoke on the front porch.

"Howdy."

"Howdy, to yourself." It was always clear when things just were not right.

He went on up the road past the Mitchell's house, past his old house, and Jenny's, almost all gone, across the creek, past the boarding house. He noticed that one end of the front porch swing was down. On past the Young's empty house, past Ma's. They were gone, off to the courthouse. Up the road, past the dynamite shack, and entered the cool dark of the mines. Turned on the electricity, that meant one dim light at the driftmouth.

He stood there. Quite still. Cool and dark. Took his hard hat and began the descent. Water was still there. Up to knees. It was just right. He went back up into a little room. The ceiling was inches high. He held his breath, went back in, eyes closed—hand outstretched, feeling for a hole. Of course, the water would be coming past "the shelf."

He waded through, and there was the high shelf. He felt around, and there was the bottle. Filled to the top with the last of the shine that he and Shine had made. He opened it. Drank. It was smooth. So much body and a good burn.

"Lord, I'm having communion." He drank more and began a dialogue with himself. "I don't understand. Now, I have experienced something that I never have." He took another swig. "I thought that seeing birth and death was the book ends, Lord, and I could take everything else between. But this is something I can't get a handle on. I can't live the rest of my life without a handle. Whata ye say?"

He was standing up to his waist in water. He had forgotten to fill the light with carbide and it was flickering. He didn't care. He was warm and the water was cool. The water was over his knees. He slipped the bottle into his pocket. Turned to go back. If he ducked down, the water would be over his head. "I need to get a handle on this." He turned around, went back inches it seemed. Reached up. There was the shelf. Dry as a bone. He was warming up, feeling good. The light flickered and fell into the darkness. He felt the dry dust and crawled up on the ledge.

"I got to get a handle. . . a handle on this." He sank into a warm sleep.

Meanwhile, Charity picked up the bucket and went to the pump. Miz McVeigh, Miz McCurg, and Aunt Ella were at the pump. She passed Smokey's house. He was sitting in the swing.

She stopped. Where was James? It was late afternoon, and he had not returned. Well, he was pouting at his mother's house. Wonder how he told her what was going on. She smiled at his discomfort. Went to the pump and waited her turn. The talk was about the revival up on School House Hill. Another topic concerned grapefruit. Did anybody get hold of them big yeller oranges that tasted bitter as gall? No, they sure don't taste nothing like oranges. Charity did not say very much, careful to keep her gums covered.

She turned to go, and who should be coming up the road but Mr. and Miz Carter. She never broke down and called them Matt or Nannie. She was surprised. Right then and there a wave of fear, of concern flooded her.

"They lau, I thought you were home."

"We've been to the courthouse. Good cases too. One going to the electric chair. How are you'all?"

"We're fine. Just fine."

"Tell James to come. It's time for supper."

"Where is he?"

"Why, I believed he was at your house."

Matt stepped up close. "How long has he been gone? A long time?"

Nothing—not a word.

"Charity, did you all quarrel?"

"That's none of your business."

"Yes, it is. You want him back? You better tell me everything you know."

"Well, if you must know, we did have a quarrel."

Matt Carter stood perfectly still. He did not speak.

"What direction did he take?"

"I don't know. I wasn't looking. I don't care what direction he took."

Nannie pulled his coattail. "Matt, let's go."

They left her standing there.

The energy of anger moved through her stomach, her knees, through her feet, into the ground. Who would take care of them, if James died? What would happen to Lois and Mickey? What would happen to her? Where would she get money? How? She walked along, one arm outstretched to balance the heavy bucket.

"I need him."

Charity had lost everything she loved. Her father, her mother, Pearlie. She had loved Pearlie. Shot by the Green boy. Nothing ever done about it. Otis died. Everything she loved, except food, had been taken from her sooner or later.

She had learned not to show love. For when she showed love, the person or thing was then taken from her. That's why she never told James she loved him. She never held the babies or ran her fingers through their hair or kissed their cheeks. That's why she loved only twin beds, and bedspreads, curtains, a sewing machine, a new dipper. Because she could lose all that and buy another one. You could not buy another James; the children could not buy another real Daddy.

"Lord, I need this man. Could you return him?"

She had to be careful, or the Lord would hear her and think that she loved James Carter. Truth was, she needed him. She did not need his love; she needed his services. The children needed him.

The girls' routine had not been interrupted. They ate supper. Washed their faces, said their prayers, and got into twin beds with pink damask bedspreads. Then in unison the prayer:

> *"Now I lay me down to sleep*
> *I pray the Lord, my soul to keep.*
> *Fi-shou-die before I wake,*
> *I pray the Lord my soul to take. Amen.*
> *God bless Daddy, Mother, and Lois and Mickey. "*

Charity turned out all the lights, went out on the front porch, and sat down on the top step. It was close to nine o'clock.

Smoky decided he'd better inform Chief Miller that James had come by in a hurry. Chief picked up the phone and put in a call to the tipple. "Any reason James Carter would go into the flooded mines?"

"Naw, he's probably at his Ma's eating cornbread and drinking buttermilk or just drinking." It was young Russ Collins. "We'll check around." Russ walked out of the driftmouth away down the hill to Carter's and yelled through the screen door.

"Howdy, and is James with y'all."

"Howdy, Russ. No, he's not here."

"Well, he's not home. Smokey saw him earlier passing up the road."

I know he's not in the mine. It's been flooded."

"Jim always seeks solitude when he is beyond settling a problem. He seems to be able to work through it alone better than with somebody else." Nannie put a glass out.

"Here, Russ, crackling cornbread and a glass of buttermilk. Matt, get in touch with Tom Becker and turn this over to him. He knows my child better than any of us." Nannie's philosophy was "what will be will be". She thought often of that part of Arthur's head between slate for all eternity.

Matt stepped to the back porch, put his fingers up to his mouth, stretched his lips tight, and blew. Out came a shrill whistle. Three times he blew. He waited. Three more times. In seven minutes, Tom was in the kitchen listening.

"Smokey was last to see him. Spoke to Chief Miller, called the drift-mouth. He's not in the mines and that's it."

"I'm going to get the boys together and we are going to have a look. Would he be huntin'? Did you go into the woods? Did he go into the flooded part of the mines?"

"I checked around, Tom." Russ was enjoying the cracklin'bread with pure apple butter and buttermilk.

"Let me get the boys." Tom stepped to the front porch and whistled as Matt had done three times, the one long whistle.

"Matt, I need a light on the porch."

Matt took two oil lamps and set one on each end of the banister. Soon there were six young men standing in the front yard. Smoking and waiting. Matt went to the banister.

"Boys, James has not been heard from since afternoon. I believe he might have had reason to go down in the mines. We are going to check it out."

The boys cleared their throats, sniffled; one or two shifted body weight, but did not speak words. But their signals were straight.

"I'm going to the shack. Ye going?" Matt said, turning to Nannie.

"I believe I'll do better here."

Russ Collins had never seen anything like this. All the boys there. Tom was standing at the door. He stopped. Matt too. They turned and looked at Russ Collins. Russ spoke to Tom. "We've all depended on you to do what you do. And you do it. You get the job done. If there's anything I can do, let me know. Otherwise. . . he trailed off. Nannie, just one more time. hit me with that cracklin' one more time."

Tom's bunch of miners started toward the diftmouth. Matt took down a miner's hat, opened the cabinet, took out his carbide light, ran his hand across the front, and there was light.

"Hey, Tom, here's you a hat." Tom came back to get it.

Shortly he returned. "Boys let's go get Jim. He's down in the mines in a place that's been closed for years, and it floods."

"Underground water floods it first. It's a fine place to hide. Where's Mudjumper?"

"Here I is, Mist Tom."

Mudjumper was the strongest, widest jumper, skinniest, pure athlete in Tways. He could outswim, outjump, and outrun anybody or anything. He could break through any door, window, and into any box or safe in Harlan or Bell County. He was very good to have in any emergency. He got his name from being able to jump over a mud puddle when he was a baby. In upper camp, he was a legend.

"Stay close to me," says Tom.

Down they went. As the boys stepped out into water, they made a place for Tom coming last. "Boys, watch out for copperheads. Sometimes a washout. Now let's all yell. . .Jim!"

Tom yelled, "Jim, oh, Jim."

Others joined. Loud.

No answer.

"M' Tom, where is the shine hid?"

"How you know that?"

"M' Tom, we never touch it. We knows they's a place somewhere."

"Follow me."

It was dark except for the little rings of light on the miners' hats.

"Hold each other; we are going in. I'm leading the way. Don't turn loose."

"M' Tom, I'll be next to you." It was Mudjumper. He had moved up and got hold of Tom's wrist. They moved up.

Suddenly a scream.

"Snake."

"Copperhead don't swim around on the bottom."

"Copperhead on dry glitches."

On they went, water to the chin. Suddenly, Tom was sinking. It happened in an instant. Mudjumper held him.

"Hold on, Tom. I na goin' let che go. Hang on. Mudjumper na goin' let che go."

Junior grabbed Mudjumper around his waist, freeing his hand. The two began wading through water. They heard coughing, then puking behind them. Finally Mudjumper felt solid ground. He reached forward a little to the left and felt dried dust. On further and he felt a warm body.

"Jim, Jim get up." Tom Becker was talking. He shook Jim—smacked at him.

A moan. A very drunk man.

"You done drunk all the shine. You white cracker, you. You done drunk the shine." Mudjumper grabbed at him, and Jim rolled into the cold water.

"Stand up, Jim. You stand up, you dumb cracker."

"You say it, M' Tom. Tell it. Praise God and tell it." This from Junior.

Jim didn't know where he was, and he didn't want to be there. He began to swing.

"Stop it! Stop it this minute," roared Tom.

"Heah, M' Tom, let me thar." Mudjumper. They changed places. "If he step in the hole, Mudjumper get him, M' Tom." Mudjumper landed one square on the chin. Jim went limp.

"Now, us kin get 'im outter thar. He's like uh wet sak uh cow feed."

They commenced passing him. The black, silky water helped his wet body slide through from hand-in-hand. They moved back toward the drift-mouth. That's when they heard Jim groan. "God, oh God." It was perfectly quiet behind him and before him. "Oh God. . . oh God." Moved forward. "Why did ye do that, Charity? Why did ye do that?"

Not a sound from the men. The whole feeling and action based on those two questions changed what the men felt. Each man could connect to betrayal. Utter, complete betrayal. Jesus in the garden betrayed by Judas. James on his back and betrayed by circumstances. By this time the boys had moved him back toward the ladder that went to the driftmouth.

Jim commenced hackin' and spitting. Coming to.

"Where in hell am I?"

"Jim, it's Tom. You got into a little trouble in the water down in number two. Jim, ye was on the ledge in number two."

"Jim, did you hear me?"

"Oh God, Tom, oh Gotamity. In the dark water."

"Boys, turn loose. This water feels good. I'm ready to go," and he trailed off.

"Jim, ye got two little girls waitin' for a good strong Daddy—Jim, two little girls!"

There was no starch in his body.

"Here's de step. We's goin up to de lite"

They squeezed two in front of Jim, and they started up. Back in the line, one asked "His face in water when you found him?"

"Another ten or fifteen minutes he'd be dead. He was out."

Matt was at the top of the steps. "Did you find him?"

"He's with us. He's fine. Just fine."

"Tom, they's no words. This is beyond words." The two men stood, each recognizing so much unfairness of things. They pulled out red bandana hand-kerchiefs and blowed into them, wiping their faces. Others gathered round.

Matt saw Jim. Hugged him. "Yer drunk. Did you drink all of it?"

"Well, Pa, it ain't there now." He turned to his rescuers.

"Boys, they's no more on the ledge. Them bottles floated away. . ."

Total silence.

Then Preacher spoke up. "Full or empty?"

Everybody laughed, slappin' each other on the back and moving out.

"We got to call Russ, tell him Jim set some dynamite and it washed out, and he was rounding it up."

"Jim, you need to get dry," said Matt.

"Matt, let me take him home so's you don't have to account for time, action and so forth. When folks ask, you can say that Jim was putting in an extree shift. And, Matt, he sure did. He sure did, Matt."

"Tom, much obliged, much obliged."

"Matt, he's close as any son I would have ever had," Tom Becker said quietly.

"I've just been baptized, but they's no doves over my head." Jim.

Matt stood close. "Yer're goin' to Tom's. Get cleaned up and go home."

"Where's yer bucket?"

"Didn't bring one."

"Get a bucket to carry home. And, Jim, go home. Them two little girls . . ."

Matt limped into the shack. His back actin' up. He opened a box and handed Jim two strawberry candy BB bats and a little jar of mercury for shining up pennies. "Fer them little girls."

Jim lifted off the lid of the bucket, took out the top where food was stored. He dropped the candy and mercury into the bottom. "Pa, do you keep an extra bucket just for this?"

"Jim, I keep it because that's Arthur's bucket and you bring it back."

Tom was waiting. Everybody else was gone to get dry. They started out.

Nannie was on the back porch. Jim and Tom waved. She waved back. Matt would tell her everything. She sighed a prayer of thanksgiving and went in. Slid a huge pot from under the bed and stirred it carefully then licked the spoon. Blackberry wine. . .

James followed Tom into Tom's house. The surprising house. Books, nice furniture, soft lamp, and a fine wife.

"Tom," she whispered, "coffee on the stove." She took hot yeast rolls from the oven. Miz Brannon's butter on the table covered with a white dish cloth. She lifted out the rolls. "Jim, go take off the wet clothes and put on some of Tom's."

For the first time, he looked down. He had on an undershirt, pants, and no socks with his two-toned shoes. "I'm fine, Miz Becker, if ye'll just get me a shirt. I'll get it back."

She put the hot rolls on the table, hot coffee and butter. Then she pulled out a drawer, took out a silver spoon, filled it full of something from a bottle.

"Swallow!"

"I, what. . . ," he sputtered.

"Open your mouth and take it!" She demanded.

He did. He felt it running down his throat, soothing, and his gorge commenced to rest.

He sat down at the table and ate hot rolls, with Ida's butter and blessed the goodness of this woman.

"Tom, is there work tonight in the mines?"

"Not in that mine, Jim."

"Tom?"

"Finish and let's go smoke."

"Let me. . . could I have one more cup of coffee, Miz Becker?"

She poured it. Hand on the back of his neck. Her curse was barrenness. And unlike Sarah, she never had an Isaac. She loved this boy as she would have her own son. Truth be told, she had seen him through many a scrape. The good thing was her heart strings were tied to his, but loosely, not as a mother's strings are tied, tuned to the agony and despair when there is a tragedy. There were blessings in not having children or, if one could have a Jim.

Tom and Jim went out to smoke. Miz Becker set the leftover rolls in the warmer and wiped all the crumbs from the smooth oil cloth.

"Tom?"

"Jim, go home and act natural. Store your hurts away. Know that what she did, she had it to do. Because of who and what she is."

"Tom, I didn't know. . ."

"Jim, we all have got to search. I always wanted. . ." He stopped. He could not verbalize his pain and loss.

"Jim, you need to get your priorities set. Set like the ten commandments. Did you notice the first one's love? Thou shalt love, Jim. You can't live without love. You can't love a lump of coal or a dollar for long. Not a car nor a tree. You have got to love something that can love back. Most of us think that we have that something the way we want it. But, we don't. Jim, you've got two little girls, bone of your bone and flesh of yer flesh. Your blood mingled with hers flows through the little girls. They love you. You love them. They are yours to cherish." He paused. "To love and to cherish, Jim. Be their protector. Spread your wings around them. Take care of them. Jim, did you see the bird in the front room?"

"Naw, can't says I did."

"Well, Jim, that bird gets the care that your little girls get. That damned bird is talked to, fed and loved. That damned bird is her child. So is the damned cat. Miz Becker's the finest woman I've ever known. She's. . ."

Jim stood in the little yard in the bowl of the dark Appalachian Mountains in Tways; a quiet peace that comes with understanding fell on him and he was ready to go home. His home to his two little girls.

"I'm much obliged for all that you've done for me; you've handed me back my life. There are no words that I can say. . ." he trailed off. "I've never been closer to another person than I am to you, Tom Becker. I would be dead more'n once if you had not been there. . ."

"Jim, read. Read. It's all in books. Jim, that's what Miz Becker taught me. The great gift of reading. It's next to having a bird!" They both laughed.

"Go home."

"I'm on my way."

He went to the screened door. "Much obliged, Miz Becker."

Wherein Every Action
Changes the Course of the Trip

He passed out the gate and started down the hill to cross the branch to make his way past the Young's, the Cloud's and others. He had on Tom's shirt and carried Arthur's bucket. There was one other thing. No more petticoat government. He would take care of her for the simple reason that she had given him two little girls who loved him unconditionally. He stopped. The thought struck him again, no rubber! This time he reacted with a broad smile. God works in mysterious ways, His wonders to perform.

He was just about to cross the branch when he stopped cold. In the middle of the branch was the automobile. The automobile, now old and rusted. The tires all washed away. Totally brown rust. The steering wheel was there and a board across the springs that one time boasted leather upholstery. He remembered when the car first appeared. A car that had run into the branch and somebody had gotten out of that car and run. Somebody else shot. Everything grew still. Next morning there set the car. Some sat at night and waited for the car to be moved. It never was. The car had been running very well. Somebody would come for that car sooner or later.

A week went by. Then came a gully washer. Some said it was a cloud burst. It ran through the camp, taking toilets that hung over the branch, routing up poke weed and other growth, back in some places into yards, washing away gardens. It went over the car, got into the tank, went all through the interior. The sun came out, but the branch washed over the automobile for days. Then it dried out. Still, nobody came to the car.

Things began to live inside the car. The windows got shot out or broken by boys throwing rocks. One Halloween a bunch of boys tore out all that they could and burned it on the inside. There was some gas in it, and it exploded, making one helluva noise and burning Junior Carter on the hands. After that it was all brown and blended in with nature.

Later a creative imagination wandering over the rusty frame and bare springs where the front seat had been brought forth a wide board that went from one side of the front seat to the other, covering the springs. Now a body or two bodies could sit and, holding onto the steering wheel, bounce all the way to Knoxville or Hollywood. "P'likin" all the way. Matt and Nannie enjoyed watching the exuberance of children playing on the old rusty car.

James' reverie was suddenly interrupted. Out stepped a little girl about the size of Lois. Came out of the bushes down to the creek and stood looking at the car. Water from the runoff was running through the car on the seat. Then she saw Jim. She stood. She was the color of coffee that had a lot of cream in it. And her eyes were blue, no green. Her hair was in braids. She had on socks and shoes and a freshly ironed yellow dress. She looked at him.

"When can we ride the car?"

"Well, not 'til some this water goes down," he replied.

Nothing back. He waited.

"What's yer name?"

"Angelique! What's yours?"

"I'm Uncle Jim." He liked that. "I'm Uncle Jim," he repeated. "You gotta last name?"

"She does." And out stepped a woman, dark woman. The tallest woman he had ever seen. No, he'd seen her before. He'd seen her when the colored women had come that day and lined up in front of the commissary for marrying one of the colored miners. She was from Alabama. She was a good six feet tall and black. All this in a flash. Suddenly James remembered his feelings. He wasn't too well. He needed to move toward home.

"You could be her sho nuff Uncle. Come on honey, it's too swift for you today." She turned and the two disappeared into the bushes.

He turned toward home. He wanted to be home. He wanted a hot meal and a long sleep. He'd been pulled inside and outside. He looked up. The sky cobalt blue. The trees were green. He knew every inch of the place and loved it; he belonged to it. He passed the little three-room shotgun houses. He rounded the curve where Miz Brannon lived. Yep. Ladies at the pump. Nell Farmer, Little Vinnie, Novella Haynes, Miz Brannon.

"Well, and Jim, was it dry enough to set dynamite?" Bless Ida Brannon's heart.

"Naw, I wasted the best part of four hours taken out what I put in."

Now that was the truth. It had taken him four hours to leave the house, get to the mines, find a shelf, drink what he found, and go to sleep. And he did take out what he brought in.

"We'll all be back to normal tomorrow. We'll all be back tomorrow. Hello, ladies."

Nell had a different slant. Russ was her brother-in-law; and he said that Jim went off in a huff. Nell would be open in her mind to what was happening next door. Jim witnessed two or three curtains moving. It was turning dusky dark. Down the road to the third house on the right. The girls were on the steps. "Daddy! Daddy, Daddy! Did you bring us something! Daddy!" He sat down on the top step, opened the bucket, lifted out the top, and in they went.

"Daddy, a B-B bat!"

"Daddy, a B-B bat!"

Lois Jean looked like him; Mickey looked like her.

"Here, look at this." Out came the mercury.

"Sit down." He reached in his pocket for an old penny. Nothing. Not a single penny did he have. Charity was peeping out from behind the window shade in the living room.

"Well, does anybody have a penny?"

"No."

"No."

There she stood, a dirty penny in her hand.

"Much obliged, but I'll find one." He got up and went inside.

He came back directly with his own penny.

"OK girls, come here."

Each claimed a knee. He laid the penny in the palm off his left hand. Took the mercury in the little nose drop bottle that he saved when Charity had used up all the neosilvole nose drops that she squirted up the girls' noses all winter long. He dropped one drop—one tiny drop. Took his finger and smoothed the liquid mercury into the dirty old penny. It began to shine like new money. It was shiny and clean. "OOOOOOOOOOOh, lookee, OOOOOOOOOOOOOOOh! Magic, ain't it, Daddy—isn't it, Daddy—fall in a can of paint. Oh, Daddy!" and Lois Jean hugged his knee. "You are magic, Daddy." Mickey was in the process of licking the B-B bat slowly to make it last.

It's a shame they have to grow up, he thought. These are special children, his girls, and he would. . .

"It's ready. Come on; let's eat."

They got up and the girls went to the table. James came in and sat down. In the middle of the table were some garden flowers in a pint jar. James reached across the table, grabbed the jar, strode to the back porch, and threw the jar and flowers as far as he could. Came back in sat down.

Lois Jean began to cry. "I picked 'em for you, Daddy. I picked 'em for you."

A curse settled over the beans, greens, bread, iced tea, the apple butter. Only Charity enjoyed the whole episode. She was in her element. She was standing at the stove, back to the table, smiling broadly, forgetting her teeth. Next morning the jar of flowers was back on the table with two shiny pennies beside the jar.

James had been up for some time. He went to the toilet. Rolled him a Duke's Mixture cigarette. Sat on the cool seat and flipped through the tool section of the Sears and Roebuck catalog. Decided he would go to Ma's for breakfast. Slipped back into the kitchen, picked up his lunch bucket, and walked out. Up the road to the three-car garage where he kept the old black Durant. Opened the car, went into the back, raised the carpet a little, reached in for half pint. Slipped it in the bottom of the bucket. Closed the car, locked it. Closed the garage door. Walked out to the path where he opened the bucket and grabbed some leaves and leafy moss. Packed it in around the bottle so it wouldn't rattle. Got back to the pump. Saw Ida before she saw him. He froze so the movement wouldn't catch her eye.

How, he wondered, had he made such a terrible mistake marrying Charity? How? He had been caught, snagged by her looks, her helpless little girl look. He had mistook who she was. Certainly, what she needed. He came to the foot bridge across the branch. The water was still a little angry. "Still water runs deep," so the saying goes. Charity was not still water. Charity was a wild branch. She had the two girls. He needed to stay with her. He had to try. She wouldn't let him into her world. She used him for the money so she could play playhouse.

He passed the Young's, Joe back in prison. Jess away at a sanitorium. And they were good boys, not as bad as some who were in the mines.

Dad was on the front porch rolling one from Duke's Mixture. "Howdy, Dad."

"I saw you comin'. Howdy yourself." James liked that greeting. It meant just one thing: the old man was in good spirits.

"Come up and sit down."

James settled in the swing. Matt stood a minute, then settled in his huge leather covered rocking chair.

"Jim, your Uncle John's dying with bad lungs."

"Yeah, that's too bad. Mines and smokin' ul do it every time."

Long pause as they sat rocking and taking long draws from cigarettes. It was the ritual. Gave a man time to think. To get hold of things. The old man continued.

"John and Ellie have had some misfortunes. John had big plans. And Ellie is a fine woman. He let things go to take care of more pressing things. The baby drowning in the lye water. His own lungs. More than a man can carry. He let things go. Now today on the courthouse steps they's going to sell his two lots in the town of Loyall for taxes. That comes to forty dollars, Jim. I want you to go down this morning with me and claim them two lots." He gave Jim time to grasp this.

"Let's go, Pa."

Jim loved his old man. The old man was wise. He knew the art of "laying low." Yet, not much passed by him. Jim listened to his dad.

"You'ens need to be there soon as you can." Ma had handed Jim biscuits.

"Pa, I'll go get the car. Take it easy and I'll meet you between here and the garage."

Nannie poured hot coffee in a blue quart jar with a spoon in it to keep it from breaking, set it in the bottom of the bucket. Stuffed catalog paper round it and placed jelly and biscuits in the top—several! The old man picked up the bucket, went down the steps down the road.

"Dad, Harlan's a pretty place in the early morning, ain't— isn't it?" Say ain't, fall in a can of paint.

"Yeah, Jim, it is." They were at the courthouse, admiring the doughboy from World War I. The war that ended all wars.

There were already many standing around. All at once Matt stood up and went to the top of the steps just as the door opened a crack and in he slipped. Everybody waiting to get in knew that Matt Carter needed to pee. It had to be worked out so's it could be worked out. The people waiting on the steps knew all about that. Especially, if it were an old man.

"You got the papers, Juanita?" He spoke to a daughter of an old friend. "How's Maude?"

"Why, she's just fine." Her voice sang. "She speaks often and fine about you, Uncle Matt. Now here's the papers you sign. Do you make the mark?"

"No, honey, I write."

"Sign right chere, Uncle Matt. And here."

"What's the date?"

"October 30, 1938."

Juanita looked over the papers. Licked her thumb and thumbed through.

"Done! The lots in Loyall are yours, Uncle Matt."

"Now, Juanita, we're coming in after awhile and I want you to transfer these to Jim."

"Why shore, Uncle Matt. No problem thar."

"Juanita, you look like your Ma. That is a fine woman. Say, I send greetings. Do you hear me?"

"Lau, yes, I hear you, Uncle Matt."

"We goin' to stroll a little; then we'll be back." He went out the door. Walked slowly He was bent over, and sometimes the affliction was a help.

Jim looked at his old man, frail, wouldn't be here much longer. Matt started slowly down the steps. The courthouse doors swung open for business.

Jim raced up the steps to the frail old man. "Come on, Dad, turn around. Let's go in."

Dad looked at James. "I'm done."

"The business, Dad. The lots!"

"I'm done, boy." He winked broadly.

"Are you sayin' you have the lots in Loyall?"

"Half of business is done. Let's sit in the car and eat a biscuit."

"Dad, how'd. . . ?"

"I got my ways, Jim. I've got my ways." The coffee was just right.

"Does Ma know your ways?"

"Son, she knows a lot. She knows a lot but not all. Never tell all. Hit's often mistook. 'All' is often mistook. You have one picture of the way that it is. You can never transfer it all to somebody else. They'll add new colors not meant to be." Pa was hard to follow sometimes. Hard to follow. The two went round to the pool hall. It had changed since Jim was a big man there. Younger bunch. Seemed meaner.

"Let's go to the A&P, Dad."

"No, let's go see Juanita."

"Who?"

"Juanita, at the courthouse."

"Yeah, she's a distant cousin."

No more was said.

So it was that they returned to the court house. "Sign right chere, Sir." They were seated in an outer office. The halls were teeming. Folks were buying land on the courthouse steps. Coming into Juanita's little outer office, getting it all sealed and delivered by laying down cash.

James Carter had never been "sir." It felt good. He signed.

He signed, and then the third time.

"Hit's yourn, sir."

"Much obliged, Ma'am."

"Uncle Matt, tell him we're related."

"You're related, distantly."

Juanita giggled.

"Dad, we got to go. I've got to eat and go to the mines."

"Thank you, Juanita. Say hello to Maude."

"Yes sir, Uncle Matt."

Riding back, both felt that something had changed forever. Neither knew what.

"Jim, every action, every action changes the course of the trip. Did you know that?"

Jim repeated, "Every action changes the course of the trip. Does that mean, because I signed some piece of paper, that my life changed?"

"Yes, it does. Here." He handed the envelope to Jim. "This is yourn. You've done for the entire family. This is yourn. Don't say anything to anybody. It's yourn."

"What is it exactly?"

"It's two lots close across from the roundhouse in Loyall, Kentucky. You can move to Loyall when this place closes up, and that's not far off."

Jim was quiet. He liked where he lived and what he was doing. He could handle anything in R.C. Tways. Anything. He had places where he could go and get back to himself. He had friends who could speak of pain and recovery from pain. Here was a place where he could use his talents. Making shine, fixing automobiles, setting dynamite, gauging a seam of coal, telling a good story, a joke, singing a song, playing a banjo, training a dog, shooting a varmint between the eyes. He learned he could wire a house with electricity. He could literally handle several volts of electricity. He could make love. He could play a good game of cards, checkers, and pool. He could get knots out of little girls' shoelaces and. . .

He really didn't want to go anywhere. He wanted to get water out of a pump, drive to Harlan on Saturday nights, eat chili and malt balls at the Little Jim Drugstore, see *Steamboat Willie* and go home with three girls. That all darted through his mind with a new awareness for the first time.

"Dad. . ."

"Jim, don't say anything. Ponder it, Jim, ponder it."

They passed the house. Girls ran out. He slowed down, picked them up.

Wherein Lois Jean and Mickey
Play with Martha Ruth

When time came around, Charity went back to Dr. C.P. Mayhall, and he extracted more teeth. She spit blood and walked towards Tways. Basil Collins picked her up. She muttered something and not a word more. She never spit or swallowed. He let her out at the commissary. She looked around and then spit a blob of bloody spit and went into the commissary.

Later, she said to the girls, "Lois Jean, Mickey, come here." Charity eased two paper pokes on the table, lifted out the lard, cabbage, dried pinto beans, pork chops, oatmeal, aspirin.

"Miz. Owens wants you to play with Martha Ruth."

Playing with Martha Ruth was a mixed blessing. Martha Ruth had every toy, every doll and her very own room filled with everything. She sat in her own wicker rocking chair that fit her. She was always clean and her hair was in ringlets to her shoulders. She wore dresses with matching hair ribbons. Everybody loved Martha Ruth. The only thing was, she didn't play like the rest did. She didn't say, "P'like I'm going to the store and p'like you drive me there and p'like we wrecked the car and fell out."

Martha Ruth liked the falling out of the car part, but she just fell in the floor and laughed. Nobody laughs when the car wrecks. Martha Ruth laughed if she felt good. Otherwise, she just sat in her wicker rocking chair, all clean, and just looked straight ahead.

The two went up on the big front porch and were met by Lennie Rue from Elcomb. Lennie Rue was a big woman who could actually lift Martha Ruth and who was named after a place, not a person. Lennie Rue's mama had met her daddy at Lennierue, Kentucky and loved him so much she named her daughter Lennie Rue. Lennie Rue cared for the house and took care of Martha Ruth. Sometimes the girls did not ever see Miz Owens.

"Come in, come in." She led them to Martha Ruth's room. New toys. And there sat Martha Ruth.

"Hello, Martha Ruth." No answer. They began looking and examining everything. Martha Ruth never moved. It took a little time to get things started. Would it be "Julie and Delee", "ride the car to the A&P", or maybe "play school?" They were winding up to get started.

Lennie Rue was going to the pump after water. "Lennie Rue, water runs out of the faucet here in the kitchen."

"I know, Miz Owens, but it's not cold. It's warm. Fine for dishes but not much else." Lennie Rue wanted to visit. She wanted news. Truth told, Miz Owens wouldn't mind some news. She didn't go out as much as some of the others.

When Lennie Rue went out, Martha Ruth got up and limped toward the door, her left arm bent, fingers splayed out. Speaking not a word.

The girls got on either side, got to the door, and giggled when all three couldn't go through at the same time. Lois Jean and Mickey stepped back. Martha Ruth went out on the porch. The girls came up on either side, taking hold of her hands. She turned, let Lois take her bad hand, and down the steps they went.

How normal it all looked, thought Miz Owens. She sometimes believed that God had cursed Vance with Martha Ruth. But, that same God had blessed her with a bunch of fine boys, whom she prayed would stay out of the mines.

The gate was closed. All three stopped. Then Mickey picked a pink petunia, put it up to her nose and sniffed hard. The petals flew up around her nose and out came a fearsome sneeze. Lois, then Martha Ruth, laughed. Mickey liked making people laugh. She did it again. More laughing. Then Martha Ruth sat down on the little path and reached over, pulled a petunia root, and all came up. She sniffed, and petals flew up around Martha Ruth's nose. Martha Ruth laughed because the petals did what they had done with Mickey. Martha Ruth had ordered the petals to do that, and they did. If only Martha Ruth could let the girls know that she knew that. She enjoyed their wonderful games. She just could not let them know that. She laughed and laughed. Lois broke off a petunia and they all laughed when the petals flew up around her nose. What fun. They pulled the petunias and laughed.

Miz Owens came out with a camera. Came out and took pictures of three little girls transported to delight putting pink and white petunias under their noses and drawing the petals up and holding them in place with deep breaths. Martha Ruth could do everything that they did. Everything. It was a splendid, glorious time. Children, the child's world, the ability to find joy with anything, anywhere, at anytime. Don't let it end. Let it go forever, she prayed.

"Miz Owens, I've got news." It was Lennie Rue opening the gate. Two buckets of water filled almost to the top and not spilling a drop.

The moment was gone. The game ended. Miz Owens was annoyed. She walked toward the house.

"Lennie Rue, fix sandwiches and lemonade for the girls and serve it on the porch."

"But, I've got news."

"I don't want to hear that cheap gossip. Fix the sandwiches."

Miz Owens went back to her stationery and fountain pen. She wrote to relatives. Sent the recipes they requested. What was the news? Truth be told, this tender-hearted woman, who bore burdens gracefully, felt that she had slighted Lennie Rue, who did the best with what she had. And Lennie Rue was pouting.

"Lennie Rue, pour us a cup of coffee and you rest awhile."

That did it. Lennie Rue poured cream into a tiny cream pitcher and put a silver sugar spoon beside the bowl. She sat on the side of her chair, twisted around until her elbows could rest on the table, but also so she could rise quickly. That showed intent. She drew in a deep breath, screwed up her nose, turned down her mouth, indicating that the news was not to be taken lightly.

"Well", she screwed up her nose the second time. "Well". . . she paused, hoping that Miz Owens would interrupt and say something to hasten her, but that did not happen.

"That woman that lived on the other side of Miz Miller, you know. The one that Mr. O. . . ." She paused and began again. "The one that somebody set up in the house on the other side of Miz Miller? Well, now. That woman got pg and didn't want. . ."

The girls were there, and Martha Ruth was restless. Without missing a beat, Lennie Rue got up, opened the refrigerator, a real one, took out the mayonnaise, jelly, and reached in the cabinet for the peanut butter and homemade blackberry jelly, without seeds.

Girls all watched as she began the sandwiches.

" . . .and didn't want the you-know-what; got her a coat hanger, untwisted it, and rammed the point home—if you know what I mean. B-l-e-d like a stuck pig. In the middle of this, somebody came in for service, and she was laying in bed. He threw back the cover, and all he saw was b-l-o-o-d." She spread a light layer of mayonnaise on one side of the bread, peanut butter and jelly on the other. Put them together and cut off the edges, sliced them diagonally, put them on saucers and set the saucers on a tray. She continued her story.

"Run out the door down to the office and they called the Harlan Hospital. They come and took her to the hospital. She died."

"Yes, Lennie Rue, she died months ago. That is old gossip. Old cheap gossip. Put that tray out on the front porch on the little table; no, put it in her bedroom."

Later Lennie Rue poured lemonade. "You'ens want Lennie Rue to make ye some dessert?"

No answer. Truth was, Lennie Rue wanted "something sweet."

She took down the vanilla wafers, got the marshmallows. Took out a pie plate. Spread a thin, thin layer of Miz Brannon's butter on it, placed a marshmallow on top of the wafer, did this ten times and popped them in hot oven. Sat back down at the table. A minute later she opened the oven.

"Perfect—just perfect."

She carried them into Martha Ruth's room, lifted them up delicately with her little finger pointed straight out.

"Here's ye some dessert, girls."

Lois took one and delicately lifted the light browned puffed up top off and ate that part first. Then the game began. Who could take three bites of one wafer 'thout it crumbling? Martha Ruth did and was pleased with her accomplishment.

Lennie Rue began cooking supper. She began by cutting up one of Miz Carter's fryers. It would take at least two, maybe three, to feed the Owens boys. Drake could eat the whole one by himself. She began singing, "Tempted and tried, we're often made to wonder why it should be thus all the day long, while there are others living in sunshine never molested, tho' in the wrong. Farther along, we'll know more about it. Farther along, we'll understand why. . ." she trailed off into a hum.

Lennie Rue was a good woman. A woman in control of herself. She liked being Lennie Rue. She never put on airs. She was saved and had been baptized in the Cumberland River. Her mama had spoiled her, but it was good spoiling. And she could make a guitar talk. She could also sing shaped notes. That was because her mama had come to Elcomb from Virginia and they had sung shaped notes in Virginia. She read, could add, and had strong ideas about meeting a good man, marrying him and raising her own children near Mama at Elcomb. And in time she would.

"Farther along we'll know more about it. . ." she sang in the hot kitchen.

Martha Ruth dozed off. Lois and Mickey sat down and looked at her books. All her books had pictures.

Miz Owens came into the room. There they sat on the floor; the linoleum was cool. Martha Ruth lay asleep on her bed, that angelic face framed in damp curls. Spinal meningitis is a terrible thing. And Martha Ruth had shown such promise. Martha Ruth could have gone to any college. She could have been the finest teacher. She could have married, not a miner, an up-and-coming physician, why. . . . She looked at the scene. Little girls whispering, reading the words that her little girl could never read. Sliding their legs back and forth across the cool linoleum, back and forth. She wiped her eyes with a pure Irish linen handkerchief, softened by Lennie Rue's washings.

"Tempted and tried, we're off made to wander. . ." Miz Owens reached into her pocket.

"Here, girls, go buy something cold over at the commissary."

Mickey looked up and took the scrip. "Lookee, Lois, lookee. It is a big quarter." Then Miz Owens gave Lois her quarter.

"Oh, thank you, Miz Owens. She ran against Miz Owens and put her head against her. Miz Owens patted her.

"Martha Ruth wants you to come again."

"We will. We will come play any ol' time." Out the door they flew.

They ran out into the road down to the commissary just across from Miz Owens' house. Got in line. It reached out on the porch. It was late afternoon and the line had formed to buy groceries for supper and next day. The girls stood in line.

"I've got a big piece of money." Mickey held up the quarter in scrip.

Miz Mitchell was in line. She seldom came to the commissary. She sent Myrtle. But today she was out of snuff and needed it badly. She had come herself.

"Well, whar'd you get hit?"

"Miz Owens. We played with Martha Ruth."

"We love Martha Ruth." That was Lois. "Miz Owens gives us quarters."

Vance Owens heard every word through the scrip window. He tallied the present transaction through the window. Said politely to the next woman who stepped up on the little wooden step so she could see through the scrip window, "Excuse me, Ann, I'll be right back."

He came out to where the girls stood.

"Hello, girls, could I see your big money?"

"Why sure, Vance Owens."

Everybody had stopped talking. They held up the scrip.

"That's a quarter. Do you know that will buy five candy bars, or five ice cream cones, or a whole bunch of candy? It will buy a cold RC and a warm Moon Pie."

The girls were speechless.

"Does anybody mind if they go to the head of the line?"

"Naw."

"Go on."

"Shore."

He took their hands and led them into the cool store, big fans whirring up a breeze. Up to Lee Haynes. Lee was getting meat out of the refrigerated cooler. He looked up.

"Lee, these girls have been visiting Martha Ruth. Could you wait on them? They have 'big pieces' of scrip." He winked.

Everybody was enjoying watching the joyful occasion. It was good to see someone bringing pleasure. Children with not a worry, not a pain. Just getting what they want—legally, without any consequences. That was an unusual sight. It was quiet; just a murmur of voices, the girls oblivious to everything except a decision.

"Well, girls," Lee said. "What will it be?" Mickey was ready.

"B-B bats. . ."

"25 B-B bats?"

Twenty-five was more than Mickey could deal with. Ten was the most. Mickey was on the fringe of understanding numbers. After "ten" Mickey would chant, "mor'n yours, mor'n yours, mor'n anything or mor'n anything, mor'n anything". That stretched things to the existential.

Mickey knew that 25 was "mor'n anything". She said, "I want one of all!" Nobody had ever heard of a thing like that. Lee liked that, and he gave her suckers, B-B bats, candy, red hots, ju–jubees, licorice, corn candy, peanut candy, Kentucky mints, and Boston beans. He did it twice, putting it altogether in a brown poke. Lois Jean stood in a trance.

"I want a Moon Pie, an RC, a Hershey bar." She trailed off.

"A Brown Cow." Somebody else.

"And a Brown Cow." Lois Jean would not forget Mother. Others watched. Two girls with money buying what tasted good and what was cold and what left no mark of sin. That was Heaven. Lee Haynes wondered if one could ever escape into their world, that tangible heaven of Moon Pies, RC colas, and cold Brown Cows.

The girls clutched their bounties, ran out, down the steps and up the road. By the time they had reached the yard, the Brown Cow ice cream was melted and running down Lois Jean's arm.

"Mother, Mother, we bought you something." There she stood with the egg turner.

"Where did you get that mess?" The Brown Cow was melting. Large pieces of the chocolate covering were beginning to slide down slowly, like a mudslide, on Lois' hand.

"Mother, Mother we bought you something."

"Mother, I got you some B-B bats."

"You know, I can't eat them things. I don't have any. . . ." She trailed off.

Lois Jean sat down on the top of the three front porch steps and was eating the Brown Cow. The cold, mushy, ice cream was so good. She licked the stick than the palm of her hand. Like Sockee! Sockee was one of many dogs that James brought in. They did not last, as Ma's did, jumping for corn pone. Sockee got mange. Daddy rubbed him in black motor oil from the mines to cure the mange. Nothing helped except a "hunting trip" that ended with a well-placed bullet that put the poor creature out of its misery.

Lois Jean licked her hand, splayed out her fingers, and licked between fingers. She opened the bag.

"Here, Mother, here is a Nickel Loaf." Charity laid the egg turner on the windowsill, sat down in the swing, tore off the paper, held it in her hand. Nothing was as good as a Nickel Loaf. Coconut with the chocolate covering. She began to swing a little, to ease down into the experience.

She was not thinking about anything except the experience of chocolate and coconut. She looked lovingly at the bar. Eating it, leaning back. Chewing gingerly on raw gums. Suddenly she looked down at the delightful concoction. Something was moving. Something moved. She sat perfectly still, waiting for her brain to take it all in, put it together, and bring it into understanding.

"Worm. worms. Shit, this candy has worms!!" The worms were white and tiny. The girls were engrossed in pleasure that only candy can bring. Lois Jean was now eating a Moon Pie. Mickey on her first B-B bat. Mickey had a plan. They all knew Mickey's plan. Save it, and savor it when Lois Jean's were gone then slowly eat the candy! Make Lois want what Mickey had. She licked the B-B bat, the strawberry B-B bat. Slowly, tongue out, sliding it around all four sides of the B-B bat—two inches long and now pointed at the end.

Charity surveyed the Nickel Loaf. She took her fingers and pulled out a worm about the size of a grain of rice. It moved. Anything white could not be bad. White was good; black was evil. She mashed the worm between her thumb and index finger and wiped it on her apron. She looked for more movement. There was none. She broke the bar into three pieces and examined it. There had to be a male worm somewhere in that nickel loaf. If there was one worm sealed inside the chocolate covering, there had to be the second. And there he was. She had him out and squeezed him to death between her fingers. Nothing more. She ate the entire thing, squeezing the soft sweet coconut against the roof of her mouth and swallowing, leaning her head against the back of the swing and sighing in deep contentment. James caught them all engrossed in the ecstasy that only candy can bring. Praise God from whom all blessings flow.

Wherein Charity Sums up the Loss

There was a strange feeling of loss—not accomplishment. She had been geared up for pain, rejection, the object of derision, the outcast. These feelings made her strong, able to go forward. Adversity. Charity thrived on adversity. She needed adversity wrapped in anger to move forward. That got you through whatever came your way. If everything was going well, look out, rest assured trouble was on the way. She had bad gums, blood, and pain. All of this agony gave her strength. This project had protected her from greater grief.

Charity's philosophy had a name: "Jerk rug." Meaning if you are rich enough to own even a small rug, trouble will find you. Sure's you step on it and feel good and things are working out, just as sure as you believe that you have turned the corner, just as sure as you believe God has given you a good life with many blessings, somebody or something is going to jerk the rug out from under you.

It followed that while you kept bloody cotton in your mouth, nothing further could happen. James would not die in the mines; the children would not die with typhoid fever; a spark from the chimney would not catch the house on fire and the twin beds with the pink brocade spreads burn up.

The bloody cotton, the ragged holes in her mouth, the pain, all talismans that prevented "jerk rug". Two weeks later Dr. Mayhall placed her new dentures in her not completely healed mouth. "The gums will conform to the dentures," he had said. He handed her a mirror. She smiled. She was beautiful. Fine bone structure, flawless skin, short blond hair framing her face. Full lips and white teeth. Neither spoke. She paid the nurse. Smiled.

"Miz Carter, you're beautiful. Come in for a checkup two weeks from today."

She was walking across the bridge when it happened. She stopped, unable to identify this somewhat familiar, yet unidentified feeling. She was pregnant and it was all her fault. A baby! The most amazing experience. For one instant, she loved the idea. She was thrilled by it. Life within life. A little baby. People would think that she was crazy standing in the road, not moving. Besides, she didn't want a baby. She didn't need another mouth to feed. James had tricked her. No, he had not tricked her. She had started this baby unknowingly. It was her actions that had started this child. She thought of the jerk rug syndrome. The baby would be born with sleepy eyes, or club-foot or dead. A wave of negatives engulfed her. She remembered Octava and George. Beautiful Octava, nervous breakdown, now in Lexington. "God, don't let me lose my mind." Silly woman. Stop in the store and get an RC and a candy bar—with worms. Hush. Sing. Just think the words:

> *"Tempted and tried, we're off moved to wonder*
> *Why it should be thus all the day long.*
> *While there are others living around us,*
> *Never molested, though in the wrong.*
> *Farther along we'll know more about it.*
> *Farther along we'll understand why.*
> *While there are others living around us,*
> *Never molested, though in the wrong."*

Next day she went to the pump late enough to meet the crowd gathered for the news. When it came her time, she pumped the bucket full, smiled broadly at all of them and went home.

Wherein the Mad Dog Comes into the House

The episode began in the late afternoon. Ella came over to see the New Home sewing machine that Charity had purchased at the Modern Electric Company in Harlan. She was back into dressing and selling fryers. Not just at Easter but all year-round. Diddles you can purchase year-round. She had purchased the sewing machine "on time." She owed Modern Electric Company two dollars a month. This New Home machine had a piece that could be attached which would actually make small gathers in the material to create ruffles. Nobody had anything like it in Tways.

Charity had bought a yard and a half of yellow material at the commissary and was going to make Lois Jean a "pinafore." It would be like an apron, except it would go all the way around, and the bib would have the ruffles beginning at the waist and going across the shoulders to the back and stopping at the waist. James attached the piece and showed Charity how to gather the ruffles. She sat down where he had left off and finished a piece of rag that was used for the lesson.

"I can do it, James. I can."

It was a warm day and the back door was open. It had a screen door. The front door was for company. No need for screen door there. She had the oscillating fan running.

In came Ella. Charity had just finished gathering the rag.

"What do you think of this?" She smiled broadly. She smiled often. Charity was a beauty. If it were not for her bow legs and if she had just been taller. . . .

"Ella, what do you think of this?"

"Well, Charity, it is modern."

"Like Modern Electric. What is modern to you, Ella?"

"Modern means the latest thing; a combination of the old in a fresh approach to produce modern."

"Ella, where'd you learn to think like that, to talk like that?"

"Why, Charity, just laid up in bed all day reading them ol' detective books."

They both laughed. Charity, flashing a glorious full set of perfect teeth. Ella did not know about the two lots that James had which had belonged to John. Charity loved a little secret.

"Now, Ella, let's make a ruffle for the pinafore."

"Do you know how to spell that, Charity?"

"Of course, and so do you."

"Spell it."

"No, no need to spell it. Let's make it."

"Not until you spell it. Sound it and spell it. Knowledge is powerful. Spell it and it's yours, correctly forever. It is as precious as a piece of gold."

"Or two lots in Layall," she thought.

"Well, if I must humor you. . . p–i–n, pin a, f–o–u–r, four."

"Very good, except for the last part that is f–o–r–e. Pinafore. Spell it."

"P i n a f o r e—-pinafore."

"Again."

"P i n a f o r e."

"Good. Now, let's ruffle up things. Could we open the front door? I'm hot."

"Well, I'm pregnant."

"Well, it will be another girl."

"Let's make a ruffle."

Charity pulled out the ruffle—a long, narrow piece that would extend from the shoulder, remaining straight, not flopping down on the shoulder.

"Charity, white rick-rack would add some definition and flair."

"I don't have any rick-rack."

"Well, I do." She stepped to the front porch and yelled across the road, "Cappie, get the white rick-rack and bring it to me, please, honey."

When she came, Ella hugged her, thanked her. "Any trouble finding it?"

"No, Mama."

Charity stopped and watched the scene. Ella would spoil her children. Charity's idea of God was: If God saw that you were attached to anything and it meant a lot to you, He'd take it surer than anything. Bless Pat, He wouldn't see her making over hers. She'd give Him no reason to think she was attached to anything except the New Home sewing machine and her dentures. She smiled.

"Here, Ella, you sew on the rick-rack while I see about the fire in the stove. Her mouth had hurt all day in one place. It dawned on her what the problem was. She went into the bedroom, got the hand mirror, opened her mouth. Couldn't see a thing except in her jaw. Dr. C. P. Mayhall had said that bone would work out. She had not believed him. She rubbed her tongue back in the vacant sockets in her jaw. The taste of salt was completely gone. She had tasted salty blood for weeks. Now it was gone. There seemed to be a tiny ridge and sure enough a little sharp end that had worked loose. She needed James' tweezers. That would take time. She put the upper dentures in and went back into the living room.

The rick-rack outlined the strip for ruffle—not yet a ruffle. Cappie lingered. Gerald was on the front porch in the swing. It was a warm, late afternoon. "Charity, let's ruffle." Ella was enjoying her success. She knew where all her children were, even the one in heaven. And she was so preoccupied that she had forgotten the cough that John had to the extent of spitting blood. She was in a safe place doing something that in the great scheme of things, came under the heading of entertainment, producing an accomplishment. An unimportant something that rode across the cooling night. All was in its place. "God's in His heaven; all's right with the world."

The rick-rack seam was straight just inside the hemming seam. Charity sat down, unscrewed the pedal foot, and screwed in the ruffler. Threaded the machine, put the piece in, and turned the gauge to adjust the thread. She used a loose number because the material was a little thick. Then she pedaled.

"Oh, look, Ella, it is working."

"Yes, it is."

Gerald and the girls came and stood around the sewing machine. Charity continued. What went in as a straight piece of material came out a ruffle with white rick-rack.

"Not a hitch in the stitch." This was Gerald, whose nose was dry.

At that very moment, the apex of perfection, the room exploded in sound and movement. No one could comprehend what was happening, but it was not good. They knew that what was happening was not good. Something had run through the opened front door and disappeared into the kitchen, the bedroom, then the girls' room and back through the living room.

It was a dog, a huge white German Shepherd. It never slowed down.

That's when they saw the foaming mouth. The dog was mad, a mad dog, a white German Shepherd. The house was filled with the chaos of the dog running in circles, the women standing frozen. Charity holding the perfect ruffle. Lois ran to the other bedroom, climbed onto the dresser, and was trying to step through the mirror. Mickey was under her bed, back in a corner and wouldn't move. Cappie and Florence were frozen in fear as the dog ran past them, circling the house. Everybody was in place screaming, and dancing in total fear. Gerald ran out the front door, only to have his mind shut down. So he ran back for his mother. To save her.

Fat Sheehan was the first to hear the commotion: door open, women and children screaming. Fat wasn't wearing his gun. This didn't sound like a human being after another human being. He ran to the open front door. Spread eagled, his arms above on both sides of the door frame, feet spread against both sides of the door frame, just as the huge white dog ran past, circling the rooms in the house. At a time like this, an unlikely energy took over and Fat was out of himself. Fat would look back and wonder how he knew what to do.

Fat Sheehan weighed close to 300 pounds and was noted for his great strength. He slid into the room, up to the side of the door that went into the kitchen. The dog was a little winded now, but still moving. Here it came through the kitchen. He leaned down and grabbed the thing around its middle and almost lost it, it being wet with lather from running.

"Get a bedspread," he yelled. "Get a bedspread. Somebody, get a bedspread, throw it over the dog." Gerald ran to Charity's bedroom. Lois still screaming and clawing. He grabbed the pink silk spread, ran back, threw the spread over Fat and the dog.

Fat had locked his hands around the dog. It was a powerful dog in a death rage.

"Son, off me, around the dog. Don't let him bite ye."

Gerald pulled the spread down off Fat's head and began tucking it around the dog. Fat waited until the head was covered and laid the dog down and both Gerald and Fat bound the spread around the body. Then Fat grabbed the mouth, clamping the teeth together and wrapping more pink satin spread around the head.

Nobody moved. "I need something to tie around this snout."

"Charity, hand me the thing in your hand! Gerald, expand it." Gerald pulled the yellow ruffle and it expanded. Fat wrapped it around and around the head. The dog still writhed in the pink spread. "Gerald, go get a gun."

"I'll do it, Fat." It was Ella. She ran over to Miz Miller's.

"I need a gun. I need a gun. Mad dog at Charity's."

Miz Miller was back in seconds with a small pearl-handle gun. "It's mine. Bring it back." She remained on the porch.

Fat was walking out on the porch. The dog wrapped in Charity's pink silk bedspread. Head tied with the yellow ruffle. "Ella, I'm a puttin' him in the yard. When I unload him, I'll hold his head down. Shoot while I hold. Watch my hand."

He put the dog down. It got its second wind and was up. Fat was on top of him.

Later, folks would say when they told the story, "It was 'rite purty, all wrapped up in James' pink satin bedspread and tied with a yellow piece of goods with white rick-rack.

"Now, Ella, now. Get close. Now!"

Ella pulled the trigger. She closed her eyes. The dog jerked three times, then relaxed. Fat stood up, wet from head to toe. "Gotamighty, 0h, God. Thank you, Jesus."

Those were his very words. He went back in the house. Mickey was missing. Where was she? They all went outside, calling her. No answer. Cappie found her under the bed and coaxed her out.

Word had reached James. Word was everywhere about the mad dog in the house. About Fat getting it out, Ella shooting it with a pearl-handle gun that no one knew she had. The bedspread and yellow ruffle. That would upset Charity. The pink bedspread. Charity had bought that bedspread soon after they were married. Every night she would fold it up and lay it gently on the chair. Often he had seen her walking around the bed, one hand smoothing along the edge of the bed, uttering the names of the dead: Pearl, Otis, William Moses, Ida Dialthea, dead and buried in the church yard at Wolf Creek.

Charity was in Lois Jean's and Mickey's bedroom. Both were asleep. She stood by the two twin beds. Suddenly she was tired. Went to her bedroom, pulled down the other white sheet, spread it on the bed, put a light blanket on top. She slept.

When James came home, he stooped over the huge pink wad of bedspread. Soft blood coming through. Pulled back the spread and saw the mouth, tied with a yellow piece of goods. He'd need to bury the dog. This was not his dog. It had come from somebody else. He went into his kitchen, washed his hands in the wash pan. Found leftovers, ate, smoked, and went to bed.

Wherein Charity Discusses Religion
and Buys a Bedspread

Ella came back the next day to finish the ruffle on the sewing machine. Charity cut a new ruffle. There was no white rick-rack. She slid the new piece under the needle. Ella looked on. It gathered nicely for about four inches, then stopped. Ella was standing, looking over her shoulder. The material caught, but no stitches formed, just a trail of white thread and no ruffle.

"Charity, let me see." Ella sat down. Nothing worked. "Did you touch it?"

"No, I didn't even sit down."

"This is strange. We saw the ruffle."

"Ella, I will make the yellow pinafore for Lois Jean. I will get more material if I need it. Today I have to buy another bedspread. I'm going to town and get it."

"Charity, we were so fortunate. That mad dog could have killed—-."

"I know, it could have killed one of us and infected the rest."

Charity pushed the New Home sewing machine against the wall. "Ella, I'm going to town, then we will finish the yellow pinafore. I won't be stopped."

She dressed in her Sunday clothes. Combed her hair, stood before the mirror, smiling broadly. Lois Jean and Mickey would stay at Aunt Ella's, playing with Cappie and Florence.

She would be back before James left, to cook and pack his lunch. Down the road she went to town. Fat Sheehan picked her up. "Whar ye goin'?"

"Into Harlan to get a bedspread. You do remember that the pink satin bedspread is gone?"

"Yeah. So is a lot of other thangs gone or changed so's you don't recognize them."

"Are you referring to Ann's new religion?"

"Have you been to a tent revival?"

"No, but I've heard about Cylo and Ann's shouting."

"Charity, hit's a shame. They're handling the fire."

"Fat, it could be the Holy Spirit."

"I heard that Ann said: 'Scheek-a-ma-shilo, give-it-to-Cylo.' That's what she said. And handed "Cylo" a handful of hot coals. And she wad'n burned. The far didn't burn them. I looked at her hands."

"How do you know she said them words?"

"A bunch of boys told it all, showed how they done it."

"Why are you shamed?"

"I don't know. I don't know."

"Fat, maybe you're under conviction."

"Them words scares me, Charity. Being under conviction. Now, I'm not a bad man. I don't beat up on Ann. I give her groceries and clothes and let her do as she will. I'm not a bad man. I can church more up on one of these mountains than I ken in a tent a passing hot coals of far."

He had something there. However, people needed the church. And it was a good place to see and be seen. You couldn't sin sitting in a church.

"Fat, I'll get out here." She got out on Main Street, leaned back through the open car window, and said, "Thank you, Fat, for everything. They's a star in your crown, Fat Sheehan."

"You're welcomed, Charity. Don't get pink this time. You are beyond a pink bedspread." He laughed and drove on down the main street.

She didn't want one of them ol' chenille things like Nannie was selling out of the back of her car. Nannie was a peddler of sorts. Out selling chenille. It was new. Chenille spreads with pictures worked in. The birds, wreaths, all worked in bright, gaudy colors. She knew that her sister could use the money. But she couldn't bear this idea of a cheap chenille spread on her bed.

"It's brocade," said the salesman. "Brocade."

"Brocade," she whispered. "I know brocade. I have twin brocade bed-spreads in pink on the twin beds."

"This washes well, won't shrink, will go through the washing machine. It is cotton with a pattern wove in. It is exquisite."

"What color is that?"

"Why it's any color you like. Mrs. J. Ray Rice bought one last week. She said it was exquisite. Marched out of here with one in pink."

"Yes, I have twin pink spreads for my daughters. Let me go think about it."

Town brought out the best in Charity. She brought a vocabulary that she used only with tradespeople.

She went to Dr. Tye's drugstore. Got a soft drink and was sitting in one of the little wire-back chairs, arms resting on the little round marble table, when in came somebody from a mining camp. Charity didn't look up. She listened carefully.

"I need some a that calomel. You know that red pill for worms. I think my children are wormy."

Dr. Tye went back to the clean, organized shelves and picked up the jar that held the red pills. "How many do you need?"

"I have seven. The youngest is two."

"I will give you 12. Don't give the two-year-old anything. The children must swallow the pill. If they chew it, it will do serious damage to the teeth. Nothing to eat or drink until a bowel movement. They will become uncomfortable until the bowel movement. Check the stools to see if they pass the worms and if they are pin worms, the very tiny ones that cause anal itching, or if they are the much larger worms living along the alimentary canal. After the bowel movement they can have food."

"How much is that, Dr. Tye?"

"Let's see, that's twelve pills. That will be exactly $1.30. And we can put it on your account."

"Thank you, Dr. Tye, but I have the money." She opened her pocketbook. Took out a two dollar bill and paid for the red worm pills. "Again, thank you."

Charity sat there thinking about long worms living inside her two girls. What a terrible thing. She got up. Stood at the counter. Bought four red shiny pills and went out in the bright sunshine to get the bedspread.

Wherein the Shiny Red Pills Are Administered

"Charity, I never of heard such thing." Charity was standing at the fence talking to Maxie Carter. Maxie had one child, little Vinnie. Little Vinnie was spoiled; she was the apple of Maxie's eye. In fact, Maxie was spoiled. Richard loved his two girls and they loved him. Maxie kept a clean house, clean toilet, clean yard, a clean apron, a clean oven. Little Vinnie was shy. She would squat in the front yard and watch Lois Jean, Mickey, and Jimmy playing "car" in the swing, all three in the swing.

Little Vinnie would watch, sitting still, never coming over. "She's bashful," said Maxie. Where she gets it, I don't know."

"Well, she's an only child. She'll come out of it later on. It would help if you took her out more often."

"And let her get sick? Never."

"Keeping children well is not easy. I'm giving mine worm pills, tomorrow."

"Say what?"

"I'm giving mine calamine worm pills tomorrow. Fact is, I need another lard bucket. Maybe you have one."

"What do you need it for?"

"When their bowels move tomorrow, I must examine the scuoose to see if there are worms, either pin or large worms."

"Oh, Charity. Mercy, Charity. You're crazy."

"Mine won't die. Get me that bucket."

Charity took it, thanking Maxie.

"I'll return it."

What a day, a new bedspread and a march forward with the worm pills. James was opposed to the whole thing.

"Charity, you are crazy. Where would these children get worms?"

"From dipping suckers in the branch, James. The toilets, some anyway, dumped into the branch. You know that as well as I do. You're going to help me. They can't chew the pills. It will cause their teeth to rot."

The next morning was a Saturday. She was up early. She woke him up. She woke up the girls.

"Come in here and take your worm pills." Lois came first, then Mickey. Mickey sat on James' lap.

"We going to play a game. Put this little pill in your mouth. Drink a big drink of water and swallow. Don't chew." He was calm. "Open up, little girl."

She did and he popped the pill. "Swallow." She did.

"Perfect! Yer Daddy's little towhead! Now just one more." Suddenly, things changed. She stiffened.

"Hurry, James, stick this in her mouth. Make her swallow it. Make her swallow it."

"Charity, be quiet." He reached for the pill. Mickey was crying and stiffening. Charity stuck the pill in her mouth and squeezed her nose. She gulped and choked on the pill. James hit her on the back. Up it came. James patted her, handed her a drink, slipped the red shiny pill in her mouth, and said, "Drink."

She opened her eyes, saw the glass, grabbed it, and drank.

"Oh, honey, one more sip. Dry your eyes." He hugged her.

"Stop it, James. You'll spoil her. And she can't eat until after 12:00 or until she has scuoosed. Now, Lois Jean, come here."

Mickey sat waiting for breakfast. And Lois rebelled.

She fought both of them. She had watched the scene and knew that whatever happened, she would not swallow the poison-ridden, bright red shiny pill. James knew that Charity had ruined any attempt at logic.

"Here, open your mouth." She sat on his knee. Not moving. "Put this in your mouth, surround it with water, and swallow it. You do that all the time."

"Don't coddle her." Charity reached for her nose, pinched it together. She opened her mouth. Charity stuck the pill in her mouth. Lois spit it across the room. Charity got on her knees and picked it up.

"Here," she said, pinching her nose together. "Swallow, don't chew it. Swallow." Again out came the not-so-shiny pill. Again Charity found it, held her nose. Lois kicked and stiffened. She felt the pill melt, filling her mouth with strong bitter, bitter taste. James realized what happened and held the glass. She drank.

"Drink all you want, honey."

"But, Dr. Tye said. . ."

"Drink all you want, honey."

"Now, honey, take this second. . ."

"Charity, leave me alone. Get out of here."

"No, she is my child and she won't have worms. Take this pill, Lois Jean."

She had the egg turner in her hand. She came over and brought it down on Lois' legs, but the second time, James grabbed her arm, took the egg turner, threw it across the room. Lois was crying.

"Charity, give me the pill. Here, open your mouth. Put this in your mouth and drink. Don't chew the pill."

She looked at her daddy and read the answer in his face about how to swallow a red worm pill. Suddenly the struggle melted into acceptance. Filling her mouth full of water, she swallowed the water and the pill at the same time. Daddy hugged her. "Yer my girl." She slid off his lap and went into the living room, sat down in the floor and took one of the encyclopedias and looked at the pictures of a strange, strange world. Mickey followed.

"James, your breakfast is ready."

"I'm not eating breakfast."

"James, the eggs and bacon are going to waste."

"I don't give a. . . I'm not eating breakfast." He went out the back door and down to the toilet. He rolled a Duke's Mixture cigarette, took a deep puff, and pondered things in his heart. The day dragged on. The girls went to sleep on the cool linoleum rug. He sat down, picked up one of the books that surrounded their dolls and doll furniture, and read about the Sistine Chapel. Then he dosed off.

Charity came in and looked at the scene. The three of them had messed up the room. She went back to the kitchen, peeled an apple. Took the sharp knife with the cut piece lying on the blade and lifted it, turning the blade over so slightly and pulling the slice into her mouth. Nothing so good as an apple. She suddenly remembered the huge red apple from the Christmas treat that had rolled out of her lap as she squatted above the toilet hole, and she heard the thump when it hit the soft scuoose.

Lois and Mickey stood before her. "Do you want to scuoose?" No answer. Do you want to scuoose, I said?" They sat down at the kitchen table.

Lois Jean heard and felt her lower body rumbling, moving; something was moving through her body. She sat still, feeling the sensation and realizing that the little red pill was working on the worms, moving them through her body, ridding her of long worms that ate her food when she swallowed it. This was the first time she had thought about the inside of herself. She took a deep breath and felt her chest expand. She breathed out the same air that she had breathed in and her chest grew smaller. It dawned on her that every inch of her insides was filled with different shaped bags like balloons that held air and food and her heart that held love. Her insides were more important than her outsides. She slid out of the chair. "I got to scuoose." Charity looked at the clock. "I got to scuoose, I said." Lois Jean ran out of the kitchen toward the toilet.

"Come back here. You've got to scuoose in the bucket! I've got to check for the worms. Come here and sit on the bucket."

She came and sat down on the syrup bucket. Her insides performed magnificently. Again came the epiphany. The inside is more important than the outside.

"Get up, Lois Jean."

"I will, Mother, when my insides tell me to."

Mickey came out and sat on her bucket. She surveyed the scene and, harking to that Anglo-Saxon period of her ancient self, announced grandly, "I've got to shit."

Charity was stunned. Mickey had learned Charity's word for burnt biscuits, broken dishes, punctured thumbs from the curtain stretchers, lumps of coal that stove caps would not cover, dresses and overalls that wound around the wringer of the washing machine, and rubbers that broke. It was a powerful word, especially spoken as a passive whisper. Because Mickey had spoken that fine old Anglo-Saxon word passed down by eight generations of Moses/Cox tribes, it must now pass from Charity's body just as the worms were going to pass from her children.

Lois closed her eyes and bore down. All that had entered her wonderful insides rushed out.

"The catalog is beside you." It was last year's Sears and Roebuck and already they were through men's clothing. When both girls had performed to her satisfaction, they went back to the living room, weak as newborn puppies.

She looked into the buckets, feeling her gorge rise. She was looking for moving worms. She carried the buckets down the steps and stood in the sunshine. Nothing. No worms. Her two girls were clean inside and outside. The two Karo Syrup buckets were emptied, cleaned with boiling water and left to sun. Cleanliness is next to Godliness.

Wherein Nannie Carter Learns
a Shattering Truth

Nannie and Matt Carter were dressed in their best clothes. She in her long-sleeved mingly goods dress, black with the tiny little flower and delicate vine pattern that women wore from about their late fifties on. Matt had his white shirt, tie, and suit on, along with the ubiquitous felt hat. Charity was at the pump. Charity came early before the others came. She really didn't care to talk to the women who congregated to laugh and exchange stories.

"Theylaume! Where are you going this early? To court?"

"No, Charity. I'm going to the doctor."

"Why, what's wrong?"

"I don't know. When I bend over to pick up something or when I sit at the table and reach long for something, I have a shooting pain below my navel that takes my breath away."

"She can't breathe, Charity, with that pain. Sometimes she screams."

"Miz Carter, I had that same pain, and it was my appendix. I had appendicitis. I was in Harlan Hospital for close to three weeks."

"Charity, don't you remember that I told you about that doctor who worked on me? He was a drunk. He was so drunk that Kaiser Stone took over when he passed out—so they say—and completed the operation. Anyway, give me a drink. Why, don't you carry a dipper, Charity?"

Nanny was bewildered by Charity's actions. Somebody might just need a drink.

"Well, no. I don't want strangers a drinking out of the dipper, Miz Carter. You'all come on by and I'll give you a cold drink."

"Well, yes, and Jim can drive us to Harlan."

Late that afternoon, when Charity was sitting on the front porch eating an apple, a car passed the house with Nannie and Matt. Earlier that day Jim had driven them to the hospital, came home and then gone to the mines.

The very next day James got up about seven o'clock, didn't eat, went out and drove Nannie and Matt to the hospital. They checked her in with Carrie Forsyth and went immediately to the operating room. Anyone could come in and watch if they cared to. Three camp doctors were standing in the hall. They nodded "good morning". Matt told Jim that he couldn't bear to watch any knife go into Nannie Caddell. They sat in chairs in the hall.

Carrie lowered the ether mask over Nannie's face. Carrie Forsyth was a nurse's nurse. Nobody had the respect that Carrie had with patients and doctors. Frankly, she was as fine as any doctor in Harlan County. She nodded, "She's out. You may proceed."

The doctor made his first cut and staggered back. "My God." A stench rose from the body. "Oh, my God, boys, this is proud flesh. Proud flesh," he continued, "in full control, grown up around anything that invades the body. Some call it puss. It is dead cells that have died trying to protect the body from an invasion of foreign matter. Now, we must find that foreign matter."

He moved his gloved hand deeper inside the body. "The human body is a beautiful system. Man has not conceived, invented, or imagined anything so magnificent, so efficient as what you boys are observing now. As the poet said, 'What a piece of work is a man. How infin...'" He stopped mid word. The only movement in the room was the electric fan overhead. His hand remained deep inside "the greatest creation in all of creation". He stood still, his eyes closed, working very slowly and then pulling his hand ever so slowly back. He pulled an object out of Nannie Carter. One half of a pair of forceps. He leaned his head back to feel the breeze on his face.

No one made a sound. He swabbed the incision, reached his hand out and Carrie placed a bottle of peroxide in it. He poured the peroxide into the abdomen. It boiled out over the freshly cut incision. He swabbed and poured.

"These organs are infected because the forceps have created holes in them. When she moved, they punctured various places in the abdomen. Miz Forsyth, how is the patient?"

"Responding well, doctor. How long will you be?"

"There is nothing more that I can do except sew up the incision."

Everything grew still. It was afternoon and the sun was shining through dirty windows.

Nannie Caddell Carter did return to Tways Mining Camp. The two of them, after a lengthy trial that, among other things, impuned her good name, left R.C. Tway Mining Camp and returned to their farm at Rockhold, Kentucky. Both she and Matt would survive the ordeal.

Wherein Dr. Clark Bailey Saves Norma Jo

Charity was in the bedroom getting clothes for the baby out of the chifforobe. By mistake, she opened the middle drawer. The middle drawer held four linen handkerchiefs with James' initials in one corner. Rubbers were in the back with the marriage certificate and three birth certificates: Lois Jean, March 10, 1931; Mickey Fowe, May 14, 1934; and Norma Jo, January 31, 1940. She hoped that this would be the last one. There were nine years difference between Lois Jean and the baby, Norma Jo.

Suddenly, she was aware of a large envelope under the ironed, linen handkerchiefs. The baby began to cry. Charity closed the drawer. The baby was hungry. Charity carried her to the kitchen and filled a bottle with three ounces of "formula" and sat down to feed her. She took some of the formula. Charity raised her, held her lovingly against her shoulder, and began to "burp" her. Out came all the formula. It shot over the back of the straight chair. The baby was choking. Charity screamed for James. He ran into the kitchen, took the baby she was handing to him. "James, she's dying. She's not breathing." He turned the baby over his knee and patted her. Suddenly she grabbed breath and began crying.

"Charity, she is fine; fix her formula and get some food in her."

He walked the baby into the front room, patting her little back. She was screaming. He stuck the end of his little finger into her mouth. She stopped crying. Charity arrived with the formula. Norma took all of it and seemed to dose off. Again, the formula ejected out of her little body. It dawned on both James and Charity that the baby could not keep food down. Something was terribly wrong. They both loved this baby. They both tried to feed her the third time. Nothing was working.

James walked down to the shack and called Dr. Clark Bailey. He also called the tipple to tell them he wouldn't be coming in until the next shift.

Two hours later Dr. Bailey was in the bedroom with Charity, James, and the baby. Charity gave her a bottle filled with two ounces of formula. Within minutes the formula shot out of the tiny mouth. Dr. Bailey took her, felt her stomach.

"I believe that this is projectile vomiting caused by a muscle that opens and closes improperly." He handed the baby back to Charity and reached for the black bag filled with bottles of pills and some with liquid. He selected one, took the medicine dropper, filled it half full. "Here, little Norma Jo, let's fix you up." This man was trusted and beloved throughout Harlan and its environs. "Look, Charity, three drops. See, three drops, just three. Three drops every three hours around the clock." He closed the bag. Started out the door.

"Do you have a biscuit? I have not eaten since morning."

Charity went to the kitchen. She opened two biscuits, placed gravy and pieces of pork chop on them, poured milk into a jar, put a lid on it, and returned in three minutes. "Here, Dr. Bailey. Thank you for coming."

"Yeah, Doc. Much obliged. If you need something else to drink, come back." James.

Dr. Bailey was eating a biscuit when he went out the door. Norma slept. James slept. Charity kept watch. James kept watch. Charity slept. Every three hours Norma was given three drops from the small bottle. Neighbors came with food. Miz Brannon had Lois and Mickey eat and play at her house after school.

Two weeks went by. Everybody knew about Norma and suggested their own cures. Hold her close to the fire; give her one drop of olive oil; hold her upside down for one minute—things would fall into place; Paregoric; Vicks salve; wine; a drop of whiskey; prayer. The last one worked. Prayers and Dr. Clark Bailey cured Norma. Norma was a well baby. A beautiful, well baby.

Charity got up and went to her bedroom and looked down. There she lay, little legs drawn under and little bottom in the air. She was a doll, and Lois would take her, change her diapers, give her bottles, and sing to her. Norma Jo Carter was welcomed with love.

Wherein Charity Reads
a Life-Changing Document

About a week later Charity was reaching for an apple, when she remembered that long envelope in the chifforobe drawer. She walked to the bedroom, opened the drawer to the chifforobe, took out the official document, walked back to the kitchen, and spread it out on the kitchen table. What was this stuff? What did this piece of paper say? What did the words say? She reached behind the cabinet, got an apple, pulled out a chair, pulled her dress above her knees, and began peeling the apple. One long strip. If she did not break the long apple peel until she had peeled the entire apple, that would be a sign. A good sign. She didn't break the peel. James had gone to work. Lois was in school, fourth grade, Miz Anderson's room. Mickey was in the first grade drawing tulips. Norma Jo was curled up in her bed taking a nap. Charity cut the apple slices thoughtfully.

The vocabulary was incomprehensible, with words sliding into words that she did not understand: "Whereas", "lot number", "two lots", "Loyall, Kentucky", "steps of the Harlan County Courthouse", "township of Loyall", "this day of our Lord", "Signed, James Lillon Carter", "Notary, Blanch Cox", "money received, $40.00". She sat thoughtfully, eating the apple and staring at the typewritten document. Epiphany. James owned two lots in the township of Loyall. Loyall was somewhere below Harlan.

"Charity, I counted six open doors between here and the mines." James came into the kitchen, poured coffee, and sat down. "There's Shine's house, ours, and Jenny's. Then the McVey's, Halley's, and Pa's. All empty. All with doors standing open. I told Uncle Tom about it, and he told me that he believes Tway Mining Camp is going to close before too long. Then, Charity, Uncle Tom told me that he is moving to Georgetown in Harlan. Ma and Pa are back on the farm…" His voice trailed off.

"James, I want to go see Loyall this Sunday. This Sunday I want to go see Loyall."

He said nothing, knowing if he sat long enough, she would unfold a plan—her plan.

"Loyall." The sound of the name brought back a flood of memories. He rolled a cigarette, lit it, and took a deep draw and waited.

"I don't want these children to grow up and marry coal miners. I want these children to have college educations and teach school like Johnny Warren. Johnny is a teacher at Rosenwald. I want them to have a better chance than I had. I want to see Loyall."

James listened and thought of his brothers. Ted was going to graduate from Berea College. Bill was working in the office in a camp in Virginia. Leige was in Knoxville, Tennessee. James knew that he was a miner. He wanted to continue mining coal. In a coal mine, James was in charge in a way that he felt comfortable with himself. "Charity, I'll take you to Loyall Sunday. Tways is going. Tways has been good for us. It is the perfect place for miners, but it is worked out. This is the only place outside of Buck Creek that I have lived. I know a little something about Loyall. I know where it is. Sunday, Charity."

When Sunday came, they got in the car for a Sunday drive. Loyall was below Harlan. He drove down to the place where he and the boys had turned up the hollow to bury Jenny. He stopped the car, got out, and approached a couple swinging in a swing on the front porch, asked for directions to the "round house". The round house was where train engines were turned around. If a train needed attention, it was fixed and turned around. They drove back up to the bridge, past the church.

This was old Loyall. The railroad was beside the road. There were two or three places of business, the R.C. Cola bottling company, the two lots. A scorched piece of land. No trees, no grass, weeds growing knee high. Charity could not hide her disappointment.

"It's two lots." She sighed.

"And it has to be surveyed."

Wherein Mr. Hampton Makes the Survey

On Monday, James went to Harlan County Courthouse, found Blanch Cox, asked her for a surveyor.

"Jim, Mr. Hampton is a fine surveyor. He will do you well. I'll call him for you."

"Hello, Dorothy, get me Mr. Hampton at his office. Yes, honey, I'm fine, and you?" After a brief exchange of pleasantries, there was a pause.

"Mr. Hampton, this is Blanch Cox up at the courthouse. James Carter out at Tways is going to need a surveyor and I told him how fine you are." She paused. "Why, thank you, Mr. Hampton."

She handed the receiver to James. "He's nice, Jim." An appointment was set. Money would be paid. It would be done one morning next week. He went back and told Charity what he had done.

"Charity, do you have twenty dollars?"

She paused. "Yes, I do. I have twenty dollars, James, for the survey."

The next Sunday Charity asked James to drive back to Loyall. The lots had not changed. But, neither had her dream of leaving the mining camp.

"James, Nannie lives in Sunshine. That's on the way home. Let's go see Nannie and Weller.

Nannie rushed out into the yard when James pulled up. "Laume, they-laume, what are you doing here? Just tell me what are you doing here?"

"Why, we've come to see you. Here, Nannie, hold the baby. This is Norma Jo." She handed the baby to Nannie.

Nannie had Jennings, Jo Ann, Betty Lou and Wilma. They walked up on the porch inside, sat down, and Charity told her about the two lots in Loyall, Kentucky.

"Now, Charity, that's good. That's real good. Why don't you move now into the empty house next door?" She laughed.

"The house next door is empty?"

"Waiting on you. Would you like a cup of coffee, Jim?"

"Yes, I would, Nannie."

Charity sat down, holding Norma Jo.

"Nannie, we can't stay long. I've got to feed the baby."

"Why, feed her right here, Charity."

"No, she's on formula."

"I don't believe in that stuff, Charity."

"Nannie, does that house have running water?"

"Yes, it does."

The plan was forming. Why was she living in that mining camp when she could have a place next to her sister, a place with running water?

"How much is the rent?"

"Fifteen dollars a month."

"James, we need to go feed the baby."

Charity had an epiphany. Epiphanies unfolded better if she was sitting at the table eating an apple. They drove home in silence. When she climbed out of the car, she said, "I'm ready to leave R.C. Tway, James."

"I think I am too, Charity."

The following week James drove down to meet Mr. Hampton, surveyor. They met on the two lots.

"James, are you thinking of building a business or a home?"

"A home, Mr. Hampton."

"This is a business section of Loyall, ugly business."

"I know, but we want to get our children out of the mining camp. R.C. Tways truth be told, is worked out. It won't last long, I don't believe."

"I'm sorry to hear that. This property would be fine for a business, but you need a better setting to raise children. The noise of that round house, the train whistle, the town whistle. It is a business setting. Now, I have a place that would be ideal to raise a family. Would you let me show it to you? It is here in Loyall."

"I've got an hour, then I've got to go to work."

"Come on. It's close. Here, you all ride with me and I'll bring you back."

They climbed into his car and drove down the road. Suddenly Jim realized that they were very close to the place where they had buried Jenny. Mr. Hampton slowed down, turned left up a dirt road, passed a house on the side of the road another few hundred feet, and stopped. James got out. He looked out and saw the side of a mountain, gently sloped to where they were standing. A ridge at the top of the slope and from there nothing but a meadow to the right and a forest beyond. It took his breath.

"That's the Herd house to the left." He pointed to a huge white bungalow. "That's the croquet court there." Then he pointed to the right. "That's the Unthank place." He pointed to the right of the house. "And that's the old cemetery, dating back, I guess, to the beginning of time. Jim, you need this place, and I need your two lots. What do you say?"

"Well, let me bring Charity down here and see what she says." Something nagged. This was too good to be true. He had seen places all over Harlan County. Nothing like this.

James went home and told Charity that there was a place she might like better and a swap could be arranged. An even swap.

The Following Saturday they went grocery shopping, but they drove to Loyall first. For the first time in his life with Charity, she was speechless. She surveyed the magnificent lay of the mountain curving into a gentle hollow. An acre "more or less". She looked at the Herd house and the Unthank house. It was a prize, and it was being offered as an even swap.

They drove to the A&P. He took the girls to the drug store, got the chili and malt balls. Ate three bowls of chili while the girls ate the malt balls and drank ice water.

"James, stop at Nannie's. We're going to rent that house. We are going to swap lots…"

"And I am going to Mary Helen and work in that mine. The equipment is fine, I understand."

They each settled in the car and did not speak again until they arrived in Tways.

Charity began, the next day, packing up the house. Taking down curtains, washing, stretching them on Miz Brannon's curtain stretchers. Packing things in boxes from the commissary. She told Miz Brannon her plan. She packed dishes, clothes, pictures, placing everything in the living room, placing quilts in the divan. By Friday everything was ready except taking down beds and the kitchen stove.

Saturday morning arrived. School was out for the summer. Lois Jean had passed fourth grade. Mickey had passed first grade. Gerald and Tom came over early. James had a truck that one of the boys had loaned him for the day. Charity had gotten up early, built a fire, cooked breakfast, and four hours later, the stove was cool enough to disassemble. The boys began with the front room. Took beds apart. Charity folded bedspreads, quilts, sheets, pillow cases on into the night. Finally the truck was full. James walked toward the truck, carrying the coal bucket and the Karo syrup cans. Finally, it was time to go. He helped Charity in the front seat with Norma. Lois Jean and Mickey Fowe next to Charity holding Norma Jo. He climbed into the truck. He drove down the road. Lights out. They got to the shack. Mr. Miller had already closed the big gates. James went into the shack. Mr. Miller came out stepped up on the running board. James drove around the commissary up the gates. Mr. Miller opened the gates. "Turn on your lights, Jim, and God bless you."

The little family rode out of the gates of the R.C. Tway Coal Company into the path of a full moon.

An Afterword

The move to Sunshine lasted from July 1940 until May 1941.
was in the fifth grade and marched in the May Day parade by Harlan. Micki
s in the second grade. We moved into the new house on the hill in Loyall
gging the swag of the ridge half way up the mountain. That was where Dr.
rk Bailey came and delivered the greatest gift—a boy—James Edward
ter, who arrived May 10, 1944.

The most precious thing we owned was the deed to this dream. That
put four children through college. I was the first to use it. Mother took
up to Mr. C. D. Cole. That was college at Cumberland College,
illiamsburg, Kentucky. Once, when the money was gone (Charity spent it
the house!), Mr. A.T. Siler extended my stay with a music scholarship.

We all received college educations, and I taught English to returning
eterans on the G.I. Bill in Wallins Creek, Kentucky for one year; then, I
aught English in Harlan High School for one year. I taught English for a
total of thirty-two years. Micki taught elementary grades for forty years.
Norma Jo taught elementary school for a few years and finished with a career
in the library at Perimeter College in Atlanta, Georgia. Eddie is top salesman
at Campbell Soup Company. All four of us have been active, all with different passions. Micki has Charity's love for houses; Norma, the midas touch;
Eddie, train displays; and me—teaching English Literature and storytelling!

The spirit and majesty of the mountains lives in our blood. We are
mountain gentry, fiercely protective of the mountain accent in our speech
that began with Chaucer and became fully developed in the speech of Queen
Elizabeth I. It is practiced in the mountains of Kentucky, North Carolina,
Virginia, and Tennessee to this day.

I attended a summer session working toward a master's degree at the
University of North Carolina. One professor worked diligently on my accent.

Then I went back to Harlan; I could not "put on" in Harlan. A group of returning Korean War veterans requested that I speak "so's we ken under stand ya."

This much I know: gentry flows through the veins. Gentry is not what you own or what your bank account is. Gentry flows through your vein based on the way you were raised and how you practiced your raising.

In 1971, James died of Black Lung. Charity is 98 years old, January 2006 Her birthday is 12-29-1907. Her greatest pleasure is "Keeblers Delux Chocolate Covered Graham Crackers". That is the way she asks for them. Every morning she dresses in a silk blouse and in winter keeps warm with cashmere sweaters. She combs her snow-white hair and puts on lipstick. At night she pulls the handmade wedding-ring quilt up over her ears and says,

> "Now I lay me down to sleep.
> I pray, Thee Lord, my soul to keep.
> If I should die before I wake,
> I pray, Thee Lord, my soul to take."
> Jubilate Dio
> Amen

Printed in the United States
46189LVS00001B/70-150

9 780977 747801